Daniel Defoe

Moll Flanders

Daniel Defoe

Moll Flanders

edited by

J. PAUL HUNTER
Emory University

THOMAS Y. CROWELL COMPANY
New York   Established 1834

3-1303-00044-6147

Appendixes

Contents

NOTES ON THIS EDITION

The Annotations

THIS edition has been annotated with the needs of the American undergraduate in mind, though a majority of the notes will also be useful to advanced students. Relevant contextual and historical information is provided, and there is an especially full glossing of words that have shifted meaning since Defoe's time. The annotations are not, however, intended to supplant the intelligent use of a good college dictionary and maps of eighteenth-century England. Students interested in Moll's peregrinations will find especially useful Ogilby's 1677 map of London, which is conveniently available at the back of Sir Walter Besant's *London in the Time of the Stuarts*. This map, of course, describes London after the Great Fire of 1666, and most of Moll's adventures presumably occurred earlier (she says she is almost seventy years old in 1683), but Defoe seems rather to have placed Moll in the London he himself knew than to have striven for technical historical accuracy.

There are, too, a few textual notes, and several critical notes where I have pointed the reader toward patterns of interest; in some cases I have tried to suggest how the novel *may*, at least, be interpreted. I hope that I have sufficiently distinguished between fact and opinion here, so that the reader may choose to read with or without my pointing hand.

The Text

This edition follows the text of the first edition and preserves the capitalization and spelling of that edition, with the few exceptions recorded below.[1] Students unfamiliar with eighteenth-century practice may find the stylistic eccentricities at first annoying, and a little confusing; but the present editor thinks that modernization sometimes misleads in the direction of simplicity and a flattening of emphasis, for modernization excludes some of the linguistic play made possible by the older (and looser) spelling and capitalization practice. For example, Moll's "Pallate Bed" or "Palate Bed" means "pallet bed," but it connotes much more in the context of her character and the action of the novel. Defoe, like many of his contemporaries, likes to explore that sort of linguistic ambiguity, and I have considered it valuable to preserve a sense of his playfulness. Admittedly, some of the variation in

[1]The present edition has been prepared from a reproduction of the copy of the first edition in the library of the University of Illinois. I should like to express my thanks to the library staff for their help in obtaining this and also the facsimile title page from that edition reproduced on p. 1 of this volume.

spelling and capitalization involves mere accident or habit, of either Defoe or his printer, and is therefore insignificant, but I have not wished to decide arbitrarily which eccentricities should be kept and which emended the reader of this edition may decide for himself. I have, however, silently corrected obvious misprints (leaving intact questionable passages), and have regularized the distinctions between the following pairs of words: whither/whether; then/than; lose/loose; ought/aught; of/off and choose (or chuse)/chose. This regularization simplifies several possible confusions, but even such modernization I have done reluctantly, for in some of these instances Defoe may still be exploiting spelling ambiguities. I have therefore included a complete list (in Appendix C) locating the instances of regularization.

The punctuation of the first edition is especially problematic, and some of it is probably as much due to printer's practice (or malpractice) as to Defoe's. Still, I have fundamentally preserved the original punctuation; in places where a modern student could be seriously misled, I have slightly altered punctuation (usually raising commas to semicolons, or adding or subtracting commas) to make the syntactic relationships more clear. The modern reader, conditioned by regularity, may sometimes be irritated by Defoe's punctuation, but he will not I think often misunderstand if he remembers that the punctuation here is often more a matter of rhetoric than of logic, and that commas and semicolons regularly indicate pauses rather than adhere to later conventions of syntax: his voice, more than his handbook, may be his guide.

In basing this edition on the first edition, I have departed from the usual practice of accepting the "third edition, corrected" as authoritative. Most modern reprints are based on this third edition,[2] on the assumption that its corrections and abridgments are the work of Defoe himself. But after completely collating the first and third editions, I find the traditional view difficult to accept. We have no external evidence of Defoe's hand in the later edition, and he seems usually to have paid little attention to the variations of subsequent editions, except to complain loudly when abridgments were issued by piratical publishers. A close look at the corrections themselves strongly suggests that they were made by someone other than the author. Some do clarify misprints and obscurities in the first edition, but others miss the crux of garbled passages. For example, in two places (pp. 144 and 201) Defoe uses the idiom "to and again" (meaning back and forth), and in both places the first edition misunderstands and misprints it as "too and again." The editor of the third edition notices something wrong, but his attempts to correct are no help because he clearly fails to

[2]An exception is the World Classics *Moll Flanders*, London, 1961.

recognize the idiom. An author might easily pass over some errors in his own work, but he is unlikely to forget completely an idiom he uses twice.[3] Sometimes the third edition allows errors to stand, sometimes it introduces new ones. In short, the person or persons who edited the third edition often show a misunderstanding of the original, missing the point in a way quite unlikely in the author himself.

In the third edition, most of the corrections are excisions, and it is usually said that the "corrections" involve rejections of redundancies. However, many lengthy repetitions of fact remain, and the pattern of excision seems rather designed to trim than to beautify: the primary purpose seems to be to make the novel shorter, not necessarily clearer or more readable. Where the first edition has paired nouns, adjectives, adverbs, and verbs, the third edition usually excises one unit of the pair (often producing a loss in meaning, or at least in precision); the third edition drops large numbers of parenthetical expressions (sometimes involving detail, sometimes involving Moll's reflections and opinions). In the third edition, shorter words and expressions are substituted for longer ones ("Countenances" becomes "Faces," "got an Opportunity" becomes "found Means," "enterprised" becomes "made," "are minded to" becomes "want to"), items are trimmed out of lists, syncopic forms and shortened spellings are increased, and occasionally sentences are rewritten to eliminate prepositional phrases and dependent clauses. Most of the cutting is, indeed, done with some care, and sometimes the greater concision makes the text easier to read; but sometimes too the editing changes the sense of the passage, and often the flavor of Moll's rambling, detailed style is severely altered. The editor of the third edition is clearly more concerned with the audience than with Moll's character. At one point, for example, when Moll lives south of the Thames, he locates her in "Rotherhith," the official name of the area; the first edition had read "Redriff," the vulgar name and the name a woman like Moll surely would have used.

But consciousness of audience was not the primary determinant of the form of the third edition. The first edition has an 11-page preface and 424 numbered pages of text (28 octavo gatherings); the third contains 6 pages of preface and 366 pages of text (24 octavo gatherings). Paper was expensive in 1722, and several characteristics of the editing suggest that the primary intention was to compress the novel into four fewer gatherings of paper. Some paper saving was achieved through the use of smaller type and through such strategies as collapsing several paragraphs into one (particularly common in passages of dialogue). But perhaps the most revealing patterns involve two

[3]For another argument against Defoe's involvement in the third edition, see the textual note (by Herbert Davis) to the World's Classics edition and see Appendix A to this volume.

practices. (1) The first edition had a large number of wasteful "trailer" lines; that is, lines of type which are less than half filled out, occurring at the end of a paragraph. The third edition has very few such lines, and two or three words are often cut near the end of a paragraph to be sure to jam the paragraph into one fewer line. (2) The third edition regularly omits phrases and parenthetical remarks which are almost precisely a type line in length, even when their omission causes a loss in meaning. The editor is obviously counting lines of type, and sometimes it seems almost as if the excision, or at least part of it, is being done by the printer at the very moment he sets the type, for some of the cuts represent the sort of space-saving opportunism that a printer could discover best. I should add that the amount of excision fluctuates widely. Sometimes almost no changes are made for several pages at a time, but such passages of stability usually follow ruthless excisions: it is almost as if the editor operates according to a directed schedule of length, and regulates the amount of his cutting, at a given point, by where he stands in respect to the schedule.

I should not give the impression that the third edition was done thoughtlessly or clumsily.[4] Rather, I mean to imply that it was done calculatedly, with decreased costs and an enlarged audience in view. Whoever did the editing was an intelligent and fairly careful reader, but his assignment forced him occasionally to change the meaning, and more often to alter the detailed and rambling style of the garrulous Moll. An author could conceivably be employed to trim his own work, but here the nature of some of the changes suggests that the hand was not Defoe's. And in the absence of persuasive evidence that Defoe *did* participate in the third edition, I believe we should consider the first edition to be the only one with his full authority.

[4]In a few places I have adopted, for this edition, third edition readings, but only in cases where the first edition was obviously garbled and where the third edition's reading seemed certainly in line with the intent of the passage.

INTRODUCTION

The critical winds have shifted favorably for *Moll Flanders* in recent years, and the book is now more highly praised, and probably more often read, than at any time since its first publication in 1722. Most undergraduate fiction courses offer *Moll* as the "representative" Defoe novel, and as this edition is being prepared for press there are already more than a dozen different editions available in bookstores. But *Moll* has not always enjoyed such popularity and prestige. A century ago, Sir Leslie Stephen, assessing Defoe's novelistic accomplishment, considered it necessary to write extensively of *Robinson Crusoe*, but he mentioned *Moll* only in passing; and his attitude was typical. Throughout the nineteenth century, Defoe was usually considered a one-novel novelist, and it was popular to classify *Moll* among the "secondary novels," distinctly a cut beneath *Crusoe* and, often, below *Journal of the Plague Year*. I confess to a certain perverse archaism in still preferring *Crusoe* to any other Defoe work, but *Moll* does not need my preference; and a debate over whether it is best or second best is likely to rest on some very fine points that turn out to be, at last, only a matter of personal taste. Clearly, *Moll*'s modern rediscovery was long overdue, and the new attention is richly deserved. The several essays at the end of this volume amply apologize for *Moll*'s present reputation and suggest some of the bases of the book's artistic power; here I shall only sketch the critical vicissitudes that earlier befell the book, and briefly "place" it in the context of Defoe's career and times.

I

Defoe's "literary" career began long after his business career and his career as a politician and journalist. Born in 1660, he was nearly fifty-nine years old when his first novel (*Robinson Crusoe*) was published in 1719 (though he had earlier published a variety of poems and prose pieces of substantial literary merit). His early life, in fact, hardly suggested that he would become one of the most prolific writers in the language — the author, according to his latest bibliographer, of 547 different titles.[1] Only twenty-two of those titles were

[1]See John Robert Moore, *A Checklist of the Writings of Daniel Defoe*, Bloomington, 1960. I have followed Professor Moore's authority in my citation of works here. The difficulties of establishing the Defoe canon are enormous because almost everything he wrote was published anony- mously. For earlier attempts to decide what Defoe wrote, see Wilson, Lee, Dottin, and the following by W. P. Trent: *The Nation* LXXXIV (1907), 515–18; LXXXV (1907), 29–32, 180–83; and the Defoe section of the Cambridge Bibliography.

published before 1700, and Defoe was busy in those early years as a ministerial student, European traveler, merchant, importer, and political agent for William and Mary. But his ever-deepening immersion in politics accelerated his writing career too, and the early years of the eighteenth century begin to show the voluminous productivity that resulted in more than 500 titles during the last thirty years of his life, *after* he was forty years old.

Many of these titles are more interesting to the political or social historian than to a student of literature, but the incredible variety of Defoe's subjects and the breadth and depth of his knowledge rank him as one of the most versatile of men. He wrote poems in praise of William, ironic tracts praising Tory persecution of Dissenters, accounts of spectral visitations, treatises on economics, defenses of government policy and attacks upon it, biographies of criminals, clergymen, and kings, proposals to reform law enforcement, didactic treatises on the conduct of families and individuals, accounts of his travels, and descriptions of divine intervention in human history. A student who wished to know the internal workings of government and trade in the early eighteenth century could hardly do better than follow the traces of Defoe's swift and furtive movements among the major men, institutions, and ideas of his time. And lurking, too, among the subjects and strategies of all those books about all those things are clues to the characteristic genius of Defoe and the artistic power that exhibited itself so clearly when Defoe turned to the fictional writing upon which his literary reputation is based.

Precisely how Defoe came to be a novelist at that late age we do not know, though we may point to common concerns the novels share with the earlier work and with the later nonfiction which he continued to write until his death in 1731. But we do know that once he began to write fiction, he maintained the sense of audience that had stood him in such good stead as a political pamphleteer and journalist. He had a shrewd eye on what the reading public was buying, and the subject matter of his novels relates closely to that of contemporary best sellers: there are action and adventure in faraway places, there are accounts of exotic customs and inexplicable occurrences, there are pirates and criminals and whores, and there is always a supplied moral. It would be a mistake not to recognize that Defoe's subjects were common in the popular literature (or subliterature) of his time and that he knew the contemporary tastes, traditions, and methods well. And it would be an equal mistake to assume that Defoe was slavish in his imitation of these traditions, that their methods became his methods, or that he simply pandered to contemporary taste. Knowing what the public wanted did not necessarily confine him to giving it to them the way they wanted it — or, in fact, giving it to them at all — but he always knew enough to pretend convincingly, sometimes so convincingly that his audience could not discriminate between his models and what he made of them, sometimes so subtly that they did not know they had been manipulated into attitudes and conclusions they had not meant to hold.

Take, for instance, Defoe's first novel, *Robinson Crusoe*. Defoe's time offered no attractive book jackets or sophisticated advertising brochures; instead, the title page served at once as a table of contents and as an advertisement. *Crusoe's* title page emphasizes the "strange and surprizing" aspects of Crusoe's long isolation, his encounters with cannibals, his domestication of Friday. Here, the title page promises, is God's plenty for the lover of suspense and adventure, for the reader fascinated by remote places and strange peoples – and all true. But the book itself offers much more; it not only satisfies the desires stimulated by the title page, but also uses those desires to accomplish more complex things that make *Crusoe*, as well as an adventure story, an account of man's encounter with God, nature, his fellow man, and himself. The expectations of the title page – expectations calculated upon what Defoe's contemporaries were reading – are satisfied, but transformed; and to see *Crusoe* clearly we should see it not only in relation to contemporary adventure stories and travel literature, but also in relation to manuals of religious piety, accounts of marvelous events wrought by Providence, spiritual biographies and autobiographies, and anthologies of anecdotes illustrating spiritual and moral lessons.[2] But *Crusoe* is not exactly like any of these kinds either; rather it draws what it needs eclectically from several traditions and transforms it into something distinctive in itself. Seeing some books that resemble *Crusoe*, in one way or another, tells us some sorts of questions to ask, but the analogues do not necessarily tell us what *Crusoe* is. Through them, we can see the audience Defoe had in mind and the expectations that audience brought to *Crusoe*, but we must still ask *how* Defoe ministered to and modified those expectations, and what he did with his relatively commonplace materials, in the text itself.

Similar considerations apply to other Defoe novels, and there are a fair number of them, for once Defoe turned to long fiction, his attention to the mode was, for six years, intense. Before the end of 1719, he had published a sequel (*The Farther Adventures of Robinson Crusoe*); in 1720 came *Memoirs of a Cavalier*, then *Captain Singleton*, and a third Crusoe book (*Serious Reflections during the Life and Surprising Adventures . . . With His Vision of the Angelic World*). *Moll Flanders* followed in 1722, along with *Journal of the Plague Year* and *Colonel Jack*; *The Fortunate Mistress* (or *Roxana*) appeared in 1724. And although such a list by itself suggests both facility and indefatigability, it represents

[2]In this paragraph I have greatly simplified the relation of these traditions to *Robinson Crusoe*. For a fuller discussion, see Hunter, *The Reluctant Pilgrim*, and Starr, *Defoe and Spiritual Autobiography*.

only a small part of Defoe's writing during those years. The year, for example, that *Moll Flanders* appeared (1722) also saw the publication of a two-volume *Collection of Miscellany Letters* (to which Defoe was a major contributor and of which he was possibly editor); *Due Preparations for the Plague* (nearly 300 pages long); *Religious Courtship* (364 pages); a political pamphlet of 38 pages; and a 420-page *Impartial History of the Life and Actions of Peter Alexowitz, the Present Czar of Muscovy*.

After 1724, although the enormous productivity continued, there is little that extends Defoe's claims as a novelist, but he does fictively embroider some essentially true biographies, and he does continue to show interest in subjects treated in *Moll Flanders*. His moralistic predilections are most prominently reflected in *A New Family Instructor* and *Conjugal Lewdness: Or, Matrimonial Whoredom* (both 1727), and his interest in geography and travel is demonstrated again by *A New Voyage Round the World* (1724), *A Tour Thro' the Whole Island of Great Britain* (3 vols., 1724–26), and several edited memoirs of real adventurers and explorers. And his concern about crime continues to emerge almost everywhere, though it is especially prominent in such works as *Augusta Triumphans: Or, The Way to Make London the Most Flourishing City in the Universe* (1728), two tracts on street robberies (1728 and 1730) and one on streetwalkers (1726). Even more dramatic evidence of this concern is provided by his various biographies of famous criminals: two of Jack Sheppard in 1724, two of Jonathan Wild in 1725, an account (with dying speech) of a man tried for barbarous murder in 1726, *An Account of the Conduct and Proceedings of the Late John Gow alias Smith, Captain of the Late Pirates, Executed for Murther and Piracy* ... (1725), *A Brief Historical Account of the Lives of the Six Notorious Street-Robbers Executed at Kingston* (1726), and *A General History of the Robberies and Murders of the Most Notorious Pyrates* (2 vols., 1724, 1728), containing thirty "lives."

II

Defoe's concern about crime and his fascination with what criminals were like reflects the intense interest of his countrymen in the 1720's, and again demonstrates his awareness of what his public was thinking about. Residents of London had every right to be concerned about the lawless directions of their civilization, for, by every measurable standard, crime of all sorts was increasing rapidly, and ordinary citizens might well fear for their lives and property. A 1731 pamphlet describes the London scene this way:

> The streets of the City are now the places of danger; men are knocked down and robb'd, nay, sometimes murdered at their own doors, and in passing and repassing from house to house, or from shop to shop.

Stage coaches are robbed in High Holbourn, Whitechapel, Pall Mall, Soho, and at almost all the avenues to the City. Hackney coaches and gentlemen's coaches are stopt in Cheapside, St. Paul's Churchyard, the Strand, and other [of] the most crowded streets, and that even while the people in throngs are passing and repassing, as it were at their elbows.

Nor are these personal violences the only grievances which we have to complain of; but the boldness and multitude of lewd and disorderly persons of both sexes, which throng the streets as soon as the evening may be said to begin, are such, that renders it not only unpleasant, but indeed unsafe, to honest and modest people to be abroad, or go from place to place, however lawful or however urgent their occasions may be.[3]

Punishment for convicted criminals became ever more severe, and by the end of the eighteenth century 200 crimes were punishable by death, but the developing rigidity of the law did little to allay actual crime until, as the century moved on, some of the underlying social causes were admitted and addressed by more meaningful reforms.

The contemporary criminal scene was, of course, only one of many reasons that the English public of 1722 had become habituated to reading criminal lives and that they relished *Moll Flanders*. Other reasons are less timely and have more to do with the continuing predilections of human nature: the desire to know how the other half lives; the need to feel the superiority of one's own values; the grasping for explanations of why the inculcated values of one's earlier life seem less relevant in times that are changing rapidly; and the quiet but intense prurience one may derive in reading of acts and patterns of behavior that one may not himself feel free to engage in. And Defoe, in *Moll Flanders*, makes use of such expectations (however much a secret they may be to readers who have them) as well as of the expectations more openly admitted by the age's concern with criminality as such. But he modifies these expectations too:

Moll turns out, except for the necessities of circumstance, to be frighteningly like us.

Her values are mainly of the same acquisitive sort that characterize respectable society.

She is a product of an earlier century (not of the present), and that century turns out, in Defoe's rendering, not to have been a place of placid serenity or symbolic order, but quite like the present. Rather than the chaos of the eighteenth-century present being comforted by secure nations of a solid seventeenth-century past, the present and past confront one another in a damning vision of human nature and its violent reactions to the complexity of social environments. Not even the comfort of the golden past is allowed.

[3]As quoted by Sir Walter Besant, *London in the Eighteenth Century*, London, 1902, pp. 495–96.

He omits the juiciest parts, though Moll's experience and her powers of vividness obviously make available possibilities of raw thrill. For real prurience or erotic stimulation the reader must wait for *Fanny Hill*, or (perhaps) read the detailed examples in more standard didactic treatises.

Defoe has always been near the center of vigorous debates about didacticism in eighteenth-century literature, and many interpreters (from that time to the present) have been skeptical about the moral aims Defoe professes. But the question becomes, in my mind, not so much one of intention in Defoe himself or of aim in his writings; rather the question involves whether the Defoe method works. Does a reader emulate the positive qualities of a character who offers herself as a kind of guide or exemplar? Does he learn from her moral mistakes, and does he, even if he believes in the validity of her repentance, take the changes in her view of herself as a model for himself? Or is the prurience paramount? Defoe pretended that his method invited, through its subject matter and through title page blurbs, the vicious reader, and that vicious tastes and expectations became reformed: he thought that those who came to scoff remained to pray. The crucial question is whether the human mind works that way, and much of the history of eighteenth-century fiction focuses around this central issue.

The question of how to teach (even when one assumes that an artist desires to teach a specific thing) remains as debatable now as when it was debated in Defoe's own time. Does example really work? Can men be laughed from their follies, or frightened from their vices? Will direct didactic statement properly affect human minds, which often perversely prefer to do the opposite of what they are told? Will ironic indirection undermine human perversity and, when properly manipulated, lead men to virtue in spite of themselves? Eighteenth century novelists raise these issues into prominence as dramatically and as fully as the literature of our own time or any other; still, the answers about effects remain locked in the mind of man.

But if I emphasize here the improbability of finding a secure formula that will once and for all separate the good and bad guys and give us an infallible method of testing the didactic hypotheses of literature, I do not mean to foreclose important questions about what *Moll Flanders* was to Defoe and his contemporaries, or may be to us. Our inability to assess certain of its effects does not prevent our seeing some of its important characteristics, and (to my mind, at least) the best way of doing this is to compare it with other books that in one way or another resemble it.

The full title *Moll Flanders* reads this way: *The Fortunes* and*

---

*Although the title page of the first edition has *Fortunes*, the title heading the first text page of the novel has *History* (as reproduced on p. 9 of this volume).

Misfortunes of the Famous Moll Flanders, & c. Who was Born in Newgate, and during a Life of continu'd Variety for Threescore Years, besides her Childhood, was Twelve Year a Whore, five times a Wife (whereof once to her own Brother) Twelve Year a Thief, Eight Year a Transported Felon in Virginia, at last grew Rich, liv'd Honest, and died a Penitent. Written from her own Memorandums. A reader of 1722 might well have associated such an advertisement with several kinds of books, and for convenience I here categorize a few of these kinds, though it should be remembered that the categories are synthetic and that few absolute conventions or borders existed in any one of them.

Most obvious is the criminal biography, an account of the life and exploits of a particular rogue. Defoe's contemporaries read genuine ones and spurious ones, and many that combined the actuality of a criminal career with incidents that were embroidered, borrowed from another criminal life, or totally fabricated. Defoe himself wrote, as I have already indicated, of such rogues as Jonathan Wild and Jack Sheppard, and he was perhaps the most distinguished writer of this kind of book, but he had plenty of contemporary competition. Besides the individual biographies (usually relatively short and sold at pamphlet prices),[4] collections of "lives" (such as Defoe's *General History of the . . . Pyrates*) were enormously popular. In 1713 a "Captain Alexander Smith" published *The History of the Lives and Robberies of the Most Noted Highway-Men, Foot-Pads, House-Breakers, Shop-Lifts and Cheats of Both Sexes in and about London and Westminster*; by 1719 it had reached a fifth edition, and later more volumes were added and the book continued to be published along with a bewildering bibliographical maze of additions from other sources. Another collection (Theophilus Lucas, *Memoirs of the Lives, Intrigues, and Comical Adventures of the Most Famous Gamesters and Celebrated Sharpers in the Reigns of Charles II, James II, William III, and Queen Anne*, 1714) suggests something of the variety to be found in criminal biography — variety of tone as well as of subject matter. Sometimes the roguery was just jolly fun and games, and sometimes it was disruptive and evil, darkly indicative of the wickedness of the age. Sometimes the crimes involved clever strategems and practical jokes; sometimes there were robbery, brutality, rape, murder, and treason.[5]

Closely related to the criminal biographies were pamphlets describing the confessions of criminals, sometimes detailing their secret undiscovered crimes, often presenting their repentance of wickedness, and almost always offering their "dying words" as they prepared to be hanged. Often such pamphlets were hawked about at the execution

[4]One of Defoe's Sheppard pamphlets, for example, sold for sixpence, the other for a shilling.

[5]For a discussion of varieties of literature involving picaros and criminals, see Frank W. Chandler, *The Literature of Roguery*, Boston and New York, 2 vols., 1907, esp. vol. I.

(with the dying words clearly having been recorded in advance); the pretense was moral edification, but of course one may wonder whether the motivation of buyers at such fiestas was not rather more complex. At any rate, the age provided plenty of occasions to write such lives and plenty of opportunities to buy, for 242 persons were hanged between 1701 and 1713.

The popularity of dying speeches is suggested by the publication in 1720 (by one of Defoe's publishers, incidentally) of a huge collection of them, *Dying Speeches and Behaviour of the Several State Prisoners that Have Been Executed the Last 300 Years.* Jonathan Swift was among the many who openly doubted the moral efficacy of such publications, and in 1722 (just a few months after *Moll Flanders* appeared) he brilliantly parodied the tradition in his *The Last Speech and Dying Words of Ebenezor Elliston.* Swift plainly thinks that no one gets reformed by sentimental twaddle, but he affects to know the true way to "teach" virtue: he has Elliston march to his death asserting, not the glory of repentance, but rather a simple fact — he has given the authorities a secret list of his accomplices and other criminals he knows. No one, he promises, will be apprehended who does not sin again, but if anyone does . . . .[6]

Criminal acts are also detailed elaborately in another tradition with more convincing religious and moral aims, the tradition of "Providence Literature."[7] Such literature describes how crime is detected through divine intervention, and recounts the horrible consequences that the criminal may expect, punishments physical as well as spiritual. William Turner's *Compleat History of the Most Remarkable Providences* (1697) anthologizes many stories of this sort, and similar in intention, if not in scope, are such books as *God's Judgment against Whoring* (1697), *God's Judgements upon Drunkards* (1659), and *The Triumphs of God's Revenge against Murther* (c. 1621).

The first two of the categories I have mentioned, and to a certain extent the third, emphasize audience interest in crime itself and relate closely to one of the stated aims of *Moll Flanders*: to prevent much crime by making the public aware of the methods and practices that criminals use. But *Moll Flanders* clearly moves beyond such exposure to less timely but more enduring human questions — questions involving motivation to criminal acts. It asks its readers to see what it would be like to be on *that* side of the law, caught in circumstances that lead progressively from acts of survival to gestures of hostility and self-destruction. And for this side of *Moll Flanders* we may profitably turn to traditions which, though perhaps not psychologically

---

[6]See *The Prose Works of Jonathan Swift* (ed. Herbert Davis), Oxford, 1948, vol. IX, pp. 35–41.

[7]See Hunter, *The Reluctant Pilgrim,* chap. 3.

analytical by modern definition, try to isolate patterns of human behavior. The traditions of the personal diary and of spiritual auto-biography and biography attempt such definitions of human pattern; at least the penitential aspects of *Moll*, and perhaps the whole struc-ture of the book, deserve consideration in the light of these traditions.[8]

The traditions I have mentioned interrelate and overlap, and the relationship between *Moll Flanders* and these contexts is a complex one, needing more appreciation and fuller description than it has ever yet received. Recent criticism of *Moll Flanders* suggests that such contextual problems are being more and more recognized, and the essays at the back of this volume take a number of important steps toward "placing" *Moll Flanders* correctly among its ancestors, contem-poraries, and descendants.

III

The first edition of *Moll Flanders* was published on January 27, 1722,[9] by W. Chetwood and T. Edlin. A second edition, published by J. Brotherton, followed in July, and before the end of the year a "third edition, corrected" was issued first by Brotherton, then by Chetwood and a group of six associated publishers that included Brotherton. In 1723, this edition was reissued, and J. Read the same year published a pirated abridgment, cutting the book approximately in half, dividing it into chapters, giving Moll a real name (Laetitia Atkins), and adding a section on her last days and death. It was this severely truncated version that was most often reprinted during the later eighteenth century, though the text of the third edition was reissued at least once, in 1741. The text of the first edition was not, so far as I know, reissued during the eighteenth century, and has seldom been reprinted since, most editors having preferred the third edition, which is considerably shorter.[10]

Five English editions within two years suggest a reasonably favor-able reception by Defoe's contemporaries, and that suggestion is confirmed by the fact that *Moll* was translated into German within a year. The book continued to be popular well into midcentury (though not nearly so popular as *The Family Instructor*), but by the late eighteenth century Defoe was already beginning to be considered a one-book novelist. Samuel Johnson singles out *Robinson Crusoe* for special mention, and in 1783 both James Beattie and Hugh Blair praise *Crusoe* but ignore *Moll* completely, foreshadowing what became

---

[8] I have been the briefer in my account here because the subject has recently been studied in some detail; see Starr, chap. 4.

[9] The title page reads 1721 because England was still using the Julian calendar, in which the new year began in March.

[10] The third edition trims about 10 per-cent from the first edition. See the textual note above.

the nineteenth-century orthodoxy of distinguishing between *Crusoe* and the "secondary novels."

The rising reputation of Defoe in the early years of the nineteenth century did not often extend wide enough to include much enthusiasm for *Moll Flanders*, and, as the century moved on, the "coarse" subject matter and style usually precluded favorable judgment, even among critics who approved of some of the other "secondary" books. Walter Wilson, in an 1830 biography of Defoe, dismisses *Moll*, even though he is relatively kind to *Roxana*, *Colonel Jack*, and several others. And sometimes *Moll* was not only dismissed as art, but openly attacked as immoral. One of the most despairing attacks (in *Cornhill Magazine*, 1871) is excerpted at the end of this volume; similar laments appear in the *London Quarterly Review* in 1882 and in the *Spectator*, 1887. Defoe's reputation suffered generally during the sixties and seventies from the discovery of papers indicating his political duplicity, but the regard for *Moll* had not been high anyway, and it was the more generally approved didactic works (*Crusoe*, *The Family Instructor*, *Journal of the Plague Year*) that felt most of the impact of that discovery. The damnation of *Moll* was not universal, on either moral or artistic grounds (see, for example, Charles Lamb's essay at the end of this volume), but the nineteenth century generally did not give *Moll* either the popular acclaim it received from Defoe's contemporaries or the critical respect that the twentieth century has offered.[10]

It is usual to cite E. M. Forster's attention to *Moll* (*Aspects of the Novel*, 1927) as the critical turning point, but several earlier critics had already singled out its excellence. In 1899, Wilbur L. Cross (*The Development of the English Novel*) had found some of the material in *Moll* "unequalled even among the modern naturalists," and in 1905 William J. Dawson (*Makers of English Fiction*) rated *Moll* higher than *Crusoe*. George Saintsbury (*The English Novel*, 1913) called *Moll* "in some respects the greatest of all [Defoe's] books," and in 1919 Virginia Woolf used the occasion of the two hundredth anniversary of *Crusoe* to defend *Moll* passionately instead.

Mrs. Woolf's defense is not based entirely on literary grounds, and her essay may be the occasion to remind us that part of the new acclaim of *Moll* in the twentieth century may well be extraliterary, having to do with our century's interest in inverting the tastes of our

---

[10]The nineteenth century excerpts at the end of this volume offer a fair sample of opinion. The fullest account of Defoe's reputation is Sidney J. Black's unpublished Boston University dissertation (1955), but more readily available are two essays by Charles Eaton Burch: "British Criticism of Defoe as a Novelist 1719–1860," *Englische Studien*, LXVII (1932), 178–98; "Defoe's British Reputation 1869–1894," *Englische Studien*, LXVIII (1934), 410–23. For a fuller account of recent criticism of *Moll Flanders*, see Ian Watt, "The Recent Critical Fortunes of *Moll Flanders*," *Eighteenth-Century Studies*, I (1967), 109–26.

Victorian forebears. But whatever the ultimate inspiration for the re-discovery of *Moll*, the book (in my opinion) speaks its own critical justification.

The twentieth-century essays included at the end of this volume also speak for themselves; they raise into prominence some of the major questions that the criticism of fiction has greeted in the last few years, when first the "new criticism" and now the "new contextualism" discovered the novel as fertile territory. Here are discussed issues of imagery, of ironic language, of intention, of structure. I might simply add that some major issues remain to be settled, and a few questions are still to be asked. What are we to make of Moll's slackening penitence? How is the retrospective point of view manipulated, and is Defoe conscious of the complicated problems of having a narrator look back sometimes in vivid detail, sometimes with more haze in between? How are we to view Moll's masks and disguises, and her refusal at last to identify herself, even if "a general Pardon should be issued"? Why does Moll habitually pun and toy with language, especially when she is frightened? What are we to make of the additive, anecdotal shape of the book? What of the book's mistakes of fact and consistency—are they Moll's or Defoe's? Why does a writer as political as Defoe assiduously avoid mentioning historical events, even though Moll lived through one of the most turbulent periods in English history? Is Defoe truly anachronistic in references to events that do not jibe with Moll's profession to have written the book in 1683, or is a complex artistic intent involved, an intent which also undercuts the claim of genuine memoirs and an editor? And, finally, what is the relation of *Moll Flanders* to the subliterature which helped to form the expectations of Defoe's readers?

THE
FORTUNES
AND
MISFORTUNES
Of the FAMOUS
Moll Flanders, &c.

Who was Born in NEWGATE, and during a
Life of continu'd Variety for Threescore Years,
besides her Childhood, was Twelve Year a
Whore, five times a *Wife* (whereof once to her
own Brother) Twelve Year a *Thief,* Eight Year a
Transported *Felon* in *Virginia,* at last grew *Rich,*
liv'd *Honest,* and died a *Penitent.*

Written from her own MEMORANDUMS.

LONDON: Printed for, and Sold by W.
CHETWOOD, at *Cato's-Head,* in *Russel-
street, Covent-Garden*; and T. EDLING, at
the *Prince's-Arms,* over-against *Exerter-Change*
in the *Strand.* MDDCXXI.

THE
PREFACE

The World is so taken up of late with Novels and Romances, that it will be hard for a private History[1] to be taken for Genuine, where the Names and other Circumstances of the Person are concealed, and on this Account we must be content to leave the Reader to pass his own Opinion upon the ensuing Sheets, and take it just as he pleases.

The Author is here suppos'd to be writing her own History, and in the very beginning of her Account, she gives the Reasons why she thinks fit to conceal her true Name, after which there is no Occasion to say any more about that.

It is true, that the original of this Story is put into new Words, and the Stile of the famous Lady we here speak of is a little alter'd, particularly she is made to tell her own Tale in modester Words than she told it at first; the Copy which came first to Hand, having been written in Language, more like one still in *Newgate*,[2] than one grown Penitent and Humble, as she afterwards pretends[3] to be.

[1]Eighteenth-century writers of prose fiction often called their works "histories" (e.g., Richardson's *Clarissa; or, The History of a Young Lady* and Fielding's *The History of Tom Jones, a Foundling*) to distinguish them from the popular "novels" and "romances," which serious writers often derided as fantastic and frivolous. Technically, "history" simply means a narrative of incidents, true or not; but those who claimed to write histories insisted either that their narrative was literally true, or that it was an accurate depiction of human nature. For a discussion of contemporary uses of the term, see *Tom Jones*, IV, i.

[2]The largest and best-known London prison of the time.

[3]Professes, claims, not necessarily suggesting fraud or falsehood. Defoe's pose of being merely an editor for genuine memoirs is a common strategy in early fiction.

The Pen employ'd in finishing her Story, and making it what you now see it to be, has had no little difficulty to put it into a Dress fit to be seen, and to make it speak Language fit to be read: When a Woman debauch'd from her Youth, nay, even being the Off-spring of Debauchery and Vice, comes to give an Account of all her vicious Practises, and even to descend to the particular Occasions and Circumstances, by which she first became wicked, and of all the progression of Crime which she run through in threescore Year, an Author must be hard put to it to wrap it up so clean, as not to give room, especially for vitious Readers to turn it to his Disadvantage.

All possible Care however has been taken to give no leud[4] Ideas, no immodest Turns in the new dressing up this Story, no not to the worst parts of her Expressions; to this Purpose some of the vicious part of her Life, which cou'd not be modestly told, is quite left out, and several other Parts, are very much shorten'd; what is left 'tis hop'd will not offend the chastest Reader, or the modestest Hearer; and as the best use is made even of the worst Story, the Moral 'tis hop'd will keep the Reader serious, even where the Story might incline him to be otherwise: To give the History of a wicked Life repented of, necessarily requires that the wick'd Part should be made as wicked, as the real History of it will bear; to illustrate and give a Beauty to the Penitent part, which is certainly the best and brightest, if related with equal Spirit and Life.

It is suggested there cannot be the same Life, the same Brightness and Beauty, in relateing the penitent Part, as is in the criminal Part: If there is any Truth in that Suggestion, I must be allow'd to say, 'tis because there is not the same taste and relish in the Reading, and indeed it is too true that the difference lyes not in the real worth of the Subject; so much as in the Gust[5] and Palate of the Reader.

But as this Work is chiefly recommended to those who know how to Read it, and how to make the good Uses of it, which the Story all along recommends to them; so it is to be hop'd that such Readers will be much more pleas'd with the Moral, than the Fable; with the Application, than with the Relation, and with the End of the Writer, than with the Life of the Person written of.

There is in this Story abundance of delightful Incidents, and all of them usefully apply'd. There is an agreeable turn Artfully given them in the relating, that naturally Instructs the Reader, either one way, or other. The first part of her leud Life with the young Gentleman at *Colchester*, has so many happy Turns given it to expose the Crime, and warn all whose Circumstances are adapted to it, of the ruinious End of such things, and the foolish Thoughtless and abhorr'd Conduct

[4]Lewd, lascivious.
[5]Taste, inclination.

of both the Parties, that it abundantly attones for all the lively Discription she gives of her Folly and Wickedness.

The Repentance[6] of her Lover at the *Bath*, and how brought by the just alarm of his fit of Sickness to abandon her; the just Caution given there against even the lawful Intimacies of the dearest Friends, and how unable they are to preserve the most solemn Resolutions of Vertue without divine Assistance; these are Parts, which to a just Discernment will appear to have more real Beauty in them, than all the amorous Chain of Story, which introduces it.

In a Word, as the whole Relation is carefully garbl'd[7] of all the Levity, and Looseness that was in it: So it is all applied, and with the utmost care to vertuous and religious Uses. None can without being guilty of manifest Injustice, cast any Reproach upon it, or upon our Design in publishing it.

The Advocates for the Stage, have in all Ages made this the great Argument to persuade People that their Plays are useful, and that they ought to be allow'd in the most civiliz'd, and in the most religious Government; Namely, That they are applyed to vertuous Purposes, and that by the most lively Representations, they fail not to recommend Vertue, and generous Principles, and to discourage and expose all sorts of Vice and Corruption of Manners; and were it true that they did so, and that they constantly adhered to that Rule, as the Test of their acting on the *Theatre*, much might be said in their Favour.

Throughout the infinite variety of this Book, this Fundamental is most strictly adhered to; there is not a wicked Action in any Part of it, but is first and last rendered Unhappy and Unfortunate: There is not a superlative Villain brought upon the Stage, but either he is brought to an unhappy End, or brought to be a Penitent: There is not an ill thing mention'd, but it is condemn'd, even in the Relation, nor a vertuous just Thing, but it carries its Praise along with it: What can more exactly answer the Rule laid down, to recommend even those Representations of things which have so many other just Objections lying against them? Namely, of Example, of bad Company, obscene Language, and the like.

Upon this Foundation this Book is recommended to the Reader, as a Work from every part of which something may be learned, and some just and religious Inference is drawn, by which the Reader will have something of Instruction, if he pleases to make use of it.

All the Exploits of this Lady of Fame, in her Depredations upon Mankind stand as so many warnings to honest People to beware of

---

[6]Eighteenth-century manuals of piety continually deplore the fact that many people repent only when they face disease or physical danger, but they also defend God's use of such means to reclaim men who otherwise would lack the will to save their own souls. For a discussion of this matter, see Hunter, *The Reluctant Pilgrim*, pp. 41–42.

[7]Sifted, purged.

them, intimating to them by what Methods innocent People are drawn in, plunder'd and robb'd, and by Consequence how to avoid them. Her robbing a little innocent Child, dress'd fine by the vanity of the Mother, to go to the Dancing-School, is a good Memento to such People hereafter; as is likewise her picking the Gold-Watch from the young Ladies side in the *Park*.

Her getting a parcel from a hair-brained Wench at the Coaches in St. *John-street*; her Booty made at the Fire, and again at *Harwich*; all give us excellent Warnings in such Cases to be more present to ourselves in sudden Surprizes of every Sort.

Her application to a sober Life, and industrious Management at last in *Virginia*, with her Transported Spouse, is a Story fruitful of Instruction, to all the unfortunate Creatures who are oblig'd to seek their Re-establishment abroad; whether by the Misery of Transportation, or other Disaster; letting them know, that Diligence and Application have their due Encouragement, even in the remotest Parts of the World, and that no Case can be so low, so despicable, or so empty of Prospect, but that an unwearied Industry will go a great way to deliver us from it, will in time raise the meanest[8] Creature to appear again in the World,[9] and give him a new Cast[10] for his Life.

These are a few of the serious Inferences which we are led by the Hand to in this Book, and these are fully sufficient to Justifie any Man in recommending it to the World, and much more to Justifie the Publication of it.

There are two of the most beautiful Parts still behind,[11] which this Story gives some Idea of, and lets us into the Parts of them, but they are either of them too long to be brought into the same Volume; and indeed are, *as I may call them* whole Volumes of themselves, (*viz.*) 1. The Life of her Governess, as she calls her, who had run thro', it seems, in a few Years all the eminent degrees of a Gentlewoman, a Whore, and a Bawd; a Midwife, and a Midwife-keeper, as *they are call'd*, a Pawn-broker, a Childtaker, a Receiver of Thieves, and of Thieves purchase, that is to say, of stolen Goods; and in a Word, her self a Thief, a Breeder up of Thieves, and the like, and yet at last a Penitent.

The second is the Life of her Transported Husband, a Highwayman; who it seems liv'd a twelve Years Life of successful Villany upon the Road, and even at last came off so well, as to be a Voluntier Transport, not a Convict; and in whose Life there is an incredible Variety.

[8]Most abject or debased.

[9]I.e., raise him to respectable status.

[10]Possibly two meanings of "cast" are merged here: (1) lot or fate, a throw of fortune; and (2) design, plan. Later Defoe further explores the rich connotations of this word, particularly in the meanings to calculate and to wreck, squander, ruin.

[11]Remaining, to come.

But as I have said, these are things too long to bring in here, so neither can I make a Promise of their coming out by themselves.[12]

We cannot say indeed, that this History is carried on quite to the full End of it, unless they can write it after they are dead; but her Husband's Life being written by a third Hand, gives a full Account of them both, how long they liv'd together in that Country, and how they came both to *England* again, after about eight Year, in which time they were grown very Rich, and where she liv'd it seems, to be very old; but was not so extraordinary a Penitent, as she was at first; it seems only that indeed she always spoke with abhorence of her former Life, and of every Part of it.

In her last Scene at *Maryland*, and *Virginia*, many pleasant things happen'd, which makes that part of her Life very agreeable, but they are not told with the same Elegancy as those accounted for by herself; so it is still to the more Advantage that we break off here.

[12]A 1730 volume (*Fortune's Fickle Distribution*) purported to offer these accounts; included was a much shortened account of Moll, plus the lives of "Jane Hackabout," the governess, and "James Macfaul," the highwayman husband. Defoe apparently had no hand in the publication.

THE
HISTORY
AND
MISFORTUNES
Of the FAMOUS
Moll Flanders, &c.

My True Name is so well known in the Records, or Registers at *Newgate*, and in the *Old-Baily*,[1] and there are some things of such Consequence still depending there, relating to my particular Conduct, that it is not to be expected I should set my Name, or the Account of my Family to this Work; perhaps, after my Death it may be better known, at present it would not be proper, no, not tho' a general Pardon should be issued, even without Exceptions and reserve of Persons or Crimes.

It is enough to tell you, that as some of my worst Comrades, who are out of the Way of doing me Harm, having gone out of the World by the Steps and the String[2] as I often expected to go, know me by the Name of *Moll Flanders*; so you may give me leave to speak of myself, under that Name till I dare own who I have been, as well as who I am.[3]

I have been told, that in one of our Neighbour Nations, whether it be in *France*, or where else, I know not; they have an Order from the King, that when any Criminal is condemn'd, either to Die, or to the Gallies, or to be Transported,[4] if they leave any Children, as such are

---

[1]A criminal court, adjoining Newgate Prison.

[2]A colloquial expression for being hanged. (steps = ladder below the gallows, string = hangman's rope)

[3]Moll's various disguises highlight her search for identity and raise significant critical questions about the psychological dimensions of Defoe's art.

[4]Capital punishment was prescribed for more than 100 crimes in Defoe's England. Theft of five shillings' value from a shop could, for example, lead to death. Exile in servitude, usually to America, was a common alternative early in the eighteenth century.

generally unprovided for, by the Poverty or Forfeiture of their Parents; so they are immediately taken into the Care of the Government, and put into an Hospital[5] call'd the *House* of *Orphans*, where they are Bred up, Cloath'd, Fed, Taught, and when fit to go out, are plac'd out to Trades, or to Services, so as to be well able to provide for themselves by an honest industrious Behaviour.

Had this been the Custom in our Country,[6] I had not been left a poor desolate Girl without Friends, without Cloaths, without Help or Helper in the World, as was my Fate; and by which, I was not only expos'd to very great Distresses, even before I was capable, either of Understanding my Case, or how to Amend it, but brought into a Course of Life,[7] which was not only scandalous in itself, but which, in its ordinary Course, tended to the swift Destruction both of Soul and Body.

But the Case was otherwise here, my Mother was convicted of Felony for a certain petty Theft, scarce worth naming, (*viz.*) Having an opportunity of borrowing[8] three Pieces of fine *Holland*,[9] of a certain Draper in *Cheapside:*[10] The Circumstances are too long to repeat, and I have heard them related so many Ways, that I can scarce be certain, which is the right Account.

However it was, this they all agree in, that my Mother pleaded her Belly,[11] and being found quick with Child; she was respited for about Seven Months, in which time having brought me into the World, and being about again, she was call'd Down, as they term it, to her former Judgment,[12] but obtain'd the Favour of being Transported to the Plantations, and left me about Half a Year old; and in bad Hands you may be sure.

This is too near the first Hours of my Life, for me to relate any thing of myself, but by hear say; 'tis enough to mention, that as I was born in such an unhappy Place, I had no Parish to have Recourse to for my

---

[5]A charitable institution for the education and maintenance of the young.

[6]Defoe's many writings show an intense sociological concern for the reform of poor laws and public institutions. For discussions of this, see the standard Defoe biographies, such as Moore and Sutherland.

[7]Terms such as "course" and "way" to describe the sequential actions of an individual's life derive from the old Christian concept of life as a journey or pilgrimage. For a discussion of the eighteenth-century significance of such terms, see Hunter, *The Reluctant Pilgrim.*

[8]Stealing (usually applied only to small thefts).

[9]Linen. (R) Hereafter (R) indicates terms which recur frequently but are glossed only on their initial appearances.

[10]The great market of London, held (before the 1666 fire) in the middle of the wide street.

[11]I.e., asked that her sentence be postponed on the ground that she was pregnant. Women criminals who claimed to be pregnant were not executed until after delivery; many women of course took advantage of the provision and falsely claimed pregnancy.

[12]I.e., her postponed sentence was now to be effected.

Nourishment in my Infancy,[13] nor can I give the least Account how I was kept alive; other than that, as I have been told, some Relation of my Mothers took me away for a while as a Nurse, but at whose Expence, or by whose Direction I know nothing at all of it.

The first account that I can Recollect, or could ever learn of myself, was, that I had wandred among a Crew of those People they call *Gypsies*, or *Egyptians*; but I believe it was but a very little while that I had been among them, for I had not had my Skin discolour'd, or blacken'd, as they do very young to all the Children they carry about with them,[14] nor can I tell how I came among them, or how I got from them.

It was at *Colchester* in *Essex*, that those People left me; and I have a Notion in my Head, that I left them there, (that is, that I hid myself and wou'd not go any farther with them) but I am not able to be particular in that Account; only this I remember, that being taken up by some of the Parish Officers of *Colchester*, I gave an Account, that I came into the Town with the *Gypsies*, but that I would not go any farther with them, and that so they had left me, but whither they were gone that I knew not, nor could they expect it of me; for tho' they sent round the Country to enquire after them, it seems they could not be found.

I was now in a Way to be provided for; for tho' I was not a Parish Charge upon this, or that part of the Town by Law; yet as my Case came to be known, and that I was too young to do any Work, being not above three Years old, Compassion mov'd the Magistrates of the Town to order some Care to be taken of me, and I became one of their own, as much as if I had been born in the Place.

In the Provision they made for me, it was my good hap to be put to Nurse, as they call it, to a Woman who was indeed Poor, but had been in better Circumstances, and who got a little Livelihood by taking such as I was suppos'd to be; and keeping them with all Necessaries, till they were at a certain Age, in which it might be suppos'd they might go to Service, or get their own Bread.

This Woman had also had a little School, which she kept to teach Children to Read and to Work; and having, as I have said, liv'd before that in good Fashion, she bred up the Children she took with a great deal of Art, as well as with a great deal of Care.

But that which was worth all the rest, she bred them up very Religiously, being herself a very sober pious Woman. (2.) Very

---

[13]Responsibility for orphans and other indigents fell to individual parishes. By law the parish was responsible only for orphans born within its limits; born in Newgate, Moll can claim no parish support. (unhappy = wretched, ill-fated [R]).

[14]Gypsies were believed to dye kidnapped children with walnut juice so that their lighter color would not betray the crime.

Housewifly and Clean, and, (3.) Very Mannerly, and with good Behaviour: So that in a Word, excepting a plain Diet, course[15] Lodging, and mean Cloths, we were brought up as Mannerly and as Genteely, as if we had been at the Dancing School.

I was continu'd here till I was eight years Old, when I was terrified with News, that the Magistrates, as I think they call'd them;[16] had order'd that I should go to Service; I was able to do but very little Service where ever I was to go, except it was to run of Errands, and be a Drudge to some Cook-Maid, and this they told me of often, which put me into a great Fright; for I had a thorough Aversion to going to Service, as they call'd it, that is to be a Servant, tho' I was so young; and I told my Nurse, as we call'd her, that I believ'd I could get my Living without going to Service if she pleas'd to let me; for she had Taught me to Work with my Needle, and Spin Worsted, which is the chief Trade of that City, and I told her that if she wou'd keep me, I wou'd Work for her, and I would Work very hard.

I talk'd to her almost every Day of Working hard; And in short, I did nothing but Work and Cry all Day, which griev'd the good kind Woman so much, that at last she began to be concern'd for me, for she lov'd me very well.

One Day after this, as she came into the Room, where all we poor Children were at Work, she sat down just over against me, not in her usual Place as Mistress, but as if she set herself on purpose to observe me, and see me Work: I was doing something she had set me to; as I remember, it was Marking some Shirts, which she had taken to Make, and after a while she began to Talk to me: Thou foolish Child, says she, thou art always Crying; (for I was Crying then) prethee, What doest Cry for? because they will take me away, *says I*, and put me to Service, and I can't Work House-Work; well Child, says she, but tho' you can't Work House-Work, as you call it, you will learn it in time, and they won't put you to hard Things at first; yes they will, says I, and if I can't do it, they will Beat me, and the Maids will Beat me to make me do great Work, and I am but a little Girl, and I can't do it, and then I cry'd again, till I could not speak any more to her.

This mov'd my good Motherly Nurse, so that she from that time resolv'd I should not go to Service yet, so she bid me not Cry, and she wou'd speak to Mr. *Mayor*, and I should not go to Service till I was bigger.

Well, this did not Satisfie me, for to think of going to Service, was such a frightful Thing to me, that if she had assur'd me I should not have gone till I was 20 years old, it wou'd have been the same to me,

---

[15]Coarse.

[16]Moll sometimes reports with great technical accuracy, but at other times reverts to a child's perspective. This may be part of Defoe's calculated attempt to manipulate a double point of view—one immediate, one retrospective.

I shou'd have cry'd, I believe, all the time, with the very Apprehension of its being to be so at last.

When she saw that I was not pacify'd yet, she began to be angry with me, and what wou'd you have? *says she*, don't I tell you that you shall not go to Service till you are bigger? Ay, says I, but then I must go at last; why, what? said she, is the Girl mad? what, would you be a Gentlewoman? Yes *says I*, and cry'd heartily, till I roar'd out again.

This set the old Gentlewoman a Laughing at me, as you may be sure it would: Well, Madam forsooth, says she, *Gibing at me*, you would be a Gentlewoman, and pray how will you come to be a Gentlewoman? what, will you do it by your Fingers Ends?

Yes, *says I again*, very innocently.

Why, what can you Earn, *says she*, what can you get a day at your Work?

Three-Pence, *said I*, when I Spin, and 4*d.* when I Work plain Work.

Alas! poor Gentlewoman, *said she again*, Laughing, what will that do for thee?

It will keep me, *says I*, if you will let me live with you; and this *I said*, in such a poor petitioning Tone, that it made the poor Womans Heart yearn to me, as she told me afterwards.

But, *says she*, that will not keep you, and buy you Cloths too; and who must buy the little Gentlewoman Cloths, *says she*, and smil'd all the while at me.

I will Work Harder then, *says I*, and you shall have it all.

Poor Child! it won't keep you, *says she*, it will hardly keep you in Victuals.

Then I will have no Victuals? *says I*, again very Innocently, let me but live with you.

Why, can you live without Victuals? *says she*; yes, *again says I*, very much like a Child, you may be sure, and still I cry'd heartily.

I Had no Policy[17] in all this, you may easily see it was all Nature,[18] but it was joyn'd with so much Innocence, and so much Passion, That in short, it set the good Motherly Creature a weeping too, and she cry'd at last as fast as I did, and then took me, and led me out of the teaching Room; come *says she*, you shan't go to Service, you shall live with me, and this pacify'd me for the present.

Sometime after this, she going to wait on the *Mayor*, and talking of such things as belong'd to her Business, at last my Story came up, and my good Nurse told Mr. *Mayor* the whole Tale: He was so pleas'd with it, that he would call his Lady, and his two Daughters to hear it, and it made Mirth enough among them, you may be sure.

[17]Craftiness, cunning.
[18]I.e., Moll acted according to her "Natural" bent.

However, not a Week had pass'd over, but on a suddain comes Mrs. *Mayoress*, and her two Daughters to the House to see my old Nurse, and to see her School and the Children: When they had look'd about them a little: Well, Mrs. ———— says the *Mayoress* to my Nurse; and pray which is the little Lass that intends to be a Gentlewoman? I heard her, and I was terrible frighted at first, tho' I did not know why neither; but Mrs. *Mayoress* comes up to me, Well Miss says she, And what are you at Work upon? The Word Miss was a Language that had hardly been heard of in our School, and I wondred what sad Name it was she call'd me; However, I stood up, made a Curtsy, and she took my Work out of my Hand, look'd on it, and said it was very well; then she took up one of my Hands, nay, says she, the Child may come to be a Gentlewoman for aught any body knows, she has a Gentlewoman's Hand, says she; this pleas'd me mightily you may be sure, but Mrs. *Mayoress* did not stop there, but giving me my Work again, she put her Hand in her Pocket, gave me a Shilling, and bid me mind my Work, and learn to Work well, and I might be a Gentlewoman for aught she knew.

Now all this while, my good old Nurse, Mrs. *Mayoress*, and all the rest of them did not understand me at all, for they meant one Sort of thing, by the Word Gentlewoman, and I meant quite another; for alas, all I understood by being a Gentlewoman, was to be able to Work for myself, and get enough to keep me without that terrible Bug-bear *going to Service*, whereas they meant to live Great, Rich, and High, and I know not what.

Well, after Mrs. *Mayoress* was gone, her two Daughters came in, and they call'd for the Gentlewoman too, and they talk'd a long while to me, and I answer'd them in my Innocent way; but always if they ask'd me whether I resolv'd to be a Gentlewoman, I answer'd YES: At last one of them ask'd me, what a Gentlewoman was? that puzzel'd me much; but however, I explain'd myself negatively, that it was one that did not go to Service, to do House-Work; they were pleas'd to be familiar with me, and lik'd my little Prattle to them, which it seems was agreeable enough to them, and they gave me Money too.[19]

As for my Money I gave it all to my Mistress Nurse, as I call'd her, and told her she should have all I got for myself when I was a Gentlewoman, as well as now; by this and some other of my talk, my old Tutress began to understand me, about what I meant by being a Gentlewoman; and that I understood by it no more, than to be able to get my Bread by my own Work, and at last, she ask'd me whether it was not so.

I told her *yes*, and insisted on it, that to do so, was to be a Gentlewoman; for says I, there is such a one, naming a Woman that mended

[19]Moll's early, and continuing, pre-occupation with money has often been considered evidence of her, or Defoe's, Protestant ethic.

Lace, and wash'd the Ladies Lac'd-heads,[20] she, *says I*, is a Gentle-woman, and they call her Madam.

Poor Child, says my good old Nurse, you may soon be such a Gentlewoman as that, for she is a Person of ill Fame, and has had two or three Bastards.

I did not understand any thing of that; but I answer'd, I am sure they call her Madam, and she does not go to Service, nor do House-Work, and therefore I insisted that she was a Gentlewoman, and I would be such a Gentlewoman as that.

The ladies were told all this again to be sure, and they made them-selves Merry with it, and every now and then the young Ladies, Mr. *Mayor's* Daughters would come and see me, and ask where the little Gentlewoman was, which made me not a little Proud of myself.

This held a great while, and I was often visited by these young Ladies, and sometimes they brought others with them; so that I was known by it, almost all over the Town.

I was now about ten Years old, and began to look a little Womanish, for I was mighty Grave[21] and Humble; very Mannerly, and as I had often heard the Ladies say I was Pretty, and would be a very handsome Woman, so you may be sure, that hearing them say so, made me not a little proud; however, that Pride had no ill effect upon me yet, only as they often gave me Money, and I gave it my old Nurse, she *honest Woman*, was so just to me, as to lay it all out again for me, and gave me Head-Dresses, and Linnen, and Gloves and Ribbons, and I went very Neat, and always Clean; for that I would do, and if I had Rags on, I would always be Clean, or else I would dabble them in Water myself; but *I say*, my good Nurse, when I had money given me, very honestly laid it out for me, and would always tell the Ladies, this, or that, was bought with their Money; and this made them oftentimes give me more; Till at last, I was indeed call'd upon by the Magistrates as I understood it, to go out to Service; but then I was come to be so good a Workwoman myself, and the Ladies were so kind to me, that it was plain I could maintain myself, that is to say, I could Earn as much for my Nurse as she was able by it to keep me; so she told them, that if they would give her leave, she would keep the Gentlewoman as she call'd me, to be her Assistant, and teach the Child-ren, which I was very well able to do; for I was very nimble at my Work, and had a good Hand with my Needle, though I was yet very young.

---

[20]Artificial heads of hair worn by ladies. Powdered and pomaded hair was drawn up over a cushion of stuffing, and dressed with gauze, ribbons, and other decoration.

[21]Serious, sober, pious; the antithesis of "gay." In the early eighteenth century, "grave" becomes a kind of all-purpose term for serious religious attitudes. Later, Fielding and especially Sterne parody the excessive and indiscriminate use of the word and suggest that gravity of countenance often really means pomposity.

But the kindness of the Ladies of the Town did not End here, for when they came to understand that I was no more maintain'd by the publick Allowance, as before, they gave me Money oftner than formerly; and as I grew up, they brought me Work to do for them; such as Linnen to Make, and Laces to Mend, and Heads to Dress up, and not only paid me for doing them, but even taught me how to do them; so that now I was a Gentlewoman indeed, as I understood that Word, and as I desir'd to be; for by the time I was twelve Years old, I not only found myself Cloaths, and paid my Nurse for my keeping, but got Money in my Pocket too before-hand.

The Ladies also gave me Cloaths frequently of their own, or their Childrens, some Stockings, some Petticoats, some Gowns, some one thing, some another, and these my old Woman Managed for me like a meer Mother,[22] and kept them for me, oblig'd me to Mend them, and turn them and twist them to the best Advantage, for she was a rare House-Wife.

At last one of the Ladies took so much Fancy to me, that she would have me Home to her House, for a Month she said, to be among her Daughters.

Now tho' this was exceeding kind in her, yet as my old good Woman said to her, unless she resolv'd to keep me for good and all she would do the little Gentlewoman more harm than good: Well, says the Lady, that's true, and therefore I'll only take her Home for a Week then, that I may see how my Daughters and she agree together, and how I like her Temper, and then I'll tell you more; and in the mean time, if any Body comes to see her as they us'd to do, you may only tell them, you have sent her out to my House.

This was prudently manag'd enough, and I went to the Ladies House, but I was so pleas'd there with the young Ladies, and they so pleas'd with me, that I had enough to do to come away, and they were as unwilling to part with me.

However, I did come away, and liv'd almost a Year more with my honest old Woman, and began now to be very helpful to her; for I was almost fourteen Years old, was tall of my Age, and look'd a little Womanish; but I had such a Tast of Genteel living at the Ladies House, that I was not so easie in my old Quarters as I us'd to be, and I thought it was fine to be a Gentlewoman indeed, for I had quite other Notions of a Gentlewoman now, than I had before; and as I thought, I say, that it was fine to be a Gentlewoman, so I lov'd to be among Gentlewomen, and therefore I long'd to be there again.

About the Time that I was fourteen Years and a quarter Old, my good old Nurse, Mother I ought rather to call her, fell Sick and

---

[22]I.e., as if she were no less than a mother.

Dyed; I was then in a sad Condition indeed, for as there is no great Bustle in putting an end to a Poor bodies Family, when once they are carried to the Grave; so the poor good Woman being Buried, the Parish Children she kept were immediately remov'd by the Church-Wardens; the School was at an End, and the Day Children of it had not more to do but just stay at Home, till they were sent some where else; and as for what she left, her Daughter a married Woman with six or seven Children, came and swept it all away at once, and removing the Goods, they had no more to say to me, than to Jest with me, and tell me, that the little Gentlewoman might set up for her self if she pleas'd.

I was frighted out of my Wits almost, and knew not what to do, for I was, as it were, turn'd out of Doors to the wide World, and that which was still worse, the old honest Woman had two and twenty Shillings of mine in her Hand,[23] which was all the Estate the little Gentlewoman had in the World; and when I ask'd the Daughter for it, she huft[24] me and laught at me, and told me, she had nothing to do with it.

It was true, the good poor Woman had told her Daughter of it, and that it lay in such a Place, that it was the Child's Money, and had call'd once or twice for me, to give it me, but I was unhappily out of the way, some where or other; and when I came back she was past being in a Condition to speak of it: However, the Daughter was so Honest afterward as to give it me, tho' at first she us'd me Cruelly about it.

Now was I a poor Gentlewoman indeed, and I was just that very Night to be turn'd into the wide World; for the Daughter remov'd all the Goods, and I had not so much as a Lodging to go to, or a bit of Bread to Eat: But it seems some of the Neighbours who had known my Circumstances took so much Compassion of me, as to acquaint the Lady in whose Family I had been a Week, as I mention'd above; and immediately she sent her Maid to fetch me away, and two of her Daughters came with the Maid tho' unsent; so I went with them Bag and Baggage, and with a glad Heart you may be sure: The fright of my Condition had made such an Impression upon me, that I did not want now to be a Gentlewoman, but was very willing to be a Servant, and that any kind of Servant they thought fit to have me be.

But my new generous Mistress had better thoughts for me; I call her generous for she exceeded the good Woman I was with before, in every Thing, as well as in the matter of Estate; I say in every Thing except Honesty; and for that, tho' this was a Lady most exactly Just,

[23]In her keeping.
[24]Treated with disdain. (huff = swell with pride and arrogance [R])

yet I must not forget to say on all Occasions, that the First tho' Poor, was as uprightly Honest as it was possible for any One to be.

I was no sooner carried away as I have said by this good Gentlewoman, but the first Lady, *that is to say*, the *Mayoress* that was, sent her two Daughters to take Care of me; and another Family which had taken Notice of me, when I was the little Gentlewoman, and had given me Work to do, sent for me after her, so that I was mightily made of, as we say; nay, and they were not a little angry, especially Madam the *Mayoress*, that her Friend had taken me away from her as she call'd it; for as she said, I was Hers by Right, she having been the first that took any Notice of me, but they that had me, wou'd not part with me; and as for me, tho' I shou'd have been very well Treated with any of the other, yet I could not be better than where I was.

Here I continu'd till I was between 17 and 18 Years old, and here I had all the Advantages for my Education that could be imagin'd; the Lady had Masters home to the House to teach her Daughters to Dance, and to speak *French*, and to Write, and others to teach them Musick; and as I was always with them, I learn'd as fast as they; and tho' the Masters were not appointed to teach me, yet I learn'd by Imitation and enquiry all that they learn'd by Instruction and Direction. So that in short, I learn'd to Dance, and speak *French* as well as any of them, and to Sing much better, for I had a better Voice than any of them; I could not so readily come at playing on the Harpsicord or Spinnet,[25] because I had no Instrument of my own to Practice on, and could only come at theirs in the intervals, when they left it, which was uncertain, but yet I learn'd tollerably well too, and the young Ladies at length got two Instruments, that is to say, a Harpsicord, and a Spinnet too, and then they Taught me themselves; But as to Dancing they could hardly help my learning Country Dances, because they always wanted me to make up even Number; and on the other Hand, they were as heartily willing to learn[26] me every thing that they had been Taught themselves, as I could be to take the Learning.

By this Means I had, as I have said above, all the Advantages of Education that I could have had, if I had been as much a Gentlewoman as they were, with whom I liv'd, and in some things I had the Advantage of my Ladies, tho' they were my Superiors; but they were all the Gifts of Nature, and which all their Fortunes could not furnish. First, I was apparently Handsomer than any of them. Secondly, I was better shap'd and Thirdly, I Sung better, by which I mean, I had a better Voice; in all which you will I hope allow me to say, I do not

---

[25]A keyed instrument, smaller than a harpsichord, very popular from the sixteenth through the eighteenth century.

[26]Teach.

speak my own Conceit of myself, but the Opinion of all that knew the Family.

I had with all these the common Vanity of my Sex (*viz.*) That being really taken for very Handsome, or if you please for a great Beauty, I very well knew it, and had as good an Opinion of myself, as any body else could have of me; and particularly I lov'd to hear any body speak of it, which could not but happen to me sometimes, and was a great Satisfaction to me.

Thus far I have had a smooth Story to tell of myself, and in all this Part of my life, I not only had the Reputation of living in a very good Family, and a Family Noted and Respected every where, for Vertue and Sobriety, and for every valluable Thing; but I had the Character too of a very sober, modest, and vertuous young Woman, and such I had always been; neither had I yet any occasion to think of any thing else, or to know what a Temptation to Wickedness meant.

But that which I was too vain of, was my Ruin,[27] or rather my vanity was the Cause of it. The Lady in the House where I was, had two Sons, young Gentlemen of very promising Parts, and of extraordinary Behaviour; and it was my Misfortune to be very well with them both, but they manag'd themselves with me in a quite different Manner.

The eldest was a gay Gentleman[28] that knew the Town, as well as the Country, and tho' he had Levity enough to do an ill natur'd thing, yet had too much Judgment of things to pay too dear for his Pleasures; he began with that unhappy Snare to all Women, (*viz.*) taking Notice upon all Occasions how pretty I was, as he call'd it; how agreeable, how well Carriaged, and the like; and this he contriv'd so subtilly, as if he had known as well, how to catch a Woman in his Net, as a Patridge when he went a Setting; for he wou'd contrive to be talking this to his Sisters when tho' I was not by, yet when he knew I was not so far off, but that I should be sure to hear him: His Sisters would return softly to him, Hush Brother, she will hear you, she is but in the next Room; then he would put it off, and Talk softlier, as if he had not known it, and begun to acknowledge he was Wrong; and then as if he had forgot himself, he would speak aloud again, and I that was so well pleas'd to hear it, was sure to Lissen for it upon all Occasions.

After he had thus baited his Hook, and found easily enough the Method how to lay it in my Way, he play'd an opener Game; and one Day going by his Sister's Chamber when I was there, doing something about Dressing her, he comes in with an Air of gayty, O!

[27]Downfall, loss of position. In the eighteenth century, "ruin" often connoted not only financial loss or sexual dishonor, but also spiritual bankruptcy.

[28]Moll uses the term here, and even more so later, in its informal sense: a man whose habits of life suggest a superior position in society and whose means enable him to live in easy circumstances without engaging in trade.

Mrs.[29] *Betty*, said he to me, How do you do Mrs. *Betty*? don't your Cheeks burn, Mrs. *Betty*? I made a Curtsy, and blush'd, but said nothing; What makes you talk so Brother, *says the Lady*; Why, says he, we have been talking of her below Stairs this half Hour; *Well says his Sister*, you can say no Harm of her, that I am sure, so 'tis no matter what you have been talking about; nay, *says he*, 'tis so far from talking Harm of her, that we have been talking a great deal of good, and a great many fine Things have been said of Mrs. *Betty*, I assure you; and particularly, that she is the Handsomest young Woman in *Colchester*; and, in short, they begin to Toast her Health in the Town.

I wonder at you Brother, *says the Sister*; *Betty* wants but one Thing, but she had as good want every Thing, for the Market is against our Sex just now;[30] and if a young Woman have Beauty, Birth, Breeding, Wit, Sense, Manners, Modesty, and all these to an Extream; yet if she have not Money, she's no Body, she had as good want them all, for nothing but Money now recommends a Woman; the Men play the Game all into their own Hands.

Her younger Brother, who was by, cry'd *Hold Sister*, you run too fast, I am an Exception to your Rule; I assure you, if I find a Woman so Accomplish'd as you Talk of, *I say*, I assure you, I would not trouble myself about the Money.

0, says the Sister, but you will take Care not to Fancy one then, without the Money.

You don't know that neither, *says the Brother*.

But why Sister, (*says the elder Brother*) why do you exclaim so at the Men, for aiming so much at the Fortune? you are none of them that want a Fortune, what ever else you want.

I understand you Brother, (*replies the Lady very smartly*,) you suppose I have the Money, and want the Beauty; but as Times go now, the first will do without the last, so I have the better of my Neighbours.

Well, *says the younger Brother*, but your Neighbours, as you call them may be even with you; for Beauty will steal a Husband sometimes in spight of Money; and when the Maid chances to be Handsomer than the Mistress, she oftentimes makes as good a Market, and rides in a Coach before her.

I thought it was time for me to withdraw, and leave them, and I did so; but not so far, but that I heard all their Discourse, in which I heard abundance of fine things said of myself, which serv'd to prompt my Vanity; but, as I soon found, was not the way to encrease my Interest in the Family; for the Sister, and the younger Brother fell

---

[29]Simply a term of courtesy, or of mock-courtesy; "Mistress," as a title, was not reserved for married women.

[30]I.e., woman's matrimonial bargaining power is poor in the present social situation.

grieviously out about it; and as he said some very dissobliging things to her, upon my Account, so I could easily see that she Resented them, by her future Conduct to me; which indeed was very unjust to me, for I had never had the least thought of what she suspected, as to her younger Brother: Indeed the elder Brother in his distant remote Way, had said a great many things, as in Jest, which I had the folly to believe were in earnest, or to flatter myself with the hopes of what I ought to have suppos'd he never intended, and perhaps never thought of.

It happen'd[31] one Day that he came running up Stairs, towards the Room where his Sisters us'd to sit and Work, as he often us'd to do; and calling to them before he came in, as was his way too, I being there alone, step'd to the Door, and said, Sir, the Ladies are not here, they are Walk'd down the Garden; as I step'd forward, to say this towards the Door, he was just got to the Door, and clasping me in his Arms, as if it had been by Chance, O! Mrs. *Betty, says he,* are you here? that's better still; I want to speak with you, more than I do with them, and then having me in his Arms he Kiss'd me three or four times.

I struggl'd to get away, and yet did it but faintly neither, and he held me fast, and still Kiss'd me, till he was almost out of Breath, and then sitting down, says, *dear Betty* I am in Love with you.

His words I must confess fir'd my Blood; all my Spirits flew about my Heart, and put me into Disorder enough, which he might easily have seen in my Face: He repeated it afterwards several times, that he was in Love with me, and my Heart spoke as plain as a Voice, that I lik'd it; nay, when ever he said, I am in Love with you, my Blushes plainly reply'd, *wou'd you were* Sir.[32]

However nothing else pass'd at that time; it was but a Surprise, and when he was gone, I soon recover'd myself again. He had stay'd longer with me, but he happen'd to look out at the Window, and see his Sisters coming up the Garden, so he took his leave, Kiss'd me again, told me he was very serious, and I should hear more of him very quickly, and away he went leaving me infinitely pleas'd tho' surpris'd, and had there not been one Misfortune in it, I had been in the Right, but the Mistake lay here, that Mrs. *Betty* was in Earnest, and the Gentleman was not.

From this time my Head run upon strange Things, and I may truly say, I was not myself; to have such a Gentleman talk to me of being in

---

[31]A favorite Defoe phrase to avoid assigning cause or responsibility for events. See Hunter, *The Reluctant Pilgrim*, pp. 151–52.

[32]According to the old love psychology which Defoe here employs, love activated the "spirits" in the blood, and, after a series of complex physical and spiritual processes, the face inevitably betrayed love feelings. For an explanation of this psychology, see Clay Hunt, *Donne's Poetry*, New Haven, 1954, pp. 62–63.

Love with me, and of my being such a charming Creature, as he told me I was, these were things I knew not how to bear, my vanity was elevated to the last Degree: It is true, I had my Head full of Pride, but knowing nothing of the Wickedness of the times, I had not one Thought of my own Safety, or of my Vertue about me; and had my young Master offer'd it at first Sight, he might have taken any Liberty he thought fit with me; but he did not see his Advantage, which was my happiness for that time.

After this Attack, it was not long, but he found an opportunity to catch me again, and almost in the same Posture, indeed it had more of Design in it on his Part, tho' not on my Part; *it was thus*; the young Ladies were all gone a Visiting with their Mother; his Brother was out of Town; and as for his Father, he had been at *London* for a Week before; he had so well watched me, that he knew where I was, tho' I did not so much as know that he was in the House; and he briskly comes up the Stairs, and seeing me at Work comes into the Room to me directly, and began just as he did before with taking me in his Arms, and Kissing me for almost a quarter of an Hour together.

It was his younger Sisters Chamber, that I was in, and as there was no Body in the House, but the Maids below Stairs, he was it may be the ruder: In short, he began to be in Earnest with me indeed; perhaps he found me a little too easie, for God knows I made no Resistance to him while he only held me in his Arms and Kiss'd me, indeed I was too well pleas'd with it, to resist him much.

However as it were, tir'd with that kind of Work,[33] we sat down, and there he talk'd with me a great while; *he said*, he was charm'd with me, and that he could not rest Night, or Day till he had told me how he was in Love with me; and if I was able to Love him again, and would make him happy, I should be the saving of his Life; and many such fine things. I said little to him again, but easily discover'd[34] that I was a Fool, and that I did not in the least perceive what he meant.

Then he walk'd about the Room and taking me by the Hand, I walk'd with him, and by and by, taking his Advantage, he threw me down upon the Bed, and Kiss'd me there most violently; but to give him his Due, offer'd no manner of Rudeness to me, only Kiss'd me a great while; after this he thought he had heard some Body come up Stairs, so he got off from the Bed, lifted me up, professing a great deal of Love for me, but told me it was all an honest Affection, and that he meant no ill to me; and with that he put five Guineas into my Hand, and went away down Stairs.

I was more confounded with the Money than I was before with the Love; and began to be so elevated, that I scarse knew the Ground I

[33]Actions. The term had not yet   [34]Showed, revealed.
gathered its full Protestant significa-
tion of grave duties.

stood on: I am the more particular in this part, that if my Story comes to be read by any innocent young Body, they may learn from it to Guard themselves against the Mischiefs which attend an early Knowledge of their own Beauty; if a young Woman once thinks herself Handsome, she never doubts the Truth of any Man, that tells her he is in love with her; for if she believes herself Charming enough to Captivate him, tis natural to expect the Effects of it.

This young Gentleman had fir'd his Inclination, as much as he had my vanity, and as if he had found that he had an opportunity, and was sorry he did not take hold of it, he comes up again in half an Hour, or thereabouts, and falls to Work with me again as before, only with a little less Introduction.

And, First, when he enter'd the Room, he turn'd about, and shut the Door. Mrs *Betty*, said he, I fancy'd before, some Body was coming up Stairs, but it was not so; however, *adds he*, if they find me in the Room with you, they shan't catch me a Kissing of you; I told him I did not know who should be coming up Stairs, for I believ'd there was no Body in the House, but the Cook, and the other Maid, and they never came up those Stairs; well my Dear, *says he*, 'tis good to be sure however, and so he sits down and we began to Talk; and now, tho' I was still all on fire with his first visit, and said little, he did as it were put Words in my Mouth, telling me how passionately he lov'd me, and that tho' he could not mention such a thing, till he came to his Estate, yet he was resolv'd to make me happy then, and himself too; *that is to say, to Marry me*, and abundance of such fine things, which I poor Fool did not understand the drift of, but acted as if there was no such thing as any kind of Love, but that which tended to Matrimony; and if he had spoke of that, I had no Room, as well as no Power, to have said No; but we were not come that length yet.

We had not sat long, but he got up, and stopping my very Breath with Kisses, threw me upon the Bed again, but then being both well warm'd, he went farther with me than Decency permits me to mention, nor had it been in my power to have deny'd him at that Moment, had he offer'd much more than he did.

However, tho' he took these Freedoms with me, it did not go to that, which they call the last Favour, which, to do him Justice, he did not attempt; and he made that self denial of his a Plea for all his Freedoms with me upon other Occasions after this: When this was over, he stay'd but a little while, but he put almost a Handful of Gold in my Hand, and left me; making a thousand Protestations of his Passion for me, and of his loving me above all the Women in the World.

It will not be strange, if I now began to think, but alas! it was but with very little solid Reflection: I had a most unbounded Stock of Vanity and Pride, and but a very little Stock of Vertue; I did indeed cast sometimes with myself[35] what my young Master aim'd at, but thought of nothing, but the fine Words, and the Gold; whether he intended to Marry me, or not to Marry me, seem'd a Matter of no great Consequence to me; nor did my Thoughts so much as suggest to me the Necessity of making any Capitulation[36] for myself, till he came to make a kind of formal Proposal to me, as you shall hear presently.

Thus I gave up myself to a readiness of being ruined without the least concern, and am a fair *Memento*[37] to all young Women, whose Vanity prevails over their Vertue: Nothing was ever so stupid on both Sides; had I acted as became me, and resisted as Vertue and Honour requir'd, this Gentleman had either Desisted his Attacks, finding no room to expect the Accomplishment of his Design, or had made fair, and honourable Proposals of Marriage; in which Case, whoever had blam'd him, no Body could have blam'd me. In short, if he had known me, and how easy the Trifle he aim'd at, was to be had, he would have troubled his Head no farther, but have given me four or five Guineas, and have lain with me the next time he had come at me; and if I had known his Thoughts, and how hard he thought I would be to be gain'd, I might have made my own Terms with him; and if I had not Capitulated for an immediate Marriage, I might for a Maintenance till Marriage, and might have had what I would; for he was already Rich to Excess, besides what he had in Expectation; but I seem'd wholly to have abandoned all such Thoughts as these, and was taken up Onely with the Pride of my Beauty, and of being belov'd by such a Gentleman; as for the Gold I spent whole Hours in looking upon it; I told[38] the Guineas over and over a thousand times a Day; Never poor vain Creature was so wrapt up with every part of the Story, as I was, not Considering what was before me, and how near my Ruin was at the Door; indeed I think, I rather wish'd for that Ruin, than studyed to avoid it.

In the mean time however, I was cunning enough, not to give the least room to any in the Family to suspect me, or to imagine that I had the least Correspondence[39] with this young Gentleman; I scarce ever look'd towards him in publick, or Answer'd if he spoke to me, if any Body was near us; but for all that, we had every now and then a little Encounter, where we had room for a Word or two, and now and then a Kiss; but no fair opportunity for the Mischief intended; and especially considering that he made more Circumlocution, than if he had known my Thoughts he had occasion for, and the Work appearing Difficult to him, he really made it so.

---

[35]Pondered, tried to think.
[36]Stipulation.
[37]Warning token.

[38]Counted. (R)
[39]Relationship, liaison. (R)

But as the Devil is an unwearied Tempter, so he never fails to find opportunity for that Wickedness he invites to: It was one Evening that I was in the Garden,[40] with his two younger Sisters, and himself, and all very innocently Merry, when he found Means to convey a Note into my Hand, by which he Directed me to understand, that he would to Morrow desire me publickly to go of an Errand for him into Town, and that I should see him somewhere by the way.

Accordingly after Dinner, he very gravely says to me, his Sisters being all by, Mrs. *Betty*, I must ask a Favour of you: What's that? *says his second Sister*; nay, Sister *says he*, very gravely, if you can't spare Mrs. *Betty* to Day, any other time will do; *yes they said*, they could spare her well enough, and the Sister beg'd Pardon for asking; which she did but of meer Course, without any Meaning; Well, but Brother? says the eldest Sister, you must tell Mrs. *Betty* what it is; if it be any private Business, that we must not hear, you may call her out, there she is. Why Sister, says the Gentleman, very gravely, What do you mean? *I* only desire her to go into the *High-street*, (and then he pulls out a Turn-Over[41]) to such a Shop, and then he tells them a long Story of two fine Neckcloths[42] he had bid Money for, and he wanted to have me go and make an Errand to buy a Neck to the Turn-Over that he showed, to see if they would take my Money[43] for the Neckcloths; to bid a Shilling more, and Haggle with them; and then he made more Errands, and so continued to have such petty Business to do, that *I* should be sure to stay a good while.

When he had given me my Errands, he told them a long Story of a Visit he was going to make to a Family they all knew, and where was to be such and such Gentlemen, and how Merry they were to be; and very formally asks his Sisters to go with him, and they as formally excus'd themselves, because of Company that they had Notice was to come and Visit them that Afternoon, which by the Way he had contriv'd on purpose.

He had scarce done speaking to them, and giving me my Errand, but his Man came up to tell him that Sir *W———— H————s* Coach stop'd at the Door; so he runs down, and comes up again immediately, alas! *says he*, aloud, there's all my Mirth spoil'd at once; Sir *W————* has sent his Coach for me, and desires to speak with me upon some earnest Business: It seems this Sir *W————* was a Gentleman, who liv'd about three Miles out of Town, to whom he had spoken on purpose the Day before, to lend him his Charriot for a particular occasion; and had appointed it to call for him, as it did about three a-Clock.

---

[40]Here Defoe seems to introduce the tempter-in-the-Garden motif; cf. pp. 27, 82, and elsewhere.

[41]Turn-down collar or neck band.
[42]Neckties.
[43]Accept the amount he had offered.

Immediately he calls for his best Wig, Hat and Sword, and ordering his Man to go to the other Place to make his Excuse, that was to say, he made an Excuse to send his Man away; he prepares to go into the Coach: As he was going, he stop'd a while, and speaks mighty earnestly to me about his Business, and finds an Opportunity to say very softly to me, *come away my Dear as soon as ever you can.* I said nothing, but made a Curtsy, as if I had done so to what he said in publick; in about a Quarter of an Hour I went out too, I had no Dress, other than before, except that I had a Hood, a Mask, a Fan and a pair of Gloves in my Pocket; so that there was not the least Suspicion in the House: He waited for me in the Coach in a back *Lane*, which he knew *I* must pass by; and had directed the Coachman whither to go, which was to a certain Place, call'd *Mile-end*,[44] where lived a Confident[45] of his, where we went in, and where was all the Convenience in the World to be as Wicked as we pleas'd.

When we were together, he began to Talk very Gravely to me; and to tell me, he did not bring me there to betray me; that his Passion for me, would not suffer him to Abuse me; that he resolv'd to Marry me as soon as he came to his Estate, that in the mean time, if *I* would grant his Request, he would Maintain me very Honourably, and made me a thousand Protestations of his Sincerity, and of his Affection to me, and That he would never abandon me, and as *I* may say, made a thousand more Preambles than he need to have done.

However as he press'd me to speak, I told him, I had no Reason to question the Sincerity of his Love to me, after so many Protestations, But — and there I stopp'd, as if I left him to Guess the rest; BUT WHAT my Dear? *says he*, I guess what you mean; what if you should be with Child, is not that it? Why then, *says he*, I'll take Care of you, and Provide for you, and the Child too, and that you may see I am not in Jest, *says he*, here's an Earnest[46] for you; and with that he pulls out a silk Purse, with an Hundred Guineas in it, and gave it me; and I'll give you such another, *says he*, every Year till I Marry you.

My Colour came, and went, at the Sight of the Purse, and with the fire of his Proposal together;[47] so that I could not say a Word, and he easily perceiv'd it; so putting the Purse into my Bosom, I made no more Resistance to him, but let him do just what he pleas'd; and as often as he pleas'd; and thus I finish'd my own Destruction at once for from this Day, being forsaken of my Vertue, and my Modesty, I had nothing of Value left to recommend me, either to God's Blessing, or Man's Assistance.

---

[44]Village just east of London, on the Great Eastern Road.

[45]Confidant. (R)

[46]Money, as tangible indication of sincerity.

[47]The joint stimulation of money and sexual expectation becomes, from this point on, characteristic of Moll's eclectic motivation.

But things did not End here, I went back to the Town, did the Business he publickly directed me to, and was at Home before any Body thought me long; as for my Gentleman, he staid out as he told me he would till late at Night, and there was not the least Suspicion in the Family, either on his Account or on mine.

We had after this, frequent Opportunities to repeat our Crime; chiefly by his Contrivance; especially at home; when his Mother and the young Ladies went Abroad a Visiting, which he watch'd so narrowly, as never to miss; knowing always before-hand when they went out; and then fail'd not to catch me all alone, and securely enough; so that we took our fill of our wicked Pleasure for near half a Year; and yet, which was the most to my Satisfaction, I was not with Child.

But before this half Year was expir'd, his younger Brother, of whom I have made some mention in the beginning of the Story, falls to work with me; and he finding me alone in the Garden one Evening, begins a Story of the same Kind to me, made good honest Professions of being in Love with me; and in short, proposes fairly and Honourably to Marry me, and that before he made any other Offer to me at all.

I was now confounded and driven to such an Extremity, as the like was never known; at least not to me; I resisted the Proposal with Obstinancy; and now I began to Arm myself with Arguments: I laid before him the inequallity of the Match, the Treatment I should meet with in the Family; the Ingratitude it wou'd be to his good Father and Mother, who had taken me into their house upon such generous Principles and when I was in such a low Condition; and in short, I said every thing to dissuade him from his Design that I could imagine, except telling him the Truth, which wou'd indeed have put an end to it all, but that I durst not think of mentioning.

But here happen'd a Circumstance that I did not expect indeed, which put me to my Shifts; for this young Gentleman, as he was plain and Honest, so he pretended to nothing with me, but what was so too; and knowing his own Innocence, he was not so careful to make his having a Kindness for Mrs. *Betty*, a Secret in the House, as his Brother was; and tho' he did not let them know that he had talk'd to me about it, yet he said enough to let his Sisters perceive he Lov'd me, and his Mother saw it too, which tho' they took no Notice of it to me, yet they did to him, and immediately I found their Carriage to me alter'd, more than ever before.

I saw the Cloud, tho' I did not foresee the Storm; it was easie, *I say,* to see that their Carriage to me was alter'd, and that it grew worse and worse every Day, till at last I got Information among the Servants, that I shou'd, in a very little while, be desired to remove.

I was not alarm'd at the News, having a full Satisfaction that I should be otherwise provided for; and especially considering that I had

Reason every Day to expect I should be with Child, and that then I should be oblig'd to remove without any Pretences for it.

After some time, the younger Gentleman took an Opportunity to tell me, that the Kindness he had for me, had got vent in the Family; he did not Charge me with it, *he said*, for he knew well enough which way it came out; he told me his plain way of Talking had been the Occasion of it, for that[48] he did not make his respect for me so much a Secret as he might have done, and the Reason was, that he was at a Point; that if I would consent to have him, he would tell them all openly that he lov'd me, and that he intended to Marry me: That it was true his Father and Mother might Resent it, and be unkind, but that he was now in a Way to live, being bred to[49] the Law, and he did not fear Maintaining me, agreeable to what I should expect; and that in short, as he believed I would not be asham'd of him, so he was resolv'd not to be asham'd of me, and that he scorn'd to be afraid to own me now, who he resolv'd to own after I was his Wife, and therefore I had nothing to do but to give him my Hand, and he would Answer for all the rest.

I was now in a dreadful Condition indeed, and now I repented heartily my easiness with the eldest Brother, not from any Reflection of Conscience, but from a View of the Happiness I might have enjoy'd, and had now made impossible; for tho' I had no great Scruples of Conscience *as I have said* to struggle with, yet I could not think of being a Whore to one Brother, and a Wife to the other; but then it came into my Thoughts, that the first Brother had promis'd to make me his Wife, when he came to his Estate; but I presently remember'd what I had often thought of, that he had never spoken a Word of having me for a Wife, after he had Conquer'd me for a Mistress; and indeed till now, tho' I said I thought of it often, yet it gave me no Disturbance at all, for as he did not seem in the least to lessen his Affection to me, so neither did he lessen his Bounty, tho' he had the Discretion himself to desire me not to lay out a Penny of what he gave me in Cloaths, or to make the least show Extraordinary, because it would necessarily give Jealousie[50] in the Family, since every Body knew I could come at such things no manner of ordinary Way; but[51] by some private Friendship, which they would presently have suspected.

But I was now in a great strait, and really knew not what to do, the main difficulty was this; the younger Brother not only laid close Siege to me, but suffered it to be seen; he would come into his Sisters Room, and his Mothers Room, and sit down, and Talk a Thousand kind things of me, and to me, even before their Faces, and when they

---

[48]Because. (R)
[49]Trained in.

[50]Arouse suspicion or indignation.
[51]Only.

were all there: This grew so Publick, that the whole House talk'd of it, and his Mother reprov'd him for it, and their Carriage to me appear'd quite Altered: In short, his Mother had let fall some Speeches, as if she intended to put me out of the Family, that is in *English*, to turn me out of Doors. Now, I was sure this could not be a Secret to his Brother, only that he might not think as indeed no Body else yet did, that the youngest Brother had made any Proposal to me about it; But as I easily cou'd see that it would go farther, so I saw likewise there was an absolute Necessity to speak of it to him, or that he would speak of it to me, and which to do first I knew not; that is, whether I should break it to him, or let it alone till he should break it to me.

Upon serious Consideration; for indeed now I began to Consider things very seriously, and never till now: I say, upon serious Consideration, I resolv'd to tell him of it first, and it was not long before I had an Opportunity, for the very next day his Brother went to *London* upon some Business, and the Family being out a Visiting, just as it had happen'd before, and as indeed was often the Case, he came according to his Custom to spend an Hour or Two with Mrs. *Betty*.

When he came and had sate down a while, he easily perceiv'd there was an alteration in my Countenance, that I was not so free and pleasant with him, as I us'd to be, and particularly, that I had been a Crying; he was not long before he took notice of it, and ask'd me in very kind Terms what was the Matter, and if any thing Troubl'd me: I wou'd have put if off if I could, but it was not to be Conceal'd; so after suffering many Importunities to draw that out of me, which I long'd as much as possible to Disclose, I told him that it was true, something did Trouble me, and something of such a Nature, that I could not Conceal from him, and yet, that I could not tell how to tell him of it neither; that it was a thing that not only Surpriz'd me, but greatly perplex'd me, and that I knew not what Course to take, unless he would Direct me: He told me with great Tenderness, that let it be what it wou'd, I should not let it Trouble me, for he would Protect me from all the World.

I then begun at a Distance, and told him I was afraid the Ladies had got some secret Information of our Correspondence; for that it was easie to see, that their Conduct was very much chang'd towards me for a great while, and that now it was come to that pass, that they frequently found Fault with me and sometimes fell quite out with me. tho' I never gave them the least Occasion: That whereas, I us'd always to lye with the Eldest Sister, I was lately put to lye by my self, or with one of the Maids; and that I had over-heard them several times talking very Unkindly about me; but that which confirm'd it all, was, that one of the Servants had told me, that she had heard I was to be

Turn'd out, and that it was not safe for the Family, that I should be any longer in the House.

He smil'd when he heard all this, and I ask'd him, how he could make so light of it, when he must needs know, that if there was any Discovery, I was Undone for ever? and that even it would hurt him, tho' not Ruin him, as it would me: I upbraided him, that he was like all the rest of the Sex, that when they had the Character and Honour of a Woman at their Mercy, often times made it their Jest, and at least look'd upon it as a Trifle, and counted the Ruin of those they had had their Will of, as a thing of no value.

He saw me Warm and Serious, and he chang'd his Stile immediately; *he told me*, he was sorry I should have such a thought of him; that he had never given me the least Occasion for it, but had been as tender of my Reputation, as he could be of his own; that he was sure our Correspondence had been manag'd with so much Address, that not one Creature in the Family had so much as a Suspicion of it; that if he smil'd when I told him my Thoughts, it was at the Assurance he lately receiv'd, that our understanding one another, was not so much as known or guess'd at; and that when he had told me, how much Reason he had to be Easie, I should Smile as he did, for he was very certain, it would give me a full Satisfaction.

This is a Mystery I cannot understand, *says I*, or how it should be to my Satisfaction, that I am to be turn'd out of Doors; for if our Correspondence is not discover'd, I know not what else I have done to change the Countenances of the whole Family to me, or to have them Treat me as they do now, who formerly used me with so much Tenderness, as if I had been one of their own Children.

Why look you Child, *says he*, that they are Uneasie about you, that is true; but that they have the least Suspicion of the Case as it is, and as it respects you and I, is so far from being True, that they suspect my Brother *Robin*;[52] and in short, they are fully persuaded he makes Love to you: Nay, the Fool has put it into their Heads too himself, for he is continually Bantring them about it, and making a Jest of Himself; I confess, I think he is wrong to do so, because he can not but see it vexes them, and makes them Unkind to you; but 'tis a Satisfaction to me, because of the Assurance it gives me, that they do not suspect me in the least, and I hope this will be to your Satisfaction too.

So it is, *says I*, one way, but this does not reach my Case at all, nor is this the chief Thing that Troubles me, tho' I have been concern'd about that too: What is it then, *says he*? With which, I fell into Tears, and could say nothing to him at all: He strove to pacifie me all he could, but began at last to be very pressing upon me, to tell what it

---

[52] A common nickname for Robert.

was; at last *I answer'd*, that I thought I ought to tell him too, and that he had some right to know it, besides, that I wanted his Direction in the Case, for I was in Such Perplexity, that I knew not what Course to take, and then I related the whole Affair to him: *I told him*, how imprudently his Brother had manag'd himself, in making himself so Publick; for that if he had kept it a Secret, as such a Thing ought to have been, I could but have Denied him Positively, without giving any Reason for it, and he would in Time have ceas'd his Sollicitations; but that he had the Vanity, first, to depend upon it that I would not Deny him, and then had taken the Freedom to tell his Resolution of having me, to the whole House.

I *told him* how far I had resisted him, and *told him* how Sincere and Honourable his Offers were, but *says I*, my Case will be doubly hard; for as they carry it Ill to me now, because he desires to have me, they'll carry it worse when they shall find I have Deny'd him; and they will presently[53] say, there's something else in it, and then out it comes, that I am Marry'd already to somebody else, or else that I would never refuse a Match so much above me as this was.

This Discourse surpriz'd him indeed very much: He *told me*, that it was a critical Point indeed for me to Manage, and he did not see which way I should get out of it; but he would consider of it, and let me know next time we met, what Resolution he was come to about it; and in the mean time, desir'd I would not give my Consent to his Brother, nor yet give him a flat Denial, but that I would hold him in Suspence a while.

I seem'd to start at his saying, I should not give him my Consent; I *told him*, he knew very well, I had no Consent to give; that he had Engag'd himself to Marry me, and that my Consent was at the same time Engag'd to him; that he had all along told me, I was his Wife, and I look'd upon myself as effectually so, as if the Ceremony had pass'd; and that it was from his own Mouth that I did so, he having all along persuaded me to call myself his Wife.

Well my Dear *says he*, don't be Concern'd at that now; if I am not your Husband, I'll be as good as a Husband to you, and do not let those things trouble you now, but let me look a little farther into this Affair, and I shall be able to say more next time we meet.

He pacify'd me as well as he could with this, but I found he was very Thoughtful, and that tho' he was very kind to me, and kiss'd me a thousand Times, and more I believe, and gave me Money too, yet he offer'd no more all the while we were together, which was above two Hours, and which I much wonder'd at, indeed at that Time, considering how it us'd to be, and what Opportunity we had.

His Brother did not come from *London*, for five or six Days, and it

[53]Immediately. (R)

was two Days more, before he got an Opportunity to talk with him; but then getting him by Himself, he began to talk very Close to him about it; and the same Evening got an Opportunity, (for we had a long Conference together) to repeat all their Discourse to me, which as near as I can remember, was to the purpose following. He *told him* he heard strange News of him since he went, (*viz.*) that he made Love to Mrs. *Betty*: Well, *says his* Brother, a little Angrily, and so *I do*, and what then? What has any body to do with that? Nay, *says his* Brother, don't be Angry *Robin*, I don't pretend to have any thing to do with it; nor do I pretend to be Angry with you about it: But I find they do concern themselves about it, and that they have used the poor Girl Ill about it, which I should take as done to my self; Who do you mean by THEY? *says* Robin; I mean my Mother, and the Girls, *says the* elder Brother.

But hark ye, *says his* Brother, are you in Earnest, do you really Love the Girl, you may be free with me you know? Why then *says* Robin, I will be free with you, I do Love her above all the Women in the World, and I will have Her, let *them say* and do what they will, I believe the Girl will not Deny me.

It stuck me to the Heart when he *told me* this, for tho' it was most rational to think I would not Deny him, yet I knew in my own Conscience, I must Deny him, and I saw my Ruin in my being oblig'd to do so; but I knew it was my business to Talk otherwise then, so I interrupted him in his Story thus.

Ay! *said I*, does he think I can not Deny him? but he shall find I can Deny him, for all that.

Well my dear *says he*, but let me give you the whole Story as it went on between us, and then say what you will.

Then he went on and *told me*, that he reply'd thus: But Brother, you know She has nothing, and you may have several Ladies with good Fortunes: 'Tis no matter for that, *said* Robin, I Love the Girl; and I will never please my Pocket in Marrying, and not please my Fancy; and so my Dear *adds he*, there is no Opposing him.

Yes, yes, *says I*, you shall see I can Oppose him, I have learnt to say NO now, tho' I had not learnt it before; if the best Lord in the Land offer'd me Marriage now, I could very chearfully say NO to him.

Well, but my Dear *says he*, What can you say to him? You know, as you said when we talk'd of it before, he will ask you many Questions about it, and all the House will wonder what the meaning of it should be.

Why *says I* smiling, I can stop all their Mouths at one Clap, by telling him and them too, that I am Married already to his elder Brother.

He smil'd a little too at the Word, but I could see it Startled him, and he could not hide the disorder it put him into; however, he return'd, Why tho' that may be true in some Sense, yet I suppose you are but in Jest, when you talk of giving such an Answer as that; it may not be Convenient on many Accounts.

No, no, *says I* pleasantly, I am not so fond of letting that Secret come out, without your Consent.

But what then can you say to him, or to them, *says he*, when they find you positive against a Match, which would be apparently so much to your Advantage?

Why, *says I*, should I be at a loss? First of all, I am not oblig'd to give them any Reason at all; on the other hand, I may tell them, I am Married already, and stop there, and that will be a full Stop too to him, for he can have no Reason to ask one Question after it.

Ay, *says he*, but the whole House will teize you about that, even to Father and Mother, and if you deny them positively, they will be disoblig'd at you and Suspicious besides.

Why, *says I*, What can I do? What would you have me do? I was in strait enough before, and as I *told you*, I was in Perplexity before, and acquainted you with the Circumstances, that I might have your Advice.

My dear *says he*, I have been considering very much upon it, you may be sure, and tho' it is a piece of Advice, that has a great many Mortifications in it to me, and may at first seem Strange to you, yet all Things consider'd, I see no better way for you, than to let him go on; and if you find him hearty and in Earnest, Marry him.

I gave him a look full of Horror at those Words, and turning Pale as Death, was at the very point of sinking down out of the Chair I sat in: When giving a start, my Dear, *says he* aloud, What's the matter with you? Where are you a going? and a great many such things; and with joging and calling to me, fetch'd me a little to my self, tho' it was a good while before I fully recover'd my Senses, and was not able to speak for several Minutes more.

When I was fully recover'd he began again; My dear *says he*, What made you so Surpriz'd at what I said, I would have you consider Seriously of it? you may see plainly how the Family stand in this Case, and they would be stark Mad if it was my Case, as it is my Brothers, and for aught I see, it would be my Ruin and yours too.

Ay! *says I*, still speaking angrily; are all your Protestations and Vows to be shaken by the dislike of the Family? Did I not always object that to you, and you made a light thing of it, as what you were above, and would not Value; and is it come to this now? *Said I*, is this your Faith and Honour, your Love, and the Solidity of your Promises?

He continued perfectly Calm, notwithstanding all my Reproaches, and I was not sparing of them at all; but *he reply'd* at last, My Dear, I have not broken one Promise with you yet; I did tell you I would Marry you when I was come to my Estate; but you see my Father is a hail healthy Man, and may live these thirty Years still, and not be

Older than several are round us in the Town; and you never propos'd my Marrying you sooner, because you know it might be my Ruin; and as to all the rest, I have not fail'd you in any thing, you have wanted for nothing.

I could not deny a Word of this, and had nothing to say to it in general; but why then, *says I*, can you perswade me to such a horrid stop, as leaving you, since you have not left me? Will you allow no Affection, no Love on my Side, where there has been so much on your Side? Have I made you no Returns? Have I given no Testimony of my Sincerity, and of my Passion? are the Sacrifices I have made of Honour and Modesty to you, no Proof of my being ty'd to you in Bonds too strong to be broken?

But here my Dear, *says he*, you may come into a safe Station, and appear with Honour, and with splendor at once, and the Remembrance of what we have done, may be wrapt up in an eternal Silence, as if it had never happen'd; you shall always have my Respect, and my sincere Affection, only then it shall be Honest, and perfectly Just to my Brother, you shall be my Dear Sister, as now you are my Dear— and there he stop'd.

Your Dear whore, *says I*, you would have said, if you had gone on; and you might as well have said it; but I understand you: However, I desire you to remember the long Discourses you have had with me, and the many Hours pains you have taken to perswade me to believe myself an honest Woman; that I was your Wife intentionally, tho' not in the Eye of the World; and that it was as effectual a Marriage that had pass'd between us, as if we had been publickly Wedded by the Parson of the Parish; you know and cannot but remember, that these have been your own Words to me.

I found this was a little too close upon him,[54] but I made it up in what follows; he stood stock still for a while, and said nothing, and I went on thus; you cannot, *says I*, without the highest injustice believe that I yielded upon all these Perswasions without a Love not to be questioned, not to be shaken again by any thing that could happen afterward: If you have such dishonourable Thoughts of me, I must ask you what Foundation in any of my Behaviour have I given for such a Suggestion.

If then I have yielded to the Importunities of my Affection; and if I have been perswaded to believe that I am really, and in the Essence of the Thing, your Wife, shall I now give the Lye to all those Arguments, and call myself your Whore, or Mistress, which is the same thing? and will you Transfer me to your Brother? Can you Transfer

---

[54]I.e., Moll touches close to a sensitive area, and he finds the issue presses hardly upon him.

my Affection? Can you bid me cease loving you, and bid me love him? is it in my Power think you to make such a Change at Demand? No Sir, *said I*, depend upon it 'tis impossible, and whatever the Change of your Side may be, I will ever be True; and I had much rather, Since it is come that unhappy Length, be Your Whore than your Brothers Wife.

He appear'd pleas'd, and touch'd with the impression of this last discourse and told me that he stood where he did before; that he had not been Unfaithful to me in any one Promise he had ever made yet, but that there were so many terrible things presented themselves to his View in the Affair before me, and that on my Account in particular, that he had thought of the other as a Remedy so effectual, as nothing could come up to it: That he thought this would not be an entire parting us, but we might love as Friends all our Days, and perhaps with more Satisfaction, than we should in the station we were now in, as things might happen: That he durst say, I could not apprehend any thing from him, as to betraying a Secret, which could not but be the Destruction of us both, if it came out: That he had but one Question to ask of me, that could lye in the way of it, and if that Question was answer'd in the Negative, he could not but think still it was the only Step I could take.

I guess'd at his Question presently, namely, Whether I was sure I was not with Child? As to that, *I told him*, he need not be concern'd about it, for I was not with Child; why then my Dear, *says he*, we have no time to Talk farther now; consider of it, and think closely about it, I cannot but be of the Opinion still, that it will be the best Course you can take; and with this, he took his Leave, and the more hastily too, his Mother and Sisters Ringing at the Gate, just at the Moment that he had risen up to go.

He left me in the utmost Confusion of Thought; and he easily perceiv'd it the next Day, and all the rest of the Week, for it was but *Tuesday* Evening when we talked; but he had no Opportunity to come at me all that Week, till the *Sunday* after, when I being indispos'd did not go to Church, and he making some Excuse for the like, stay'd at Home.

And now he had me an Hour and a Half again by myself, and we fell into the same Arguments all over again, or at least so near the same, as it would be to no purpose to repeat them; at last, *I ask'd him* warmly what Opinion he must have of my Modesty,[55] that he could suppose, I should so much as Entertain a thought of lying with two Brothers? And assur'd him it could never be: *I added* if he was to tell me that he would never see me more, than which nothing but Death could be more Terrible, yet I could never entertain a thought so

---

[55]Propriety, sense of shame.

Dishonourable to my self, and so Base to him; and therefore, I entreated him if he had one Grain of Respect or Affection left for me, that he would speak no more of it to me, or that he would pull his Sword out and Kill me. He appear'd surpriz'd at my Obstinacy as he call'd it, *told me* I was unkind to my self, and unkind to him in it; that it was a Crisis unlook'd for upon us both, and impossible for either of us to foresee; but that he did not see any other way to save us both from Ruin, and therefore he thought it the more Unkind; but that if he must say no more of it to me, he added with an unusual Coldness, that he did not know any thing else we had to talk of; and so he rose up to take his leave; I rose up too, as if with the same Indifference, but when he came to give me as it were a parting Kiss, I burst out into such a Passion of Crying, that tho' I would have spoke, I could not, and only pressing his Hand, seem'd to give him the Adieu, but cry'd vehemently.

He was sensibly mov'd with this; so he sat down again, and said a great many kind things to me, to abate the excess of my Passion; but still urg'd the necessity of what he had proposed; all the while insisting, that if I did refuse, he would notwithstanding provide for me; but letting me plainly see, that he would decline me in the main Point; nay, even as a Mistress; making it a point of Honour not to lye with the Woman, that for aught he knew, might come to be his Brothers Wife.

The bare loss of him as a Gallant was not so much my Affliction, as the loss of his Person,[56] whom indeed I Lov'd to Distraction; and the loss of all the Expectations I had, and which I always had built my Hopes upon, of having him one Day for my Husband: These things oppress'd my Mind so much, that in short, I fell very ill, the agonies of my Mind, in a word, threw me into a high Feaver, and long it was, that none in the family expected my Life.

I was reduc'd very low indeed, and was often Delirious and light Headed; but nothing lay so near me, as the fear, that when I was light Headed, I should say something or other to his Prejudice; I was distress'd in my Mind also to see him, and so he was to see me, for he really Lov'd me most passionately; but it could not be; there was not the least Room to desire it, on one side, or other, or so much as to make it Decent.

It was near five Weeks that I kept my Bed, and tho' the violence of my Feaver abated in three Weeks, yet it several times Return'd; and the Physicians said two or three times, they could do no more for me, but that they must leave Nature[57] and the Distemper[58] to fight it Out; only strengthening the first with Cordials to maintain the

---

[56]I.e., the loss of him as an individual.
[57]Normal bodily strength and vigor. Behind the physicians' judgment is a naturopathic assumption about the body's recuperative powers.
[58]Illness.

Strugle: After the end of five Weeks I grew better, but was so Weak, so Alter'd, so Melancholly, and recover'd so Slowly, that the Physicians apprehended I should go into a Consumption; and which vex'd me most, they gave it as their Opinion, that my Mind was Oppress'd, that something Troubl'd me, and in short, that I was IN LOVE; upon this, the whole House was set upon me to Examine me, and to press me to tell, whether I was in Love or not, and with who? but as I well might, I deny'd my being in Love at all.

They had on this Occasion a Squable one Day about me at Table, that had like to have put the whole Family in an Uproar, and for sometime did so; they happen'd to be all at Table, but the Father; as for me I was Ill, and in my Chamber: at the beginning of the Talk, which was just as they had finish'd their Dinner, the old Gentlewoman who had sent me somewhat to Eat, call'd her Maid to go up; and ask me if I would have any more; but the Maid brought down Word, I had not Eaten half what she had sent me already.

Alas, *says the* old Lady, that poor Girl; I am afraid she will never be well.

Well! *says the* elder Brother, How should Mrs. *Betty* be well, *they say* she is in Love?

I believe nothing of it *says the* old Gentlewoman.

I don't know *says the* eldest Sister, what to say to it, they have made such a rout about her being so Handsome, and so Charming, and I know not what, and that in her hearing too, that has turn'd the Creatures Head[59] I believe, and who knows what possessions[60] may follow such Doings? for my Part I don't know what to make of it.

Why Sister, you must acknowledge she is very Handsome, *says the* elder Brother.

Ay, and a great deal Handsomer than you Sister, *says* Robin, and that's your Mortification.

Well, well, that is not the Question, *says his* Sister, the Girl is well enough, and she knows it well enough; she need not be told of it to make her Vain.

We are not a talking of her being Vain, *says the* elder Brother, but of her being in Love; it may be she is in Love with herself, it seems my Sisters think so.

I would she was in Love with me, *says* Robin, I'd quickly put her out of her Pain.

What d'ye mean by that Son, *says the* old Lady, How can you talk so?

Why Madam, *says* Robin again, very honestly, Do you think I'd let the poor Girl Die for Love, and of one that is near at hand to be had too.

---

[59]Destroyed her perspective.   [60]Irrational impulses.

Fye Brother, *says the* second Sister, how can you talk so? would you take a Creature that has not a Groat[61] in the World?

Prethee Child *says* Robin, Beauties[62] a Portion, and good Humour with it, is a double Portion;[63] I wish thou hadst half her Stock of both for thy Portion: So there was her Mouth stopp'd.

I find, *says the* eldest Sister, if *Betty* is not in Love, my Brother is; I wonder he has not broke his Mind to *Betty*, I warrant she won't say NO.

They that yield when they're ask'd *says* Robin, are one step before them that were never ask'd to yield, Sister, and two Steps before them that yield before they are ask'd: And that's an Answer to you Sister.

This fir'd the Sister, and she flew into a Passion, and said, things were come to that pass, that it was time the Wench, *meaning me*, was out of the Family; and but that she was not fit to be turn'd out,[64] she hop'd her Father and Mother would consider of it, as soon as she could be remov'd.

Robin reply'd, That was business for the Master and Mistress of the Family, who were not to be taught by One, that had so little Judgment as his eldest Sister.

It run up a great deal farther; the Sister Scolded, *Robin* Rally'd[65] and Banter'd, but poor *Betty* loss'd Ground by it extreamly in the Family: I heard of it, and I cry'd heartily, and the old Lady came up to me, some body having told her that I was so much concern'd about it: I complain'd to her, that it was very hard the Doctors should pass such a Censure[66] upon me, for which they had no Ground; and that it was still harder, considering the Circumstances I was under in the Family; that I hop'd I had done nothing to lessen her Esteem for me, or given any Occasion for the Bickering between her Sons and Daughters; and I had more need to think of a Coffin, than of being in Love, and beg'd she would not let me suffer in her Opinion for any bodies Mistakes, but my own.

She was sensible of the Justice of what I said, but *told me*, since there had been such a Clamour among them, and that her younger Son Talk'd after such a rattling way as he did; she desir'd I Would be so Faithful to her, as to Answer her but one Question sincerely; I told her I would with all my heart, and with the utmost plainess and sincerity: Why then the Question was, Whether there was any thing

---

[61]I.e., is penniless. A groat was original-ly a small coin and became proverbial as an insignificant amount.

[62]Beauty's; i.e., beauty is.

[63]An eighteenth-century commonplace. Cf. Clarissa's speech in Pope's *Rape of the Lock*, V, 9ff.

[64]Except for the fact that she was not yet recovered from illness.

[65]Teasingly ridiculed.

[66]Diagnosis, professional opinion.

between her Son *Robert* and me? I told her with all the Protestations of Sincerity that I was able to make, and as I might well do, that there was not, nor ever had been; I *told her,* that Mr. *Robert* had rattled and jested, as she knew it was his way, and that I took it always as I suppos'd he meant it, to be a wild airy way of Discourse that had no Signification in it: And again assured her, that there was not the least tittle of what she understood by it between us; and that those who had Suggested it, had done me a great deal of Wrong, and Mr. *Robert* no Service at all.

The old Lady was fully satisfy'd, and kiss'd me, spoke chearfully to me, and bid me take care of my Health, and want for nothing, and so took her leave: But when she came down, she found the Brother and all his Sisters together by the Ears; they were Angry even to Passion, at his upbraiding them with their being Homely, and having never had any Sweet-heart, never having been ask'd the Question, and their being so forward as almost to ask first: He rallied them upon the Subject of Mrs. *Betty*; how Pretty, how good Humour'd, how she Sung better than they did, and Danc'd better, and how much Handsomer she was; and in doing this, he omitted no Ill-natur'd Thing that could vex them, and indeed, push'd too hard upon them: The old Lady came down in the height of it, and to put a stop to it, told them all the Discourse she had had with me, and how I answer'd, that there was nothing between Mr. *Robert* and I.

She's wrong there, *says* Robin, for if there was not a great deal between us, we should be closer together than we are: I told her I Lov'd her hugely, *says he,* but I could never make the Jade believe I was in Earnest; I do not know how you should *say his* Mother, no body in their Senses could believe you were in Earnest, to Talk so to a poor Girl, whose Circumstances you know well.

But prethee Son *adds she,* since you tell me that you could not make her believe you were in Earnest, what must we believe about it? for you ramble so in your Discourse, that no body knows whether you are in Earnest or in Jest: But as I find the Girl by your own Confession has answer'd truely, I wish you would do so too, and tell me seriously, so that I may depend upon it; Is there any thing in it or no? Are you in Earnest or no? Are you Distracted indeed, or are you not? 'Tis a weighty Question, and I wish you would make us easie about it.

By my Faith Madam, *says* Robin, 'tis in vain to mince[67] the Matter, or tell any more Lyes about it, I am in Earnest, as much as a Man is, that's going to be Hang'd. If Mrs. *Betty* would say she Lov'd me, and that she would Marry me, I'd have her to morrow Morning fasting; and say, *To have, and to hold,* instead of eating my Breakfast.

[67]Make light of.

Well, *says the Mother*, then there's one Son lost; and she said it in a very mournful Tone, as one greatly concern'd at it.

I hope not Madam, *says* Robin, no Man is lost, when a good Wife has found him.

Why but Child, *says the* old Lady, she is a Beggar.

Why then Madam, she has the more need of Charity *says* Robin; I'll take her off of the hands of the Parish, and she and I'll Beg together.

Its bad Jesting with such things, *says the Mother*.

I don't Jest Madam, *says* Robin: We'll come and beg your Pardon Madam; and your Blessing Madam, and my Fathers.

This is all out of the way Son, *says the Mother*, if you are in Earnest you are Undone.

I am afraid not *says he*, for I am really afraid she won't have me, after all my Sisters huffing and blustring; I believe I shall never be able to persuade her to it.

That's a fine Tale indeed, she is not so far out of her Senses neither; Mrs. *Betty* is no Fool, *says the youngest Sister*, Do you think she has learnt to say NO, any more than other People?

No Mrs. *Mirth-Wit*[68] says Robin, Mrs. *Betty*'s no Fool; but Mrs. *Betty* may be Engag'd some other way, And what then?

Nay, *says the eldest Sister*, we can say nothing to that, Who must it be to then? She is never out of the Doors, it must be between you.

I have nothing to say to that *says* Robin, I have been Examin'd enough; there's my Brother, if it must be *between us*, go to Work with him.

This stung *the elder Brother* to the Quick, and he concluded that *Robin* had discover'd something: However, he kept himself from appearing disturb'd; Prethee *says he*, don't go to sham your Stories off upon me, I tell you, I deal in no such Ware; I have nothing to say to Mrs. *Betty* nor to any of the *Miss Betty*'s in the Parish; and with that he rose up and brush'd off.

No, *says the eldest Sister*, I dare answer for my Brother, he knows the World better.

Thus the Discourse ended; but it left *the elder Brother* quite confounded: He concluded his Brother had made a full Discovery, and he began to doubt, whether I had been concern'd in it, or not; but with all his Management,[69] he could not bring it about to get at me; at last, he was so perplex'd, that he was quite Desperate, and resolv'd he wou'd come into my Chamber and see me, whatever came of it: In order to this, he contriv'd it so; that one Day after Dinner, watching *his eldest Sister*, till he could see her go up Stairs, he runs after her,

[68]Robin mockingly gives his sister a name like those given to type characters in contemporary stage comedies. [69]Manipulation.

Hark ye Sister, says he, Where is this sick Woman? may not a body see her? YES, *says the Sister,* I believe you may, but let me go first a little, and I'll tell you; so she run up to the Door, and gave me notice; and presently call'd to him again: BROTHER, *says she,* you may come if you please; so in he came, just in the same kind of Rant: Well, *says he,* at the Door *as he came in,* Where is this sick Body that's in Love? How do ye do Mrs. *Betty?* I would have got up out of my Chair, but was so Weak I could not for a good while; and he saw it and his Sister too, and she said, *Come do not strive to stand up,* my Brother desires no Ceremony, especially, now you are so Weak. No, No, Mrs. *Betty,* pray sit still *says he,* and so sits himself down in a Chair over-against me, and appear'd as if he was mighty Merry.

He talk'd a deal of rambling Stuff to his Sister, and to me; sometimes of one thing, sometimes of another, on purpose to Amuse[70] his Sister; and every now and then, would turn it upon the old Story, directing it to me: Poor Mrs. *Betty, says he,* it is a sad thing to be in Love, why it has reduced[71] you sadly; at last I spoke a little, I am glad to see you so Merry, Sir *says I,* but I think the Doctor might have found some thing better to do, than to make his Game at his Patients: If I had been Ill of no other Distemper, I know the Proverb too well to have let him come to me: What Proverb *says he?* O! I remember it now: What,

> *Where Love is the Case,*
> *The* Doctor's *an Ass.*[72]

Is not that it Mrs. *Betty?* I smil'd, and said nothing: Nay, *says he,* I think the effect has prov'd it to be Love; for it seems the Doctor has been able to do you but little Service, you mend very slowly they say, I doubt[73] there's somewhat in it Mrs. *Betty,* I doubt you are Sick of the Incureables, and that is Love; I smil'd and said, No, *indeed Sir,* that's none of my Distemper.

We had a deal of such Discourse, and sometimes others that signify'd as little; by and by He ask'd me to Sing them a Song; at which I smil'd, and said, my singing Days were over: At last he ask'd me, if he should Play upon his Flute to me; his Sister said, she believ'd it wou'd hurt me, and that my Head could not bear it; I bow'd and said, No, it would not hurt me: And pray Madam, *said I;* do not hinder it, I love the Musick of the Flute very much; then his Sister said, well do then Brother; with that he pull'd out the Key of his Closet, Dear Sister, *says he,* I am very Lazy, do step to my Closet and fetch my

---

[70]Deceive, divert her attention from the issue.

[71]Brought down to a deplorable condition or state of mind.

[72]The proverb appears in Roger L'Estrange's translation of Quevedo's *Visions,* 1667.

[73]Suspect. (R)

Flute, it lies in *such a Drawer*, naming a Place where he was sure it was not, that she might be a little while a looking for it.

As soon as she was gone, he related the whole Story to me, of the Discourse his Brother had about me, and of his pushing it at him, and his concern about it, which was the Reason of his contriving this Visit to me: I assur'd him, I had never open'd my Mouth either to his Brother, or to any Body else: I told him the dreadful Exigence I was in; that my Love to him, and his offering to have me forget that Affection, and remove it to another, had thrown me down; and that I had a thousand Times wish'd I might Die, rather than Recover, and to have the same Circumstances to strugle with as I had before; and that this backwardness to Life, had been the great Reason of the slowness of my Recovering: I added, that I foresaw, that as soon as I was well, I must quit the Family; and that as for Marrying his *Brother*, I abhor'd the thoughts of it, after what had been my Case with him, and that he might depend upon it, I would never see his Brother again upon that Subject: That if he would break all his Vows and Oaths, and Engagements with me, be that between his Conscience and his Honour, and himself: But he should never be able to say, that I who he had persuaded to call my self his Wife, and who had given him the Liberty to use me as a Wife, was not as Faithful to him as a Wife ought to be, what ever he might be to me.

He was going to reply, and had said, That he was sorry I could not be persuaded, and was a going to say more, but he heard his Sister a coming, and so did I; and yet I forc'd out these few Words as a reply, That I could never be persuaded to Love one Brother, and Marry another: He shook his Head and said, *Then I am Ruin'd*, meaning himself; and that Moment his Sister enter'd the Room, and told him she could not find the Flute; Well, *says he* merrily, this Laziness won't do, so he gets up, and goes himself to go to look for it, but comes back without too; not but that he could have found it, but because his Mind was a little Disturb'd, and he had no mind to Play; and besides, the Errand he sent his Sister of, was answer'd another way; for he only wanted an Opportunity to speak to me, which he gain'd, tho' not much to his Satisfaction.

I had however, a great deal of Satisfaction in having spoken my Mind to him with Freedom, and with such an honest Plainess, as I have related; and tho' it did not at all Work that way I desir'd, *that is to say*, to oblige the Person to me the more; yet it took from him all possibility of quiting me, but by a down right breach of Honour,[74] and giving up all the Faith of a Gentleman to me, which he had so

[74]An early instance of Moll's instinctive cunning, a pattern of behavior that alternates with her naiveté.

often engaged by, never to abandon me, but to make me his Wife as soon as he came to his Estate.

It was not many Weeks after this, before I was about the House again, and began to grow well; but I continu'd Melancholly, silent, dull, and retir'd, which amaz'd the whole Family, except he that knew the Reason of it; yet it was a great while before he took any Notice of it, and I *as backward to speak, as he,* carried[75] respectfully to him, but never offer'd to speak a Word to him, that was particular of any kind whatsoever; and this continu'd for sixteen or seventeen Weeks, so that as I expected every Day to be dismiss'd the Family, on Account of what Distaste they had taken another Way, in which I had no Guilt; so I expected to hear no more of this Gentleman, after all his solemn Vows, and Protestations, but to be ruin'd and abandon'd.

At last I broke[76] the way myself in the Family, for my Removing; for being talking seriously with the old Lady one Day, about my own Circumstances in the World, and how my Distemper had left a heaviness upon my Spirits, that I was not the same thing I was before: The old Lady said, I am afraid *Betty,* what I have said to you, about my Son, has had some influence upon you, and that you are Melancholly on his Account; Pray will you let me know how the Matter stands with you both? if it may not be improper, for as for *Robin,* he does nothing but Rally and Banter when I speak of it to him: Why truly Madam, *said I,* that Matter stands as I wish it did not, and I shall be very sincere with you in it, what ever befalls me for it, Mr. *Robert* has several times propos'd Marriage to me, which is what I had no Reason to expect, my poor Circumstances consider'd; but I have always resisted him, and that perhaps in Terms more positive than became[77] me, considering the Regard that I ought to have for every Branch of your Family: But *said I,* Madam, I could never so far forget my Obligations to you, and all your House, to offer to Consent to a Thing, which I know must needs be Disobliging to you, and this I have made my Argument to him, and have possitively told him, that I would never entertain a Thought of that kind, unless I had your Consent, and his Fathers also, to whom I was bound by so many invincible Obligations.

And is this possible Mrs. *Betty,* says the old Lady? then you have been much Juster to us, than we have been to you; for we have all look'd upon you as a kind of a Snare[78] to my Son; and I had a Proposal to make to you, for your Removing, for fear of it; but I had not yet mention'd it to you, because I thought you were not thorough Well, and I was afraid of grieving you too much, least it should

---

[75]Behaved. (R)
[76]Opened; brought the subject out into the open.
[77]Were proper to.

[78]Attractive deception. In the eighteenth century, the term often bore strong religious overtones of leading a soul to destruction.

throw you down again, for we have all a Respect for you still, tho' not so much, as to have it be the Ruin of my Son; but if it be as you say, we have all wrong'd you very much.

As to the Truth of what I say, Madam, *said I*, I refer you to your Son himself; if he will do me any Justice, he must tell you the Story just as I have told it.

Away goes the old Lady to her Daughters, and tells them, the whole Story, just as I had told it her, and they were surpris'd at it, you may be sure, as I believ'd they would be; one *said*, she could never have thought it; another said, *Robin* was a Fool, a *Third* said, she would not believe a Word of it, and she would warrant that *Robin* would tell the Story another way; but the old Gentlewoman, who was resolv'd to go to the bottom of it, before I could have the least Opportunity of Acquainting her Son with what had pass'd, resolv'd too, that she would Talk with her Son immediately, and to that purpose sent for him, for he was gone but to a Lawyers House in the Town, upon some petty Business of his own, and upon her sending, he return'd immediately.

Upon his coming up to them, for they were all still together; sit down *Robin*, *says the old Lady*, I must have some talk with you; with all my Heart, Madam, *says* Robin, *looking very Merry*; I hope it is about a good Wife, for I am at a great loss in that Affair: How can that be, *says his Mother*, did not you say, you resolved to have Mrs. *Betty*? Ay Madam, says *Robin*; but there is one has *forbid the Banns*: Forbid the Banns! *says his Mother*, who can that be? Even Mrs. *Betty* herself, says *Robin*. How so, *says his Mother*; Have you ask'd her the Question then? *Yes, indeed Madam, says* Robin; I have attack'd her in Form,[79] five times since she was Sick, and am beaten off; the Jade is so stout,[80] she won't Capitulate, nor yield upon any Terms, except such as I cannot effectually Grant: Explain your self, *says the Mother*, for I am surpris'd, I do not understand you, I hope you are not in Earnest.

Why, Madam, *says he*, the Case is plain enough upon me, it explains itself; she wont have me, *she says*; is not that plain enough? I think 'tis plain, and pretty rough too; well but *says the Mother*, you talk of Conditions, that you cannot Grant; what, does she want a Settlement? her Jointure ought to be according to her Portion; but what Fortune does she bring you? Nay, as to Fortune, *says* Robin, she is rich enough; I am satisfy'd in that Point; but *'tis I* that am not able to come up to her Terms, and she is positive she will not have me without.

Here the Sisters put in, Madam, *says the second Sister*, 'tis impossible to be serious with him; he will never give a direct Answer to any thing; you had better let him alone, and talk no more of it to him; you know

---

[79]According to the prescribed methods or rules.

[80]Resolute, unyielding; or possibly, proud, obstinate.

how to dispose of her out of his way, if you thought there was any thing in it; *Robin* was a little warm'd with his Sisters rudeness, but he was even with her; and yet with good Manners too: There are two sorts of People, Madam, *says he, turning to his Mother*, that there is no contending with, that is a wise Body and a Fool; 'tis a little hard I should engage with both of them together.

The younger Sister then put in, we must be Fools indeed, *says she*, in my Brother's Opinion, that he should think we can believe, he has seriously ask'd Mrs. *Betty* to Marry him, and that she has refus'd him.

Answer, and *Answer not*, says *Solomon*,[81] *replyed her Brother*: When your Brother had said to your Mother, that he had ask'd her no less than five Times, and that it was so, that she positively Denied him; methinks a younger Sister need not question the Truth of it, when her Mother did not: My Mother you see did not understand it, *says the second Sister*: There's some difference *says* Robin, between desiring me to Explain it, and telling me she did not believe it.

Well but Son, *says the old Lady*, if you are dispos'd to let us into the Mystery of it, What were these hard Conditions? Yes Madam *says* Robin, I had done it before now, if the *Teazers* here had not worried me by way of Interruption: The Conditions are, that I bring my Father and you to Consent to it, and without that, she protests she will never see me more upon that Head; and these Conditions *as I said*, I suppose I shall never be able to Grant; I hope my warm Sisters will be Answer'd now, and Blush a little; if not, I have no more to say till I hear farther.

This Answer was surprizing to them all, tho' less to the Mother, because of what I had said to her; as to the Daughters they stood Mute a great while; but the Mother said with some Passion, Well, I had heard this before, *but I cou'd not believe it*; but if it is so, then we have all done *Betty* wrong, and she has behav'd better than I ever expected: Nay, *says the eldest Sister*, if it is so, she has acted Handsomely[82] indeed: I confess *says the Mother*, it was none of her Fault, if he was Fool enough to take a Fancy to her; but to give such an Answer to him, shews more Respect to your Father and me, than I can tell how to Express; I shall value the Girl the better for it, as long as I know her. But I shall not *says* Robin, unless you will give your Consent: I'll consider of that a while *says the Mother*; I assure you, if there were not some other Objections in the way, this Conduct of hers would go a great way to bring me to Consent: I wish it would go quite thro' with it, *says* Robin; if you had as much thought about making me Easie,[83] as you have about making me Rich, you would soon Consent to it.

---

[81]See Proverbs 26: 4, 5. Robin again calls his sister a fool, this time by allusion.

[82]Appropriately.
[83]I.e., relieving his mental anxiety.

Why *Robin, says the Mother again*, Are you really in Earnest? Would you so fain have her as you pretend? Really Madam *says* Robin, I think 'tis hard you should Question me upon that Head, after all I have said: I won't say that I will have her, how can I resolve that point, when you see I cannot have her without your Consent? besides I am not bound to Marry at all: But this I will say I am in Earnest in, that I will never have any body else, if I can help it; so you may Determine for me, *Betty*, or no Body, is the Word; and the Question which of the Two shall be in your Breast to decide Madam; provided only, that *my good humour'd Sisters here, may have no Vote in it.*

All this was dreadful to me, for the Mother began to yield, and *Robin* press'd her Home in it: On the other hand, she advised with the eldest Son, and he used all the Arguments in the World to persuade her to Consent; alledging his Brothers passionate Love for me, and my generous Regard to the Family, in refusing my own Advantages, upon such a nice point of Honour, and a thousand such Things: And as to the Father, he was a Man in a hurry of publick Affairs, and getting Money, seldom at Home, thoughtful of the main Chance;[84] but left all those Things to his Wife.

You may easily believe, that when the Plot was thus, as *they thought* broke out,[85] and that every one thought they knew how Things were carried: It was not so Difficult, or so Dangerous, for the elder Brother, who no body suspected of any thing, to have a freer Access to me than before: Nay the Mother, *which was just as he wish'd*, Propos'd it to him to Talk with Mrs. *Betty*; for it may be Son *said she*, you may see farther into the Thing than I; and see if you think she has been so Positive as *Robin* says she has been, or no. This was as well as he could wish, and he as it were yielding to Talk with me at his Mother's Request, She brought me to him into her own Chamber; told me her Son had some Business with me at her Request, and desir'd me to be very Sincere with him; and then she left us together, and he went and shut the Door after her.

He came back to me, and took me in his Arms and kiss'd me very Tenderly; but told me, he had a long Discourse to hold with me, and it was now come to that Crisis, that I should make myself Happy or Miserable, as long as I Liv'd: That the Thing was now gone so far, that if I could not comply with his Desire, we should be both Ruin'd: Then he told me the whole Story between *Robin*, as he call'd him, and his Mother, and Sisters, and himself; as it is above: And now dear Child, *says he*, consider what it will be to Marry a Gentleman of a good

---

[84]I.e., interested primarily in getting gain and raising his position. The phrase was, according to the OED, already cant by 1669. In late nineteenth- and early twentieth-century Defoe criticism, the phrase was often used to describe the predilections of Defoe's main characters, and sometimes of Defoe himself.

[85]I.e., the family thought that the full scheme had been revealed.

Family, in good Circumstances, and with the Consent of the whole House, and to enjoy all that the World can give you: And what, on the other Hand, to be sunk into the dark Circumstances of a Woman that has lost her Reputation; and that tho' I shall be a private Friend to you while I live, yet as I shall be suspected always; so you will be afraid to see me, and I shall be afraid to own you.

He gave me no time to Reply, but went on with me thus: What has happen'd between us Child, so long as we both agree to do so, may be buried and forgotten: I shall always be your sincere Friend, without any Inclination to nearer Intimacy, when you become my Sister; and we shall have all the honest part of Conversation without any Reproaches between us, of having done amiss: I beg of you to consider it, and do not stand in the way of your own Safety and Prosperity; and to satisfie you that I am Sincere, *added he*, I here offer you 500 *l.* in Money, to make you some Amends for the Freedoms I have taken with you, which we shall look upon as some of the Follies of our Lives, which 'tis hop'd we may Repent of.

He spoke this in so much more moving Terms than it is possible for me to Express, and with so much greater force of Argument than I can repeat: That I only recommend it to those who Read the Story, to suppose, that as he held me above an Hour and Half in that Discourse, so he answer'd all my Objections, and fortified his Discourse with all the Arguments that humane[86] Wit and Art could Devise.

I cannot say however, that any thing he said, made Impression enough upon me, so as to give me any thought of the Matter; till he told me at last very plainly, that if I refus'd, he was sorry to add that he could never go on with me in that Station as we stood before; that tho' he Lov'd me as well as ever, and that I was as agreeable to him, as ever; yet, Sense of Vertue had not so far forsaken him, as to suffer him to lye with a Woman that his Brother Courted to make his Wife; and if he took his leave of me, with a denial in this Affair, whatever he might do for me in the Point of support, grounded on his first Engagement of maintaining me, yet he would not have me be surpriz'd, that he was oblig'd to tell me, he could not allow himself to see me any more; and that indeed I could not expect it of him.

I receiv'd this last part with some tokens of Surprize and Disorder, and had much ado,[87] to avoid sinking down, for indeed I lov'd him to an Extravagance, not easie to imagine; but he perceiv'd my Disorder, he entreated me to consider seriously of it, assur'd me that it was the only way to Preserve our mutual Affection, that in this Station we might love as Friends, with the utmost Passion, and with a love of Relation untainted, free from our just Reproaches, and free from

---

[86]Human. [87]Found it difficult.

other Peoples Suspicions; that he should ever acknowledge his happiness owing to me; that he would be Debtor to me as long as he liv'd, and would be paying that Debt as long as he had Breath; Thus he wrought me up, in short, to a kind of Hesitation in the Matter; having the Dangers on one Side represented in lively Figures, and indeed heightn'd by my Imagination of being turn'd out to the wide World, a meer cast off Whore, *for it was no less*, and perhaps expos'd as such; with little to provide for myself; with no Friend, no Acquaintance in the whole World, *out of*[88] *that Town*, and there I could not pretend to stay; all this terrify'd me to the last Degree, and he took care upon all Occasions to lay it home[89] to me, in the worst Colours that it could be possible to be drawn in; on the other Hand, he fail'd not to set forth the easy prosperous Life, which I was going to live.

He answer'd all that I could object from Affection, and from former Engagements, with telling me the Necessity that was before us of taking other Measures now; and as to his Promises of Marriage, the nature of things[90] *he said*, had put an End to that, by the probability of my being his Brothers Wife, before the time to which his Promises all referr'd.

Thus in a Word, I may say, he Reason'd me out of my Reason; he conquer'd all my Arguments, and I began to see a Danger that I was in, which I had not consider'd of before, and that was of being drop'd by both of them, and left alone in the World to shift for myself.

This, and his perswasion, at length Prevail'd with me to Consent, tho' with so much Reluctance, that it was easie to see I should go to Church, like a Bear to the Stake; I had some little Apprehensions about me too, least my new Spouse, who by the way, I had not the least Affection for, should he be skilful enough to Challenge me on another Account, upon our first coming to Bed together; but whether he did it with Design, or not, I know not; but his elder Brother took care to make him very much Fuddled before he went to Bed; so that I had the Satisfaction of a drunken Bedfellow the first Night: How he did it I know not, but I concluded that he certainly contriv'd it, that his Brother might be able to make no Judgment of the difference between a Maid and a married Woman; nor did he ever Entertain any Notions of it, or disturb his Thoughts about it.

I should go back a little here, to where I left off; the elder Brother, having thus manag'd me, his next business was to Manage his Mother, and he never left till he had brought her to acquiesce, and be passive in the thing; Even without acquainting the Father, other than by Post

---

[88]Outside of.

[89]Dramatize it.

[90]The way things had happened. Compare the brother's conception of nature here with Moll's summary, four paragraphs later, of how men "naturally" act. For Defoe's conception of human nature, see Novak, *Defoe and the Nature of Man*.

Letters: So that she consented to our Marrying privately, and leaving her to manage the Father afterwards.

Then he Cajol'd with his Brother, and perswaded him what Service he had done him, and how he had brought his Mother to Consent, which *tho' True*, was not indeed done to serve him, but to serve himself; but thus diligently did he cheat him, and had the Thanks of a faithful Friend for shifting off his Whore into his Brothers Arms for a Wife. So certainly does Interest banish all manner of Affection, and so naturally[91] do Men give up Honour and Justice, Humanity, and even Christianity, to secure themselves.

I must now come back to Brother *Robin*, as we always call'd him; who having got his Mother's Consent *as above*, came big[92] with the News to me, and told me the whole Story of it, with a Sincerity so visible, that I must confess it griev'd me, that I must be the Instrument to abuse so honest a Gentleman; but there was no Remedy, he would have me, and I was not oblig'd to tell him, that I was his Brother's Whore, tho' I had no other way to put him off; so I came gradually into it, to his Satisfaction, and behold, we were Married.

Modesty forbids me to reveal the Secrets of the Marriage Bed,[93] but nothing could have happen'd more suitable to my Circumstances than that, *as above*, my Husband was so Fuddled when he came to Bed, that he could not remember in the Morning, whether he had had any Conversation[94] with me or no, and I was oblig'd to tell him *he had*, tho' in reallity *he had not*, that I might be sure he could make no enquiry about any thing else.

It concerns the Story in hand very little, to enter into the farther particulars of the Family, or of myself, for the five Years that I liv'd with this Husband; only to observe that I had two Children by him, and that at the end of five Year he Died: He had been really a very good Husband to me, and we liv'd very agreeably together; But as he had not receiv'd much from them, and had in the little time he liv'd acquir'd no great Matters, so my Circumstances were not great; nor was I much mended[95] by the Match: Indeed I had preserv'd the elder Brother's Bonds to me, to pay me 500 *l.* which he offer'd me for my Consent to Marry his Brother; and this with what I had saved of the Money he formerly gave me, and about as much more by my Husband, left me a Widow with about 1200 *l.* in my Pocket.

My two Children were indeed taken happily[96] off of my Hands, by

---

[91]I.e., in a state of nature, rather than of grace.

[92]Literally, pregnant; i.e., Robin was anxious to communicate the news to Moll.

[93]Defoe was less modest than Moll and in 1727 published a 406-page

Treatise Concerning the Use and Abuse of the Marriage Bed (its first edition was titled *Conjugal Lewdness*).

[94]Sexual intercourse.

[95]Financially improved.

[96]By chance. Or possibly Moll means fortunately. (R)

my Husband's Father and Mother, and that by the way was all they got by Mrs. *Betty.*

I confess I was not suitably affected with the loss of my Husband; nor indeed can I say, that I ever Lov'd him as I ought to have done, or as was proportionable to the good Usage I had from him, for he was a tender, kind, good humour'd Man as any Woman could desire; but his Brother being so always in my sight, *at least* while we were in the Country, was a continual Snare to me; and I never was in Bed with my Husband, but I wish'd my self in the Arms of his Brother; and tho' his Brother never offer'd me the least Kindness[97] that way, after our Marriage, but carried it just as a Brother ought to do; yet, it was impossible for me to do so to him: In short, I committed Adultery and Incest with him every Day in my Desires, which without doubt, was as effectually Criminal in the Nature of the Guilt, as if I had actually done it.

Before my Husband Died, his elder Brother was Married, and we being then remov'd to *London*, were written to by the old Lady to come, and be at the Wedding; my Husband went, but I pretended Indisposition, and that I could not possibly Travel, so I staid behind; for in short, I could not bear the sight of his being given to another Woman, tho' I knew I was never to have him my self.

I was now *as above*, left loose to the World, and being still Young and Handsome, as every body said of me, *and I assure you, I thought my self so*, and with a tollerable Fortune in my Pocket, I put no small value upon my self.[98] I was Courted by several very considerable Tradesmen; and particularly, very warmly by one, a *Linnen-Draper*, at whose House after my Husband's Death I took a Lodging, his Sister being my Acquaintance; here I had all the Liberty, and all the Opportunity to be Gay, and appear in Company that I could desire; my Landlord's Sister being one of the Madest, Gayest things alive, and not so much Mistress of her Vertue, as I thought at first she had been: She brought me into a World of wild Company, and even brought home several Persons, *such as she lik'd well enough to Gratifie*, to see her pretty Widow, *so she was pleas'd to call me*, and that Name I got in a little time in Publick; now as Fame and Fools make an Assembly, I was here wonderfully Caress'd;[99] had abundance of Admirers, and such as call'd themselves *Lovers*; but I found not one fair Proposal among them all; as for their common Design, that I understood too well to be drawn into any more Snares of that Kind: The Case was alter'd with me, I had Money in my Pocket, and had nothing to say to them: I had been trick'd once by *that Cheat* call'd,

[97]Possibly a pun on "Kind" meaning family or kin.

[98]I.e., Moll places a high marital price tag on herself.

[99]Surprisingly sought after, courted.

LOVE, but the Game was over; I was resolv'd now to be Married, or Nothing, and to be well Married, or not at all.

I lov'd the Company indeed of Men of Mirth and Wit, Men of Gallantry and Figure, and was often entertain'd with such, as I was also with others; but I found by just Observation, that the brightest Men came upon the dullest Errand, *that is to say*, the Dullest, as to what I aim'd at; on the other Hand, those who came with the best Proposals, were the Dullest and most disagreeable Part of the World: I was not averse to a Tradesman, but then I would have a Tradesman for sooth, that was something of a Gentleman too; that when my Husband had a mind to carry me to the Court, or to the Play, he might become[100] a Sword, and look as like a Gentleman, as another Man; and not be one that had the mark of his Apron-strings upon his Coat, or the mark of his Hat upon his Perriwig;[101] that should look as if he was set on to his Sword, when his Sword was put on to him, and that carried his Trade in his Countenance.

Well, at last I found this amphibious Creature, this *Land-water-thing*, call'd, a *Gentleman-Tradesman*; and as a just Plague upon my Folly, I was catch'd in the very Snare, which *as I might say*, I laid for myself; *I say laid for my self*, for I was not Trepan'd[102] I confess, but I betray'd my self.

This was a *Draper* too, for tho' my Comrade would have brought me to a Bargain with her Brother; yet when it came to the Point, it was it seems for a Mistress, not a Wife, and I kept true to this Notion, that a Woman should never be kept for a Mistress, that had Money to keep her self.[103]

Thus my Pride, not my Principle, my Money, not my Vertue, kept me Honest; tho' as it prov'd, I found I had much better have been Sold by my *She Comrade* to her Brother, than have Sold my self as I did to a Tradesman, that was Rake, Gentleman, Shop keeper, and Beggar all together.

But I was hurried on[104] (by my Fancy to a Gentleman) to Ruin my self in the grossest Manner that ever Woman did; for my new Husband coming to a lump of Money at once, fell into such a profusion of Expence, that all I had, and all he had before, if he had any thing worth mentioning, would not have held it out above one Year.

He was very fond of me for about a quarter of a Year, and what I got

---

[100]Look well with, wear with fitting grace.

[101]Wig. The "marks" Moll speaks of would betray the "gentleman" and show him to be a tradesman by day, an appearance that at this point she pretentiously wishes to avoid.

[102]Entrapped, swindled.

[103]The third edition is, here, more aphoristic: "... a Woman should never be kept for a Mistress, that had Money to make her self a Wife." Such a change is not typical of the third edition.

[104]Driven along. This is a favorite Defoe phrase to express psychological necessity.

by that, was, that I had the pleasure of seeing a great deal of my Money spent upon my self, and as I may say, had some of the spending it too: Come, my dear, *says he to me one Day*, Shall we go and take a turn into the Country for about a Week? Ay, my Dear, *says I*, Whither would you go? I care not whither *says he*, but I have a mind to look like Quality for a Week; we'll go to OXFORD *says he*: How *says I*, shall we go, I am no Horse Woman, and 'tis too far for a Coach; too far *says he*, no Place is too far for a Coach and Six: If I carry you out, you shall Travel like a Dutchess;[105] hum *says I*, my Dear 'tis a Frolick, but if you have a mind to it I don't care. Well the time was appointed, we had a rich Coach, very good Horses, a Coachman, Postilion, and two Footmen in very good Liveries; a Gentleman on Horseback, and a Page with a Feather in his Hat upon another Horse; The Servants all call'd him my Lord, and the Inn-Keepers you may be sure did the like, and I was *her Honour* the Countess; and thus we Travel'd to OXFORD, and a very pleasant Journey we had; for, give him his due, not a Beggar alive knew better how to be a Lord than my Husband: We saw all the Rareties[106] at OXFORD, talk'd with two or three Fellows of Colleges, about putting out a young Nephew that was left to his Lordship's Care to the University, and of their being his Tutors; we diverted our selves with bantering several other poor Scholars, with hopes of being at least his Lordship's Chaplains and putting on a Scarf;[107] and thus having liv'd like Quality indeed, as to Expence; we went away for *Northampton,* and in a word, in about twelve Days ramble came Home again, to the Tune of about 93 *l.* Expence.

Vanity is the perfection of a Fop; my Husband had this Excellence, that he valued nothing of Expence,[108] and as his History you may be sure has very little weight[109] in it, 'tis enough to tell you, that in about two Years and a Quarter he Broke, and was not so happy to get over into the *Mint*,[110] but got into a *Spunging-House,*[111] being Arrested in an Action too heavy for him to give Bail to, so he sent for me to come to him.

---

[105]Technically, the wife of a duke, but the word was also used colloquially to describe any woman of imposing demeanor or showy appearance.

[106]Usually in the eighteenth-century this word suggests freaks of nature, such as the three-breasted woman, hairy man, and big-headed boy exhibited at fairs. But here Moll probably means antiquarian curiosities of the sort later displayed in the Ashmolean Museum. In *Tour* Defoe speaks of "the Museum, or Chamber of Rareties" as one of Oxford's sights. But if the reference is here to the Ash-molean, Defoe was anachronistic, for the Ashmolean did not open until 1682.

[107]A nobleman's chaplain wore, as part of his clerical garb, a neck scarf, the ends of which hung from his shoulders in front.

[108]Thought nothing of spending money.

[109]Persuasive or convincing power.

[110]Legal sanctuary for insolvent debtors, in Southwark, so called because Henry VIII had kept a mint there.

[111]A place of preliminary confinement for debtors, kept by a bailiff or sheriff's officer.

It was no surprize to me, for I had foreseen *sometime*, that all was going to Wreck, and had been taking care to reserve something if I could, *tho' it was not much* for myself: But when he sent for me, he behav'd much better than I expected, and told me plainly, he had plaid the Fool[112] and suffer'd himself to be Surpriz'd which he might have prevented; that now he foresaw he could not stand it, and therefore he would have me go Home, and in the Night take away every thing I had in the House of any Value and secure it; and after that, he told me, that if I could get away 100 *l.* or 200 *l.* in Goods out of the Shop, I should do it; only says he, let me know nothing of it; neither what you take, or whither you carry it; for as for me *says he*, I am re-solv'd to get out of this House and be gone; and if you never hear of me more, my Dear, *says he*, I wish you well; I am only sorry for the Injury I have done you: He said some very handsome Things to me indeed at Parting; for *I told you* he was a *Gentleman*, and that was all the benefit I had of his being so; that he used me very handsomely, and with good Manners upon all Occasions, even to the last, only spent all I had, and left me to Rob the Creditors for something to Subsist on.

However, I did as he bad me, *that you may be sure,*[113] and having thus taken my leave of him, I never saw him more; for he found means to break out of the Bailiff's House that Night, or the next, and got over into *France*; and for the rest, the Creditors scrambl'd for it as well as they could: How I knew not, for I could come at no Knowledge of any thing, more than this; that he came Home about three a Clock in the Morning, caus'd the rest of his Goods to be remov'd into the *Mint*, and the Shop to be shut up; and having rais'd what Money he could get together, he got over as I said to *France*, from whence I had one or two[114] Letters from him, and no more.

I did not see him when he came Home, for he having given me such Instructions as above, and I having made the best of my Time, I had no more Business back again at the House, not knowing but I might have been stop'd there by the Creditors; for a *Commission of Bankrupt,* being soon after Issued, they might have stop'd me by Orders from the *Commissioners*: But my Husband having so dextrously got out of the Bailiff's House by letting himself down in a most desperate Manner, from almost the top of the House, to the top of another

---

[112]The proverbial expression "play the Fool" derives from King Saul's admission of guilt; see I Samuel 26:21. (plaid = played [R])

[113]Moll's cynical hardness, in phrases like this one, contrasts rather sharply with her younger expressions and conduct.

[114]Moll sometimes affects approxima-tion, but she keeps close track of precise detail when she wishes to; note the statistics two paragraphs below. Such alternation between approximation and precision is characteristic of Defoe's "realistic" style, and Swift parodied it in the opening paragraphs of *Gulliver's Travels*.

Building, and leaping from thence which was almost two Stories, and which was enough indeed to have broken his Neck: He came home and got away his Goods, before the Creditors could come to Seize, *that is to say*, before they could get out the Commission,[115] and be ready to send their Officers to take Possession.

My Husband was so civil to me, *for still I say, he was much of a Gentleman*, that in the first Letter he wrote me from *France*, he let me know where he had Pawn'd 20 Pieces of fine *Holland* for 30 *l*. which were really worth above 90 *l*. and enclos'd me the Token, and an order for the taking them up, paying the Money, which I did, and made in time above 100 *l*. of them, having Leisure to cut them and sell them, some and some,[116] to private Families, as opportunity offer'd.

However with all this, and all that I had secur'd before, I found upon casting things up, my Case was very much alter'd, and my Fortune much lessen'd, for including the Hollands, and a parcel of fine Muslins, which I carry'd off before, and some Plate, and other things; I found I could hardly muster up 500 *l*. and my Condition was very odd, for tho' I had no Child, (*I had had one by my Gentleman* Draper, *but it was buried*, yet I was a Widow bewitch'd, I had a Husband, and no Husband, and I could not pretend[117] to Marry again, tho' I knew well enough my Husband would never see *England* any more, if he liv'd fifty Years: *Thus I say*, I was limitted from Marriage, what Offer soever might be made me; and I had not one Friend to advise with, in the Condition I was in, at least not one I durst Trust the Secret of my Circumstances to, for if the Commissioners were to have been inform'd where I was, I should have been fetch'd up, and examin'd upon Oath, and all I had sav'd be taken away from me.

Upon these Apprehensions the first thing I did, was to go quite out of my Knowledge,[118] and go by another Name: This I did effectually, for I went into the *Mint* too, took Lodgings in a very private Place, drest me up in the Habit of a Widow, and call'd myself Mrs. *Flanders*.

Here, however I conceal'd myself, and tho' my new Acquaintances knew nothing of me, yet I soon got a great deal of Company about me; and whether it be that Women are scarce among the Sorts of People that generally are to be found there; or that some Consolation in the Miseries of the Place, are more Requisite than on other Occasions; I soon found an agreeable Woman was exceedingly valuable among the Sons of Affliction there; and that those that wanted Money to pay Half a Crown in the Pound to their Creditors,

---

[115]I.e., get legal authority to confiscate the goods.

[116]Some here, some there.

[117]Presume, claim the right to.

[118]Moll may mean that she went beyond her previous experience, but she probably means that she moved beyond her circle of acquaintances.

and that run in Debt at the Sign of the *Bull*[119] for their Dinners, would yet find Money for a Supper, if they lik'd the Woman.

However, I kept myself Safe yet, tho' I began, like my Lord *Rochester's*[120] Mistress, that lov'd his Company, but would not admit him farther, to have the Scandal of a Whore, without the Joy; and upon this score tir'd with the Place, and indeed with the Company too, I began to think of Removing.

It was indeed a Subject of strange Reflection to me, to see Men who were overwhelm'd in perplex'd Circumstances; who were reduc'd some Degrees below being Ruin'd; whose Families were Objects of their own Terror and other Peoples Charity; yet while a Penny lasted, nay, even beyond it, endeavouring to drown their Sorrow in their Wickedness; heaping up more Guilt upon themselves, labouring to forget former things, which now it was the proper time to remember, making more Work for Repentance, and Sinning on, as a Remedy for Sin past.

But it is none of my Talent to preach; these Men were too wicked, even for me; there was something horrid and absurd in their way of Sinning, for it was all a Force even upon themselves;[121] they did not only act against Conscience, but against Nature; they put a Rape upon their Temper to drown the Reflections, which their Circumstances continually gave them; and nothing was more easie than to see how Sighs would interrupt their Songs, and paleness, and anguish sit upon their Brows, in spight of the forc'd Smiles they put on; nay, sometimes it would break out at their very Mouths, when they had parted with their Money for a lewd Treat, or a wicked Embrace; I have heard them, turning about, fetch a deep Sigh, and cry *what a Dog am I!* Well *Betty*, my Dear, I'll drink thy Health tho', *meaning the Honest Wife*, that perhaps had not a Half a Crown for herself, and three or four Children: The next Morning they are at their Penitentials again, and perhaps the poor weeping Wife comes over to him, either brings him some Account of what his Creditors are doing, and how she and the Children are turn'd out of Doors, or some other dreadful News; and this adds to his self Reproaches; but when he has Thought and Por'd on it till he is almost Mad, having no Principles to Support him, nothing within him, or above him, to Comfort him; but finding it all Darkness on every Side, he flyes to the same Relief again, (*viz.*) to Drink it away, Debauch it away, and falling into Company of Men in just the same Condition with himself, he repeats the Crime, and thus he goes every Day one Step onward of his way to Destruction.

---

[119]The identifying sign of a tavern.

[120]John Wilmot, Earl of Rochester, was perhaps the most famous rake in Charles II's court, and in the eighteenth century his amorous exploits were as famous as his poetry. Moll apparently refers to one of his less successful adventures.

[121]I.e., they acted unnaturally, against their own impulses.

I was not wicked enough for such Fellows as these *yet*; on the contrary, I began to consider here *very seriously* what I had to do; how things stood with me, and what Course I ought to take: I knew I had no Friends, no not one Friend, or Relation in the World; and that little I had left apparently wasted, which when it was gone, I saw nothing but Misery and Starving was before me: Upon these Considerations, I say, and fill'd with Horror at the Place I was in, and the dreadful Objects, which I had always before me, *I resolv'd to be gone.*

I had made an Acquaintance with a very sober good sort of a Woman, who was a Widow too, like me, but in better Circumstances; her Husband had been a Captain of a Merchant Ship, and having had the Misfortune to be Cast away coming Home on a Voyage from the *West-Indies*, which would have been very profitable, if he had come safe; was so reduc'd by the Loss, that tho' he had saved his Life then, it broke his Heart, and kill'd him afterwards, and his Widow being per-sued by the Creditors was forc'd to take Shelter in the *Mint*: She soon made things up with the help of Friends, and was at Liberty again; and finding that I rather was there to be conceal'd, than by any particular Prosecutions, and finding also that I agreed with her, *or rather she with me* in a just Abhorrence of the Place, and of the Company; she invited me to go Home with her, till I could put myself in some posture of settling in the World to my Mind; withal telling me, that it was ten to one, but some good Captain of a Ship might take a Fancy to me, and Court me, in that part of the Town where she liv'd.

I accepted her offer, and was with her Half a Year, and should have been longer; but in that interval what she propos'd to me happen'd to herself, and she marry'd very much to her Advantage; but whose Fortune soever was upon the Encrease, mine seem'd to be upon the Wane, and I found nothing present, except two or three Boatswains, or such Fellows, but as for the Commanders they were generally of two Sorts. 1. Such as having good Business, *that is to say*, a good Ship, resolv'd not to Marry, but with Advantage, that is, with a good Fortune. 2. Such as being out of Employ, wanted a Wife to help them to a Ship, I mean. (1.) A Wife, who having some Money could enable them to hold, as they call it, a good part of a Ship themselves, so to en-courage Owners to come in; Or. (2.) A Wife who if she had not Money, had Friends who were concern'd in Shipping, and so could help to put the young Man into a good Ship, which to them is as good as a Portion, and neither of these was my Case; so I look'd like one that was to *lye on Hand.*[122]

This Knowledge I soon learnt by Experience, (*viz.*) That the State of things was altered, as to Matrimony, and that I was not to expect at

---

[122]Again Moll uses a shop metaphor to describe her marriageability.

London, what I had found in the Country; that Marriages were here the Consequences of politick Schemes, for forming Interests, and carrying on Business, and that LOVE had no Share, or but very little in the Matter.

That, as my Sister in Law, at *Colchester* had said; Beauty, Wit, Manners, Sence, good Humour, good Behaviour, Education, Vertue, Piety, or any other Qualification, whether of Body or Mind, had no power to recomend: That Money only made a Woman agreeable: That Men chose Mistresses indeed by the gust of their Affection, and it was requisite to a Whore to be Handsome, well shap'd, have a good Mein, and a graceful Behaviour; but that for a Wife, no Deformity would shock the Fancy, no ill Qualities, the Judgement; the Money was the thing; the Portion was neither crooked, or Monstrous, but the Money was always agreeable, whatever the Wife was.

On the other Hand, as the Market run very Unhappily on the Mens side, I found the Women had lost the Privilege of saying No, that it was a Favour now for a Woman to have THE QUESTION ask'd, and if any young Lady had so much Arrogance as to Counterfeit a Negative, she never had the Opportunity given her of denying twice; much less of Recovering that false Step, and accepting what she had but seem'd to decline: The Men had such Choice every where, that the Case of the Women was very unhappy; for they seem'd to Plie at every Door, and if the Man was by great Chance refus'd at one House, he was sure to be receiv'd at the next.

Besides this, I observ'd that the Men made no scruple to set themselves out, and to go a Fortune Hunting, *as they call it*, when they had really no Fortune themselves to Demand it, or Merit to deserve it; and That they carry'd it so high, that a Woman was scarce allow'd to enquire after the Character, or Estate of the Person that pretended to her: This, I had an Example of, in a young Lady at the next House to me, and with whom I had Contracted an intimacy; she was Courted by a young Captain, and though she had near 2000 *l.* to her Fortune, she did but enquire of some of his Neighbours about his Character, his Morals, or Substance; and he took Occasion at the next Visit to let her know, truly, that he took it very ill, and that he should not give her the Trouble of his Visits any more: I heard of it, and as I had begun my Acquaintance with her, I went to see her upon it: She enter'd into a close Conversation with me about it, and unbosom'd herself very freely; I perceiv'd presently that tho' she thought herself very ill us'd, yet she had no power to resent it, and was exceedingly Piqu'd that she had lost him, and particularly that another of less Fortune had gain'd him.

I fortify'd her Mind against such a Meanness, *as I call'd it*; I told her, that as low as I was in the World, I would have despis'd a Man that should think I ought to take him upon his own Recommendation only, without having the liberty to inform myself of his Fortune and of his Character; also *I told her*, that as she had a good Fortune, she had no need to stoop to the Disaster of the times; that it was enough that the Men could insult us that had but little Money to recommend us; but if she suffer'd such an Affront to pass upon her without Resenting it, she would be render'd low-priz'd upon all Occasions, and would be the Contempt of all the Women in that part of the Town; that a Woman can never want an Opportunity to be Reveng'd of a Man that has us'd her ill, and that there were ways enough to humble such a Fellow as that, or else certainly Women were the most unhappy Creatures in the World.

I found she was very well pleas'd with the Discourse, and she told me seriously that she would be very glad to make him sensible of her just Resentment, and either to bring him on again, or have the Satisfaction of her Revenge being as publick as possible.

I told her, that if she would take my Advice, I would tell her she should obtain her Wishes in both those things; and that I would engage I would bring the Man to her Door again, and make him beg to be let in: *She smil'd at that*, and soon let me see, that if he came to her Door, her Resentment was not so great as to give her leave to let him stand long there.

However, she lissened very willingly to my offer of Advice; so *I told her*, that the first thing she ought to do, was a piece of Justice to herself; namely, that whereas she had been told by several People, that he had reported among the Ladies, that he had left her, and pretended to give the Advantage of the Negative to himself; she should take care to have it well spread among the Women, which she could not fail of an Opportunity to do in a Neighbourhood so addicted to Family News, as that she liv'd in was; that she had enquired into his Circumstances, and found he was not the Man as to Estate he pretended to be: Let them be told Madam, *said I*, that you had been well inform'd that he was not the Man that you expected, and that you thought it was not safe to meddle with him, that you heard he was of an ill Temper, and that he boasted how he had us'd the Women ill upon many Occasions, and that particularly he was Debauch'd in his Morals, *& c*. The last of which indeed had some Truth in it; but at the same time, I did not find that she seem'd to like him much the worse for that part.

As I had put this into her Head, she came most readily into it; immediately she went to Work to find Instruments, and she had very little difficulty in the Search; for telling her Story in general to a Couple of Gossips in the Neighbourhood, it was the Chat of the Tea Table all over that part of the Town, and I met with it where ever I visited: Also, as it was known that I was Acquainted with the young Lady herself, my Opinion was ask'd very often, and I confirm'd it with all the necessary Aggravations, and set out his Character in the blackest

Colours; but then as a piece of secret Intelligence, I added, as what the other Gossips knew nothing of (*viz.*) That I had heard he was in very bad Circumstances; that he was under a Necessity of a Fortune to support his Interest with the Owners of the Ship he Commanded: That his own Part was not paid for, and if it was not paid quickly his Owners would put him out of the Ship, and his Chief Mate was likely to Command it, who offer'd to buy that Part which the Captain had promis'd to take.

I added, for I confess I was heartily piqu'd at the Rogue, *as I call'd him*, that I had heard a Rumour too, that he had a Wife alive at *Plymouth*, and another in the *West Indies*, a thing which they all knew was not very uncommon for such kind of Gentlemen.

This work'd as we both desir'd it, for presently the young Lady at next Door, *who had a Father and Mother that Govern'd, both her, and her Fortune*, was shut up, and her Father forbid him the House: Also in one Place more where he went, the Woman had the Courage, *however strange it was*, to say No, and he could try no where but he was Reproached with his Pride, and that he pretended not to give the Women leave to enquire into his Character, *and the like.*

Well, by this time he began to be sensible of his mistake, and having allarm'd[123] all the Women on that side the Water, he went over to *Ratcliff*,[124] and got access to some of the Ladies there; but tho' the young Women there too were, according to the Fate of the Day, pretty willing to be ask'd, yet such was his ill luck, that his Character follow'd him over the Water, and his good Name was much the same there, as it was on our side; so that tho' he might have had Wives enough, yet it did not happen among the Women that had good Fortunes, which was what he wanted.

But this was not all, she very ingeniously manag'd another thing herself, for she got a young Gentleman, who was a Relation, and was indeed a marry'd Man, to come and visit her Two or Three times a Week in a very fine Chariot and good Liveries, and her Two Agents and I also, presently spread a Report all over, that this Gentleman came to Court her; that he was a Gentleman of a Thousand Pounds a Year, and that he was fallen in Love with her, and that she was going to her Aunt's in the City, because it was inconvenient for the Gentleman to come to her with his Coach in *Redriff*,[125] the Streets being so narrow and difficult.

This took immediately, the Captain was laugh'd at in all Companies, and was ready to hang himself; he tryed all the ways possible to come at her again, and wrote the most passionate Letters to her in the

---

[123]I.e., he became aware that the rumors had alerted all women to guard against his advances.

[124]A parish east of London on the north bank of the Thames.

[125]A slang name for Rotherhithe, an area on the south bank of the Thames, inhabited by people involved in sea trade.

World, excusing his former Rashness, and in short, by great Application, obtained leave to wait on her again, *as he said*, to clear his
Reputation.

At this meeting she had her full Revenge of him; for *she told him*
she wondred what he took her to be, that she should admit any Man
to a Treaty of so much Consequence, as that of Marriage, without
enquiring very well into his Circumstances; that if he thought she was
to be huff'd into Wedlock, and that she was in the same Circumstances
which her Neighbours might be in, (*viz.*) to take up with the first
good Christian that came, he was mistaken; that in a word his Character was really bad, or he was very ill beholding to his Neighbours; and
that unless he could clear up some Points, in which she had justly
been Prejudiced, she had no more to say to him, but to do herself
Justice, and give him the Satisfaction of knowing, that she was not
afraid to say NO, either to him, or any Man else.

With that she told him what she had heard, *or rather rais'd*[126] *herself
by my means, of his Character*; his not having paid for the Part he
pretended to Own of the Ship he Commanded; of the Resolution of
his Owners to put him out of the Command, and to put his Mate in his
stead; and of the Scandal rais'd on his Morals; his having been
reproach'd with such and such Women; and his having a Wife at
Plymouth and in the *West-Indies, and the like*; and she ask'd him,
whether he could deny that she had good Reason, if these things were
not clear'd up, to refuse him, and in the mean time to insist upon
having Satisfaction in Points so significant as they were?

He was so confounded at her Discourse that he could not answer a
word, and she almost began to believe that all was true, by his disorder,
tho' at the same time she knew that she had been the raiser of all
those Reports herself.

After some time he recover'd himself a little, and from that time
became the most humble, the most modest, and most importunate
Man alive in his Courtship.

She carried her jest on a great way, she ask'd him, if he thought she
was so at her last shift[127] that she could or ought to bear such Treatment, and if he did not see that she did not want[128] those who thought
it worth their while to come farther to her than he did, meaning the
Gentleman who she had brought to visit her by way of sham.

She brought him by these tricks to submit to all possible measures
to satisfie her, as well of his Circumstances, as of his Behaviour. He
brought her undeniable Evidence of his having paid for his part of the
Ship; he brought her Certificates from his Owners, that the Report of
their intending to remove him from the Command of the Ship, and

---

[126]I.e., rumors she had made up herself
and spread about.

[127]Last resort.

[128]Lack. (R)

put his chief Mate in, was false and groundless; in short, he was quite the reverse of what he was before.

Thus I convinc'd her, that if the Men made their Advantage of our Sex in the Affair of Marriage, upon the supposition of there being such Choice to be had, and of the Women being so easie; it was only owing to this, that the Women wanted Courage to maintain their Ground, and to play their Part; and that according to my Lord *Rochester*,

> *A Woman's ne'er so ruin'd but she can*
> *Revenge herself on her undoer, Man.*[129]

After these things, this young Lady plaid her part so well, that tho' she resolved to have him, and that indeed having him was the main bent of her design, yet she made his obtaining her be TO HIM the most difficult thing in the World; and this she did, not by a haughty Reserv'd Carriage,[130] but by a just Policy, turning the Tables upon him, and playing back upon him his own Game; for as he pretended by a kind of lofty Carriage, to place himself above the occasion of a Character, and to make enquiring into his Character a kind of an affront to him; she broke with him upon that Subject; and at the same time that she made him submit to all possible enquiry after his Affairs, she apparently shut the Door against his looking into her own.

It was enough to him to obtain her for a Wife; as to what she had, she told him plainly, that as he knew her Circumstances, it was but just she should know his; and tho' at the same time he had only known her Circumstances by common Fame, yet he had made so many Protestations of his Passion for her, that he could ask no more but her Hand to his grand Request, *and the like ramble according to the Custom of Lovers*: In short, he left himself no room to ask any more questions about her Estate, and she took the advantage of it like a prudent Woman, for she plac'd part of her Fortune so in Trustees, without letting him know any thing of it, that it was quite out of his reach, and made him be very well content with the rest.

It is true she was pretty well besides, that is to say, she had about 1400 *l.* in Money, which she gave him, and the other, after some time, she brought to light, as a perquisite to her self; which he was to accept as a mighty Favour, seeing though it was not to be his, it might ease him in the Article of her particular Expences; and I must add, that by this Conduct the Gentleman himself became not only the more humble in his Applications to her to obtain her, but also was much the more an obliging Husband to her when he had her: I cannot but

---

[129]Slightly misquoted from Rochester's "A Letter from Artemisa...," 11. 185–86. Defoe is probably making a point about Moll's tastes by having her quote Rochester.

[130]Conduct, demeanor. (R)

remind the Ladies here how much they place themselves below the common Station of a Wife, which if I may be allow'd not to be Partial is low enough already; *I say* they place themselves below their common Station, and prepare their own Mortifications, by their submitting so to be insulted by the Men before-hand, which I confess I see no Necessity of.

This Relation may serve[131] therefore to let the Ladies see, that the Advantage is not so much on the other Side, as the Men think it is; and tho' it may be true, that the Men have but too much Choice among us; and that some Women may be found, who will dishonour themselves, be Cheap, and Easy to come at, and will scarce wait to be ask'd; yet if they will have Women, *as I may say*, worth having, they may find them as uncomatable as ever; and that those that are otherwise, are a Sort of People that have such Defficiencies, *when had*, as rather recommend the Ladies that are Difficult than encourage the Men to go on with their easie Courtship, and expect Wives equally valluable that will come at first call.

Nothing is more certain, than that the Ladies always gain of the Men, by keeping their Ground, and letting their pretended Lovers see they can Resent being slighted, and that they are not affraid of saying NO. They, I observe, insult us mightily, with telling us of the Number of Women; that the Wars and the Sea, and Trade, and other Incidents have carried the Men so much away, that there is no Proportion between the Numbers of the Sexes; and therefore the Women have the Disadvantage; but I am far from Granting that the Number of the Women is so great, or the Number of the Men so small; but if they will have me tell the Truth, the Disadvantage of the Women, is a terrible Scandal upon the Men, and it lyes here, and here only; *Namely*, that the Age is so Wicked, and the Sex so Debauch'd, that in short the Number of such Men, as an honest Woman ought to meddle with, is small indeed, and it is but here and there that a Man is to be found who is fit for a Woman to venture upon.

But the Consequence even of that too amounts to no more than this; that Women ought to be the more Nice;[132] For how do we know the just Character of the Man that makes the offer? To say, that the Woman should be the more easie on this Occasion, is to say, we should be the forwarder to venture, because of the greatness of the Danger; which in my way of Reasoning is very absurd.

On the contrary, the Women have ten Thousand times the more Reason to be wary, and backward, by how much the hazard of being

---

[131]The emphasis here upon the ethical and practical usefulness of the story is rather like that in contemporary conduct books such as *The Bride Woman's Counselor* (1709), *The Whole Duty of a Woman* (1718), *The Young Man's Duty* (1670), or Defoe's own *The Family Instructor* (1715–18) and *Religious Courtship* (1722).

[132]Scrupulous.

betray'd is the greater; and would the Ladies consider this, and act the wary Part, they would discover every Cheat that offer'd; for, *in short*, the Lives of very few Men now a-Days will bear a Character; and if the Ladies do but make a little Enquiry, they will soon be able to distinguish the Men, and deliver themselves: As for Women that do not think their own Safety worth their Thought, that impatient of their present State, resolve *as they call it* to take the first good Christian that comes; that runs into Matrimony, as a Horse rushes into the Battle; I can say nothing to them, but this, that they are a Sort of Ladies that are to be pray'd for among the rest of distemper'd People; and to me they look like People that venture their whole Estates in a Lottery where there is a Hundred Thousand Blanks to one Prize.

No Man of common Sense will value a Woman the less, for not giving up herself at the first Attack, or for not accepting his Proposal without enquiring into his Person or Character; on the contrary, he must think her the weakest of all Creatures in the World, as the Rate of Men now goes; In short, he must have a very contemptible Opinion of her Capacities, nay, even of her Understanding, that having but one Cast[133] for her Life, shall cast that Life away at once, and make Matrimony like Death, be *a Leap in the Dark*.[134]

I would fain have the Conduct of my Sex a little Regulated[135] in this particular, which is the Thing in which of all the parts of Life, I think at this Time we suffer most in: 'Tis nothing but lack of Courage, the fear of not being Marry'd at all, and of that frightful State of Life, call'd *an old Maid*; of which I have a Story to tell by itself: This I say, is the Woman's Snare; but would the Ladies once but get above that Fear, and manage rightly, they would more certainly avoid it by standing their Ground, in a Case so absolutely Necessary to their Felicity, than by exposing themselves as they do; and if they did not Marry so soon as they may do otherwise, they would make themselves amends by Marrying safer; she is always Married too soon, who gets a bad Husband, and she is never Married too late, who gets a good one: In a Word, there is no Woman, *Deformity, or lost Reputation excepted*, but if she manages well, may be Marry'd safely one time or other; but if she Precipitates herself, it is ten Thousand to one but she is undone.

But I come now to my own Case, in which there was at this time no little Nicety. The Circumstances I was in, made the offer of a good

---

[133]Throw of fortune. Here the term seems to move close to an angling metaphor, with which it later merges. "Cast" in its various senses is one of the most frequently manipulated words in *Moll Flanders*; note, e.g., the use of such variations as "cast away," "cast up," "cast with myself," "cast off," etc.

[134]I.e., to be hanged, a common seventeenth- and eighteenth-century slang expression. "To be cast" is slang for the same thing.

[135]Restrained; i.e., Moll wishes women would be more self-disciplined and rational in considering marriage offers.

Husband, the most necessary Thing in the World to me; but I found soon that to be made Cheap, and Easy, was not the way: It soon began to be found that the Widow had no Fortune, and to say this, was to say all that was Ill of me; for I began to be dropt in all the Discourses of Matrimony: Being well Bred, Handsome, Witty, Modest and agreeable; all which I had allowed to my Character, whether justly, or no, is not to the Purpose; I say, all these would not do without the Dross, which was now become more valuable than Virtue itself. In short, *The Widow*, they said, *had no Money*.

I resolv'd therefore, as to the State of my present Circumstances, that it was absolutely Necessary to change my Station,[136] and make a new Appearance in some other Place where I was not known, and even to pass by another Name if I found Occasion.

I Communicated my Thoughts to my intimate Friend the Captain's Lady; who I had so faithfully serv'd in her Case with the Captain; and who was as ready to serve me in the same kind as I could desire: I made no scruple to lay my Circumstances open to her, my Stock was but low, for I had made but about 540 *l*. at the Close of my last Affair, and I had wasted some of that; However, I had about 460 *l*. left, a great many very rich Cloaths, a gold Watch, and some Jewels, tho' of no extraordinary value, and about 30 or 40 *l*. left in Linnen not dispos'd of.

My Dear and faithful Friend, the Captain's Wife was so sensible of the Service I had done her in the Affair above, that she was not only a steddy Friend to me, but knowing my Circumstances, she frequently made me Presents as Money came into her Hands; such as fully amounted to a Maintenance; so that I spent none of my own; and at last she made this unhappy Proposal to me (*viz.*) that as we had observ'd, *as above*, how the Men made no scruple to set themselves out as Persons meriting a Woman of Fortune, when they had really no Fortune of their own; it was but just to deal with them in their own way, and if it was possible, to Deceive the Deceiver.

The Captain's Lady, in short, put this Project into my Head, and told me if I would be rul'd by her I should certainly get a Husband of Fortune, without leaving him any room to Reproach me with want of my own; I told her as I had Reason to do, That I would give up myself wholly to her Directions, and that I would have neither Tongue to speak, or Feet to step, in that Affair, but as she should direct me; depending that she would Extricate me out of every Difficulty that she brought me into, which she said she would Answer for.

The first step she put me upon, was to call her Cousin, and go to a Relations House of hers in the Country, where she directed me, and where she brought her Husband to visit me, and calling me Cousin,

---

[136]Changing one's station or calling is regularly condemned in the common Christian manuals of piety available to Defoe's readers. For a discussion of the implications of such a change, see Hunter, *The Reluctant Pilgrim*, pp. 34 ff.

she work'd Matters so about, that her Husband and she together
Invited me most passionately to come to Town and be with them, for
they now liv'd in a quite different Place from where they were before.
In the next Place she tells her Husband, that I had at least 1500 *l.*
Fortune, and that after some of my Relations I was like to have a great
deal more.

It was enough to tell her Husband this, there needed nothing on my
Side; I was but to sit still and wait the Event, for it presently went all
over the Neighbourhood that the young Widow at Captain———s
was a Fortune, that she had at least 1500 *l.* and perhaps a great deal
more and *that the Captain said so*; and if the Captain was ask'd at any
time about me, he made no scruple to affirm it, tho' he knew not one
Word of the Matter, other than that his Wife had told him so; and in
this he thought no Harm, for he really believ'd it to be so, because he
had it from his Wife; so slender a Foundation will those Fellows build
upon, if they do but think there is a Fortune in the Game: With the
Reputation of this Fortune, I presently found myself bless'd with
admirers enough, and that I had my Choice of Men, as scarce as they
said they were, *which by the way confirms what I was saying before*: This
being my Case, I who had a subtle Game to play, had nothing now
to do but to single out from them all, the properest Man that might be
for my Purpose; *that is to say*, the Man who was most likely to depend
upon the *hear say* of a Fortune, and not enquire too far into the
particulars; and unless I did this, *I did nothing*, for my Case would not
bare[137] much Enquiry.

I Pick'd out my Man without much difficulty, by the judgement I
made of his way of Courting me; I had let him run on with his Protestations and Oaths that he lov'd me above all the World; that if I would
make him happy, that was enough; all which I knew was upon Supposition, nay, it was upon a full Satisfaction,[138] that I was very Rich,
tho' I never told him a Word of it myself.

This was my Man, but I was to try him to the bottom, and indeed in
that consisted my Safety; for if he baulk'd, I knew I was undone, as
surely as he was undone if he took me; and if I did not make some
scruple about his Fortune, it was the way to lead him to raise some
about mine; and first therefore, I pretended on all occasions to doubt
his Sincerity, and told him, perhaps he only courted me for my
Fortune; he stop'd my Mouth in that part, with the Thunder of his
Protestations, *as above*, but still I pretended to doubt.

One Morning he pulls off his Diamond Ring, and writes upon the
Glass of the Sash[139] in my Chamber this Line,

You I love, and you alone.

[137]Bear.
[138]Conviction.
[139]Window.

I read it, and ask'd him to lend me his Ring, with which I wrote under it thus,

> *And so in Love says every one.*[140]

He takes his Ring again, and writes another Line thus,

> *Virtue alone is an Estate.*

I borrow'd it again, and I wrote under it,

> *But Money's Vertue; Gold is Fate.*

He colour'd[141] as red as Fire to see me turn so quick upon him, and in a kind of a Rage told me he would Conquer me, and writes again *thus*,

> *I scorn your Gold, and yet I Love.*

I ventur'd all upon the last cast of Poetry, as you'll see, for I wrote boldly under his last,

> *I'm Poor: Let's see how kind you'll prove.*

This was a sad Truth to me, whether he believ'd me or no I cou'd not tell; I supposed then that he did not. However he flew to me, took me in his Arms, and kissing me very eagerly, and with the greatest Passion imaginable he held me fast till he call'd for a Pen and Ink, and then *told me* he could not wait the tedious writing on the Glass, but pulling out a piece of paper, he began and wrote again,

> *Be mine, with all your Poverty.*

I took his Pen and follow'd him immediately thus,

> *Yet secretly you hope I lie.*

He told me that was unkind, because it was not just, and that I put him upon contradicting me, which did not consist with good Manners, any more than with his Affection; and therefore since I had insensibly drawn him into his poetical scribble, he beg'd I would not oblige him to break it off, so he writes again,

> *Let Love alone be our Debate.*

---

[140]The "wit battle" here, a couplet version of stichomythia, resembles bargain scenes in contemporary plays. [141]Blushed.

I wrote again,

She Loves enough, that does not hate.

This he took for a favour, and so laid down the Cudgels, that is to say the Pen; I say he took it for a favour, and a mighty one it was, if he had known all. However he took it as I meant it, that is, to let him think I was inclin'd to go on with him, as indeed I had all the Reason in the World to do, for he was the best humoured merry sort of a Fellow that I ever met with; and I often reflected on my self, how doubly criminal it was to deceive such a Man; but that Necessity,[142] which press'd me to a Settlement suitable to my Condition, was my Authority for it, and certainly his Affection to me, and the Goodness of his Temper, however they might argue against using him ill, yet they strongly argued to me, that he would better take the Disappointment, than some fiery tempered Wretch, who might have nothing to recommend him but those Passions which would serve only to make a Woman miserable all her Days.

Besides, tho' I had jested with him, as he suppos'd it, so often about my Poverty, yet, when he found it to be true, he had fore-closed all manner of objection, seeing[143] whether he was in jest or in earnest, he had declar'd he took me without any regard to my Portion, and whether I was in jest or in earnest, I had declar'd my self to be very Poor, so that in a word, I had him fast both ways; and tho' he might say afterwards he was cheated, yet he could never say that I had cheated him.

He persued me close after this, and as I saw there was no need to fear losing him, I play'd the indifferent part with him longer than Prudence[144] might otherwise have dictated to me: But I considered how much this caution and indifference would give me the advantage over him, when I should come to be under the Necessity of owning my own Circumstances to him; and I manag'd it the more warily, because I found he inferr'd from thence, as indeed he ought to do, that I either had the more Money, or the more Judgment, and would not venture at all.

I took the freedom one Day, after we had talk'd pretty close to the Subject, to tell him, that it was true I had receiv'd the Compliment of a Lover from him; namely, that he would take me without enquiring into my Forture, and I would make him a suitable return in this, (*viz.*) that I would make as little enquiry into his as consisted with Reason, but I hoped he would allow me to ask a few Questions, which he should answer or not as he thought fit; and that I would

[142]For a discussion of the concept of necessity in Defoe, see Novak, *Defoe and the Nature of Man*, chap. 3.

[143]Seeing that, because.

[144]Practical wisdom, a politic course of action. The concept of prudence is prominent in much eighteenth-century literature, most notably in *Tom Jones*.

not be offended if he did not answer me at all; one of these Questions related to our manner of living, and the place where, because I had heard he had a great Plantation in *Virginia*, and that he had talk'd of going to live there, and I told him I did not care to be Transported.[145]

He began from this Discourse to let me voluntarily into all his Affairs, and to tell me in a frank open way, all his Circumstances, by which I found he was very well to pass in the World; but that great part of his Estate consisted of three Plantations, which he had in *Virginia*, which brought him in a very good Income, generally speaking, to the tune of 300 *l*. a Year; but that if he was to live upon them, would bring him in four times as much; very well, thought I, you shall carry me thither as soon as you please, tho' I won't tell you so before-hand.

I jested with him extremely about the Figure he would make in *Virginia*; but I found he would do any thing I desired, tho' he did not seem glad to have me undervalue his Plantations, so I turn'd my Tale; I told him I had good reason not to desire to go there to live, because if his Plantations were worth so much there, I had not a Fortune suitable to a Gentleman of 1200 *l*. a Year, as he said his Estate would be.

He reply'd generously, he did not ask what my Fortune was, he had told me from the beginning he would not, and he would be as good as his word; but whatever it was, he assur'd me he would never desire me to go to *Virginia* with him, or go thither himself without me, unless I was perfectly willing, and made it my Choice.

All this, you may be sure, was as I wish'd, and indeed nothing could have happen'd more perfectly agreeable; I carried it on as far as this with a sort of indifferency, that he often wondred at, more than at first, But which was the only support of his Courtship;[146] and I mention it the rather to intimate again to the Ladies, that nothing but want of Courage for such an Indifferency,[147] makes our Sex so cheap, and prepares them to be ill us'd as they are; would they venture the loss of a pretending Fop now and then, who carries it high upon the point of his own Merit, they would certainly be slighted less, and courted more; had I discovered[148] really and truly what my great Fortune was, and that in all I had not full 500 *l*. when he expected 1500 *l*., yet I had hook'd him so fast, and play'd him so long,

---

[145]Transferred to another place of abode. Being transported does not necessarily imply criminal banishment, though the ambiguity of the word gives force, in the light of Moll's early confession and later activity, to her comment. Later, Moll puns further on the word,
using it to describe the state of being carried out of one's normal mental condition.

[146]I.e., his interest in Moll was due to her apparent lack of interest in him.

[147]I.e., they fear to pretend indifference.

[148]Revealed. (R)

that I was satisfied he would have had me in my worst Circumstances; and indeed it was less a surprize to him when he learnt the Truth, than it would have been, because having not the least blame to lay on me, who had carried it with an air of indifference to the last, he could not say one word, except that indeed he thought it had been more, but that if it had been less he did not repent his bargain; only that he should not be able to maintain me so well as he intended.

In short, we were married, and very happily married on my side I assure you, *as to the Man*; for he was the best humour'd Man that ever Woman had, but his Circumstances were not so good as I imagined, as on the other hand he had not bettered himself by marrying so much as he expected.

When we were married I was shrewdly put to it to bring him that little Stock I had, and to let him see it was no more; but there was a necessity for it, so I took my opportunity one Day when we were alone, to enter into a short Dialogue with him about it; MY DEAR, *said I*, we have been married a Fortnight, is it not time to let you know whether you have got a Wife with something, or with nothing; your own time for that, my Dear, *says he*, I am satisfied that I have got the Wife I love, I have not troubled you much, says he, with my enquiry about it.

That's true, *said I*, but I have a great difficulty upon me about it, which I scarce know how to manage.

What's that, my Dear, *says he*?

Why, *says I*, 'tis a little hard upon me, and 'tis harder upon you; I am told that Captain ———— (meaning my Friend's Husband) has told you I had a great deal more Money than I ever pretended to have, and I am sure I never employ'd him to do so.

Well, *says he*, Captain ———— may have told me so, but what then; if you have not so much, that may lye at his Door, but you never told me what you had, so I have no reason to blame you if you have nothing at all.

That is so just, *said I*, and so generous, that it makes my having but a little a double Affliction to me.

The less you have, *my Dear, says he*, the worse for us both; but I hope your Affliction you speak of, is not caus'd for fear I should be unkind to you, for want of a Portion, NO NO, if you have nothing tell me plainly, and at once; I may perhaps tell the Captain he has cheated me, but I can never say you have cheated me, for did you not give it under your Hand that you were Poor, and so I ought to expect you to be.

Well, said I, *my Dear*, I am glad I have not been concern'd in deceiving you before Marriage; if I deceive you since, 'tis ne'er the worse; *that I am Poor* is too true, but not so Poor as to have nothing neither; so I pull'd out some Bank Bills, and gave him about a Hundred and Sixty Pounds, there's something, my Dear, *says I*, and not quite all neither.

I had brought him so near to expecting nothing, by what I had said before, that the Money, tho' the Sum was small in it self, was doubly welcome to him; he own'd it was more than he look'd for, and that he did not question by my Discourse to him, but that my fine Cloths, Gold Watch, and a Diamond Ring or two had been all my Fortune.

I let him please himself with that 160 *l.* two or three Days, and then having been abroad that Day, and as if I had been to fetch it, I brought him a Hundred Pounds more home in Gold, and told him there was a little more Portion for him; and in short, in about a Week more I brought him 180 *l.* more, and about 60 *l.* in Linnen, which I made him believe I had been oblig'd to take with the 100 *l.* which I gave him in Gold, as a Composition for a Debt of 600 *l.*, being little more than Five Shilling in the Pound, and overvalued too.

And now, MY DEAR, *says I to him*, I am very sorry to tell you, that there is all, and that I have given you my whole Fortune; I added, that if the Person who had my 600 *l.* had not abus'd me, I had been worth a Thousand Pound to him, but that as it was, I had been faithful to him, and reserv'd nothing to my self, but if it had been more he should have had it.

He was so oblig'd by the Manner, and so pleas'd with the Sum, for he had been in a terrible fright least it had been nothing at all, that he accepted it very thankfully: And thus I got over the Fraud of *passing for a Fortune without Money*, and cheating a Man into Marrying me on pretence of a Fortune; which, *by the way*, I take to be one of the most dangerous Steps a Woman can take, and in which she runs the most hazard of being ill us'd afterwards.

My Husband, *to give him his due*, was a Man of infinite good Nature, but he was no Fool; and finding his Income not suited to the manner of Living which he had intended, if I had brought him what he expected, and being under a Disappointment in his return of[149] his Plantations in *Virginia*, he discover'd many times his inclination of going over to *Virginia* to live upon his own; and often would be magnifying the way of living there, how cheap, how plentiful, how pleasant, *and the like.*

I began presently to understand his meaning, and I took him up very plainly one Morning, and told him that I did so; that I found his Estate turn'd to no account at this distance, compar'd to what it would do if he liv'd upon the spot, and that I found he had a mind to go and live there; and I added, that I was sensible he had been disappointed in a Wife, and that finding his Expectations not answer'd

---

[149]Profit from.

that way, I could do no less to make him amends than tell him, that I was very willing to go over to *Virginia* with him and live there.

He said a thousand kind things to me upon the subject of my making such a Proposal to him: He told me, that however he was disappointed in his Expectations of a Fortune, he was not disappointed in a Wife; and that I was all to him that a Wife could be, and he was more than satisfied in the whole when the particulars were put together; but that this offer was so kind, that it was more than he could express.

To bring the story short, we agreed to go; *he told me*, that he had a very good House there, that it was well Furnish'd, that his Mother was alive and liv'd in it, and one Sister, which was all the Relations he had; that as soon as he came there, his Mother would remove to another House which was her own for life, and his after her Decease; so that I should have all the House to my self; and I found all this to be exactly as he had said.

To make this part of the story short, we put on board the Ship *which we went in*, a large quantity of good Furniture for our House, with stores of Linnen and other Necessaries, and a good Cargoe for Sale, and away we went.

To give an account of the manner of our Voyage, which was long and full of Dangers, is out of my way, I kept no Journal, neither did my Husband; all that I can say is, that after a terrible passage, frighted twice with dreadful Storms, and once with what was still more terrible, I mean a Pyrate, who came on board and took away almost all our Provisions; and, which would have been beyond all to me, they had once taken my Husband to go along with them, but by entreaties were prevail'd with to leave him: I say, after all these terrible things we arriv'd in *York River* in *Virginia*, and coming to our Plantation, we were receiv'd with all the Demonstrations of Tenderness and Affection (by my Husband's Mother) that were possible to be express'd.

We liv'd here all together, my Mother-in-law, *at my entreaty*, continuing in the House, for she was too kind a Mother to be parted with; my Husband likewise continued the same as at first, and I thought my self the happiest Creature alive; when an odd and surprizing[150] Event put an end to all that Felicity in a moment, and rendred my Condition the most uncomfortable, if not the most miserable, in the World.

My Mother was a mighty chearful good humour'd old Woman, I may call her old Woman, for her Son was above Thirty; I say she was very pleasant, good Company, and us'd to entertain *me, in particular,*

---

[150]Astonishing, full of wonder. The word was much more powerful in the eighteenth century than now, and carried a sense of awe.

with abundance of Stories to divert me, as well of the Country we were in, as of the People.

Among the rest, she often told me how the greatest part of the Inhabitants of the Colony came thither in very indifferent Circumstances from *England*; that, generally speaking, they were of two sorts, either (1.) such as were brought over by Masters of Ships to be sold as Servants, *such we call them*, my Dear, *says she*, but they are more properly call'd *Slaves*. Or, (2.) Such as are Transported from *Newgate* and other Prisons, after having been found guilty of Felony and other crimes punishable with Death.

When they come here, *says she*, we make no difference, the Planters buy them, and they work together in the Field till their time is out; when 'tis expir'd, *said she*, they have Encouragement given them to Plant for themselves; for they have a certain number of Acres of Land allotted them by the Country, and they go to work to Clear and Cure[151] the Land, and then to Plant it with Tobacco and Corn[152] for their own use; and as the Tradesmen and Merchants will trust them with Tools, and Cloaths, and other Necessaries, upon the Credit of their Crop before it is grown, so they again Plant every Year a little more than the Year before, and so buy whatever they want with the Crop that is before them.

Hence Child, *says she*, many a *Newgate* Bird[153] becomes a great Man, and we have, *continued she*, several Justices of the Peace, Officers of the Train Bands,[154] and Magistrates of the Towns they live in, that have been burnt in the Hand.[155]

She was going on with that part of the Story, when her own part in it interrupted her, and with a great deal of good-humour'd Confidence she told me, she was one of the second sort of Inhabitants herself; that she came away openly, having ventur'd too far in a particular Case, so that she was become a Criminal, and here's the Mark of it, CHILD, *says she*, and pulling off her Glove, look ye here, *says she*, turning up the Palm of her Hand, and shewed me a very fine white Arm and Hand, but branded in the inside of the Hand, as in such cases it must be.

This Story was very moving to me, but my Mother (smiling) said, you need not think such a thing strange, *Daughter*, for as I told you, some of the best Men in this Country are burnt in the Hand, and they are not asham'd to own it; there's Major ——— *says she*, he was an Eminent Pickpocket; there's Justice *Ba*———*r* was a Shoplifter,

---

[151]Clear from timber and prepare for tilling.
[152]Grain. (R)
[153]Jailbird.
[154]Trained companies of citizen soldiery, organized in London and elsewhere during the sixteenth, seventeenth, and eighteenth centuries.
[155]Branded as criminals.

and both of them were burnt in the Hand, and I could name you several, such as they are.

We had frequent Discourses of this kind, and abundance of instances she gave me of the like; after some time, as she was telling some Stories of one that was Transported but a few Weeks ago, I began in an intimate kind of way to ask her to tell me something of her own Story, which she did with the utmost plainness and Sincerity; how she had fallen into very ill Company in *London* in her young Days, occasion'd by her Mother sending her frequently to carry Victuals and other Relief to a Kinswoman of hers who was a Prisoner in *Newgate*, and who lay in a miserable starving Condition, was afterwards Condemned to be Hang'd, but having got Respite by pleading her Belly, dyed afterwards in the Prison.

Here my Mother-in-Law ran out in a long account of the wicked practices in that dreadful Place, and how it ruin'd more young People than all the Town besides; and Child, *says my Mother*, perhaps you may know little of it, or it may be have heard nothing about it, but depend upon it, *says she*, we all know here, that there are more Thieves and Rogues made by that one Prison of *Newgate*, than by all the Clubs and Societies of Villains in the Nation; 'tis that cursed Place, *says my Mother*, that half Peoples this Colony.

Here she went on with her own Story so long, and in so particular a manner, that I began to be very uneasy, but coming to one Particular that requir'd telling her Name, I thought I should have sunk down in the place; she perceived I was out of order, and asked me if I was not well, and what ail'd me? I told her I was so affected with the melancholy Story she had told, and the terrible things she had gone thro', that it had overcome me; and I beg'd of her to talk no more of it: *Why*, my Dear, *says she, very kindly,* what need these things trouble you? These Passages were long before your time, and they give me no trouble at all now, nay I look back on them with a particular Satisfaction, as they have been a means to bring me to this place. Then she went on to tell me how she very luckily fell into a good Family, where behaving herself well, and her Mistress dying, her Master married her, by whom she had my Husband and his Sister; and that by her Diligence and good Management after her Husband's Death, she had improv'd the Plantations to such a degree as they then were, so that most of the Estate was of her getting, not her Husband's, for she had been a Widow upwards of sixteen Year.

I heard this part of the Story with very little attention, because I wanted much to retire and give vent to my Passions, which I did soon after; and let any one judge what must be the Anguish of my Mind, when I came to reflect, that this was certainly no more or less *than my own Mother*, and I had now had two Children, and was big with another by my own Brother, and lay with him still every Night.

I was now the most unhappy of all Women in the World:[156] O had the Story never been told me, all had been well; it had been no Crime to have lain with my Husband, since as to his being my Relation, I had known nothing of it.

I had now such a load on my Mind that it kept me perpetually waking; to reveal it, *which would have been some ease to me*, I cou'd not find wou'd be to any purpose, and yet to conceal it wou'd be next to impossible; nay, I did not doubt but I should talk of it in my sleep, and tell my Husband of it whether I would or no: If I discover'd it, the least thing I could expect was to lose my Husband, for he was too nice and too honest a Man to have continued my Husband after he had known I had been his Sister, so that I was perplex'd to the last degree.

I leave it to any Man to judge what Difficulties presented to my view: I was away from my native Country at a distance prodigious, and the return to me unpassable; I liv'd very well, but in a Circumstance unsufferable in it self; if I had discover'd my self to my Mother, it might be difficult to convince her of the Particulars, and I had no way to prove them: *On the other hand*, if she had question'd or doubted me, I had been undone, for the bare Suggestion would have immediately separated me from my Husband, without gaining[157] my Mother or him, who would have been neither a Husband or a Brother; so that between the surprise on one hand, and the uncertainty on the other, I had been sure to be undone.

In the mean time, as I was but too sure of the Fact, I liv'd therefore in open avowed Incest and Whoredom, and all under the appearance of an honest Wife; and tho' I was not much touched with the Crime of it, yet the Action had something in it shocking to Nature,[158] and made my Husband, *as he thought himself*, even nauseous to me.

However, upon the most sedate Consideration, I resolv'd that it was absolutely necessary to conceal it all, and not make the least Discovery of it either to Mother or Husband; and thus I liv'd with the greatest Pressure imaginable for three Year more, but had no more Children.

During this time my Mother used to be frequently telling me old Stories of her former Adventures, which however were no ways pleasant to me; for by it, tho' she did not tell it me in plain terms, yet I could easily understand, joyn'd with what I had heard my self, of my first Tutors; that in her younger Days she had been both WHORE

---

[156]Moll tends to speak in extremes; just before, she was "the happiest Creature alive."

[157]Giving advantage to.

[158]Moll here distinguishes between social morality and her own personal intuitive morality; the moral abstraction bothers her less than the physical presence of the husband.

and THIEF; but I verily believe she had lived to repent sincerely of both, and that she was then a very Pious sober and religious Woman.

Well, let her Life have been what it would then, it was certain that my Life was very uneasie to me; for I liv'd, as I have said, but in the worst sort of Whoredom, and as I cou'd expect no Good of it, so really no good Issue came of it, and all my seeming Prosperity wore off and ended in Misery and Destruction; it was some time indeed before it came to this, for, but I know not by what ill Fate guided, every thing went wrong with us afterwards, and that which was worse, my Husband grew strangely alter'd; froward, jealous, and unkind, and I was as impatient of bearing his Carriage, as the Carriage was unreasonable and unjust: These things proceeded so far, and we came at last to be in such ill Terms with one another, that I claim'd a promise of him which he entered willingly into with me, when I consented to come from *England* with him (*viz.*) that if I found the Country not to agree with me or that I did not like to live there, I should come away to *England* again when I pleas'd, giving him a Year's warning to settle his Affairs.

I say *I now claim'd this promise of him*, and I must confess I did it not in the most obliging Terms that could be in the World neither; but I insisted that he treated me ill, that I was remote from my Friends, and could do my self no Justice, and that he was Jealous without cause, my Conversation having been unblameable, and he having no pretence for it, and that to remove to *England*, would take away all Occasion from him.

I insisted so peremptorily upon it, that he could not avoid coming to a point, either to keep his word with me or to break it; and this notwithstanding he used all the skill he was master of, and employ'd his Mother and other Agents to prevail with me to alter my Resolutions; indeed the bottom of the thing[159] lay at my Heart, and that made all his Endeavours fruitless, for my Heart was alienated from him, *as a Husband*; I loathed the Thoughts of Bedding with him, and used a thousand Pretences of Illness and Humour[160] to prevent his touching me, fearing nothing more than to be with Child again by him, which to be sure would have prevented, or at least delay'd my going over to *England*.

However, at last I put him so out of Humour, that he took up a rash and fatal Resolution. In short I should not go to *England*; and tho' he had promis'd me, yet it was an unreasonable thing for me to desire it, that it would be ruinous to his Affairs, would Unhinge his whole Family, and be next to an Undoing him in the World; That therefore I ought not to desire it of him, and that no Wife in the World that valu'd her Family and her Husbands prosperity would insist upon such a thing.

---

[159]I.e., the basis (incest) of the difficulty.   [160]Temperament, mood.

This plung'd[161] me again, for when I considered the thing calmly, and took my Husband as he really was, a diligent careful Man in the main Work of laying up an Estate for his Children, and that he knew nothing of the dreadful Circumstances that he was in; I could not but confess to myself that my Proposal was very unreasonable, and what no Wife that had the good of her Family at Heart wou'd have desir'd.

But my Discontents were of another Nature; I look'd upon him no longer as a Husband, but as a near Relation, the Son of my own Mother, and I resolv'd some how or other to be clear of him, but which way I did not know, nor did it seem possible.

It is said *by the ill-natured World* of our Sex, that if we are set on a thing, it is impossible to turn us from our Resolutions: *In short,* I never ceas'd poreing upon the Means to bring to pass my Voyage, and came that length with my Husband at last, as to propose going without him. This provok'd him to the last degree, and he call'd me not only an unkind Wife, but an unnatural Mother, and ask'd me how I could entertain such a Thought without horror as that of leaving my two Children (for one was dead) without a Mother, and to be brought up by Strangers, and never to see them more? *It was true,* had things been right, I should not have done it, but now, *it was* my real desire never to see them, or him either any more; and as to the Charge of unnatural I could easily answer it to myself, while I knew that the whole Relation was Unnatural in the highest degree in the World.

However, it was plain there was no bringing my Husband to any thing; he would neither go with me, or let me go without him, and it was quite out of my Power to stir without his Consent, as any one that knows the Constitution of the Country I was in, knows very well.

We had many Family quarrels about it, and they began (in time) to grow up to a dangerous Height, for as I was quite Estrang'd from my Husband (*as he was call'd*) in Affection, so I took no heed to my Words, but sometimes gave him Language that was provoking: And, *in short,* strove all I could to bring him to a parting with me, which was what above all things in the World I desir'd most.

He took my Carriage very ill, and indeed he might well do so, for at last I refus'd to Bed with him, and carrying on the Breach upon all occasions to extremity he told me once he thought I was Mad, and if I did not alter my Conduct, he would put me under Cure; *that is to say, into a Mad-House*: I told him he should find I was far enough from Mad, and that it was not in his power, or any other Villians to Murther me; I Confess at the same time I was heartily frighted at his Thoughts of putting me into a *Mad-House*, which would at once have destroy'd all the possibility of breaking the Truth out, whatever the occasion

---

[161]Overwhelmed, depressed.

might be; for that then, no one would have given Credit to a word of it. This therefore brought me to a Resolution, *whatever came of it* to lay open my whole Case; but which way to do it, or to whom, was an inextricable Difficulty, and took me up many Months to Resolve; *in the mean time*, another Quarrel with my Husband happen'd, which came up to such a mad Extream as almost push'd me on to tell it him all to his Face; but tho' I kept it in so as not to come to the particulars, I spoke so much as put him into the utmost Confusion, and in the End brought out the whole Story.

He began with a calm Expostulation upon my being so resolute to go to *England*; I defended it; and one hard Word bringing on another as is usual in all Family strife, *he told me*, I did not Treat him as if he was my Husband, or talk of my Children, as if I was a Mother, and *in short*, that I did not deserve to be us'd as a Wife: That he had us'd all the fair Means possible with me; that he had Argu'd with all the kindness and calmness, that a Husband or a Christian ought to do, and that I made him such a vile return, that I Treated him rather like a Dog than a Man, and rather like the most contemptible Stranger than a Husband: That he was very loth to use Violence with me, but that *in short*, he saw a Necessity of it now, and that for the future he should be oblig'd to take such Measures as should reduce me to my Duty.

My blood was now fir'd[162] to the utmost, *tho' I knew what he had said was very true*, and nothing could appear more provok'd; I told him for his fair means and his foul they were equally condemn'd by me; that for my going to *England*, I was resolv'd on it, come what would; and that as to treating him not like a Husband, and not showing my self a Mother to my Children, there might be something more in it than he understood at present; but, for his farther consideration, I thought fit to tell him thus much, that he neither was my lawful Husband, nor they lawful Children, and that I had reason to regard neither of them more than I did.

I confess I was mov'd to pity him when I spoke it, for he turn'd pale as Death, and stood mute as one Thunderstruck, and once or twice I thought he would have fainted; *in short*, it put him in a Fit something like an Apoplex; he trembl'd, a Sweat or Dew ran off his Face, and yet he was cold as a Clod, so that I was forced to run and fetch something for him to keep Life in him; when he recover'd of that, he grew sick and vomited, and in a little after was put to Bed, and in the next Morning was, as he had been indeed all Night, in a violent Fever.

However it went off again, and he recovered tho' but slowly, and when he came to be a little better, he told me, I had given him a mortal Wound with my Tongue, and he had only one thing to ask

[162]Blood was often considered the seat of anger, as well as of other passions.

before he desir'd an Explanation; I interrupted him, and told him I was sorry I had gone so far, since I saw what disorder it put him into, but I desir'd him not to talk to me of Explanations, for that would but make things worse.

This heighten'd his impatience, and indeed perplex'd him beyond all bearing; for now he began to suspect that there was some Mystery yet unfolded, but could not make the least guess at the real Particulars of it; all that run in his Brain was, that I had another Husband alive, which I could not say in fact might not be true; but I assur'd him however, there was not the least of that in it; and indeed as to my other Husband he was effectually dead in Law to me, and had told me I should look on him as such, so I had not the least uneasiness on that score.

But now I found the thing too far gone to conceal it much longer, and my Husband himself gave me an opportunity to ease my self of the Secret much to my Satisfaction; he had laboured with me three or four Weeks, *but to no purpose*, only to tell him, whether I had spoken those words only as the effect of my Passion, to put him in a Passion? Or whether there was any thing of Truth in the bottom of them? But I continued inflexible, and would explain nothing, unless he would first consent to my going to *England*, which he would never do, *he said*, while he liv'd; on the other hand I said it was in my power to make him willing when I pleas'd, NAY to make him entreat me to go; and this increased his Curiosity, and made him importunate to the highest degree, *but it was all to no purpose*.

At length he tells all this Story to his Mother, and sets her upon me to get the main Secret out of me, and she us'd her utmost Skill with me indeed; but I put her to a full stop at once, *by telling her* that the Reason and Mystery of the whole matter lay in herself; and that it was my Respect to her that had made me conceal it, and that in short I could go no farther, and therefore conjur'd[163] her not to insist upon it.

She was struck dumb at this Suggestion, and could not tell what to say or to think; but laying aside the supposition as a Policy[164] of mine, continued her importunity on account of her Son, and if possible to make up the breach between us two; as to that, *I told her*, that it was indeed a good design in her, but that it was impossible to be done; and that if I should reveal to her the Truth of what she desir'd, she would grant it to be impossible, and cease to desire it: At last I seem'd to be prevail'd on by the importunity, and told her I dar'd trust her with a Secret of the greatest Importance, and she would soon see that this was so, and that I would consent to lodge it in her Breast, if she would engage solemnly not to acquaint her Son with it without my consent.

She was long in promising this part, but rather than not come at the main Secret she agreed to that too, and after a great many other

---

[163]Implored.   [164]Devious scheme, cunning trick.

Preliminaries, I began and told her the whole Story: First I told her how much she was concern'd in all the unhappy breach which had happen'd between her Son and me, by telling me her own Story, and her *London* Name; and that the surprize she see I was in, was upon that Occasion:[165] Then I told her my own Story and my Name, and assur'd her by such other Tokens as she could not deny that I was no other, nor more or less than her own Child, *her Daughter* born of her Body in *Newgate*; the same that had sav'd her from the Gallows by being in her Belly, and the same that she left in such and such Hands when she was Transported.

It is impossible to express the Astonishment she was in; she was not inclin'd to believe the Story, or to remember the Particulars; for she immediately foresaw the Confusions that must follow in the Family upon it; but every thing concurr'd so exactly with the Stories she had told me of her self, and which if she had not told me, she would perhaps have been content to have denied, that she had stop'd her own Mouth, and she had nothing to do but to take me about the Neck and kiss me, and cry most vehemently over me, without speaking one word for a long time together; at last she broke out, *Unhappy Child!* *says she*, what miserable chance could bring thee hither? And in the Arms of my own Son too! *Dreadful Girl!* says she, *why we are all undone!* Married to thy own Brother! Three Children, and two alive, all of the same Flesh and Blood! My Son and my Daughter lying together as Husband and Wife! All Confusion and Destraction[166] for ever! *miserable Family!* what will become of us? what is to be said? what is to be done? and thus she run on for a great while, nor had I any power to speak, or if I had, did I know what to say, for every word wounded me to the Soul: With this kind of Amasement on our Thoughts we parted for the first time, tho' my Mother was more surpriz'd than I was, because it was more News to her than to me: However, she promis'd again to me at parting, that she would say nothing of it to her Son, till we had talk'd of it again.

It was not long, you may be sure, before we had a second Conference upon the same Subject; when, as if she had been willing to forget the Story she had told me of herself, or to suppose that I had forgot some of the Particulars, she began to tell them with Alterations and Omissions; but I refresh'd her Memory, and set her to rights in many things which I supposed she had forgot, and then came in so opportunely with the whole History, that it was impossible for her to go from it; and then she fell into her Rhapsodies[167] again, and Exclamations at the Severity of her Misfortunes: When these things were a little over with her, we fell into a close Debate about what should be

[165]Because of that.
[166]Distraction.

[167]Exaggerated and extravagant expressions of feeling.

first done before we gave an account of the matter to my Husband, but to what purpose could be all our Consultations? we could neither of us see our way thro' it, nor see how it could be safe to open such a Scene to him; it was impossible to make any judgment, or give any guess at what Temper he would receive it in, or what Measures he would take upon it; and if he should have so little Government of himself, as to make it publick, we easily foresaw that it would be the ruin of the whole Family, and expose my Mother and me to the last degree; and if at last he should take the Advantage the Law would give him, he might put me away with disdain, and leave me to Sue for the little Portion that I had, and perhaps wast it all in the Suit, and then be a Beggar; the Children would be ruin'd too, having no legal Claim to any of his Effects; and thus I should see him perhaps in the Arms of another Wife in a few Months, and be myself the most miserable Creature alive.

My Mother was as sensible of this as I; and upon the whole, we knew not what to do; after some time, we came to more sober Resolutions, but then it was with this Misfortune too, that my Mother's Opinion and mine were quite different from one another, and indeed inconsistent with one another; for my Mother's Opinion was, that I should bury the whole thing entirely, and continue to live with him as my Husband, till some other Event should make the discovery of it more convenient; and that in the mean time she would endeavour to reconcile us together again, and restore our mutual Comfort and Family Peace, that we might lie as we us'd to do together, and so let the whole matter remain a secret as close as Death, for Child, *says she*, we are both undone if it comes out.

To encourage me to this, she promis'd to make me easy in my Circumstances as far as she was able, and to leave me what she could at her Death, secur'd for me separately from my Husband; so that if it should come out afterwards, I should not be left destitute, but be able to stand on my own Feet, and procure Justice from him.

This Proposal did not agree at all with my Judgment of the thing, tho' it was very fair and kind in my Mother, but my Thoughts run quite another way.

As to keeping the thing in our own Breasts, and letting it all remain as it was, I told her it was impossible; and I ask'd her how she cou'd think I cou'd bear the thoughts of lying with my own Brother? In the next place I told her that her being alive was the only support of the Discovery, and that while she own'd me for her Child, and saw reason to be satisfyed that I was so, no body else would doubt it; but that if she should die before the Discovery, I should be taken for an impudent Creature that had forg'd such a thing to go away from my Husband, or should be counted Craz'd and Distracted: Then I told her how he had threaten'd already to put me into a Mad-house, and what concern I had been in about it, and how that was the thing that drove me to the necessity of discovering it to her as I had done.

From all which I told her, that I had on the most serious Reflections I was able to make in the Case, come to this Resolution, which I hop'd she would like, as a medium between both, (*viz.*) that she should use her endeavours with her Son to give me leave to go for *England*, as I had desired, and to furnish me with a sufficient Sum of Money, either in Goods along with me, or in Bills for my Support there, all along suggesting, that he might one time or other think it proper to come over to me.

That when I was gone she should then in cold Blood, and after first obliging him in the solemnest manner possible to Secresie, discover the Case to him; doing it gradually, and as her own Discretion should guide her, so that he might not be surpriz'd with it, and fly out into any Passions and Excesses on my account, or on hers; and that she should concern herself to prevent his slighting the Children, or Marrying again, unless he had a certain account of my being Dead.

This was my Scheme, and my Reasons were good; I was really alienated from him in the Consequence of these things; indeed I mortally hated him as a Husband, and it was impossible to remove that riveted[168] Aversion I had to him; *at the same time* it being an unlawful incestuous living added to that Aversion; and tho' I had no great concern about it in point of Conscience, yet every thing added to make Cohabiting with him the most nauseous thing to me in the World; and I think verily it was come to such a height, that I could almost as willingly have embrac'd a Dog, as have let him offer any thing of that kind to me, for which Reason I could not bear the thoughts of coming between the Sheets with him; I cannot say that I was right in point of Policy in carrying it such a length, while at the same time I did not resolve to discover the thing to him; but I am giving an account of what was, not of what ought or ought not to be.

In this directly opposite Opinion to one another my Mother and I continued a long time, and it was impossible to reconcile our Judgments; many Disputes we had about it, but we could never either of us yield our own, or bring over the other.

I insisted on my Aversion to lying with my own Brother; and she insisted upon its being impossible to bring him to consent to my going from him to *England*; and in this uncertainty we continued, not differing so as to quarrel, or any thing like it; but so as not to be able to resolve what we should do to make up that terrible breach that was before us.

At last I resolv'd on a desperate course, and *told my Mother* my Resolution, (*viz.*) that in short, I would tell him of it myself; my

---

[168]Fixed, firmly established.

Resolution (viz.) that in short, I would tell him of it myself; my Mother was frighted to the last degree at the very thoughts of it; but *I bid her be easie*, told her I would do it gradually and softly, and with all the Art and good Humour I was Mistress of, and time it also as well as I could, taking him in good Humour too: *I told her* I did not question but if I cou'd be Hypocrite enough to feign more Affection to him than I really had, I should succeed in all my Design, and we might part by Consent, and with a good Agreement, for I might love him well enough for a Brother, tho' I could not for a Husband.

All this while he lay at my Mother to find out, if possible, what was the meaning of that dreadful Expression of mine, as he call'd it, which I mention'd before; namely, *That I was not his lawful Wife, nor my Children his legal Children*: My Mother put him off, told him she could bring me to no Explanations, but found there was something that disturb'd me very much, and she hop'd she should get it out of me in time, and in the mean time recommended to him earnestly to use me more tenderly, and win me with his usual good Carriage; *told him* of his terrifying and affrighting me with his Threats of sending me to a Mad-house, and the like, and advis'd him not to make a Woman Desperate on any account whatever.

He promis'd her to soften his Behaviour, and bid her assure me that he lov'd me as well as ever, and that he had no such design as that of sending me to a Mad-house, whatever he might say in his Passion; also he desir'd my Mother to use the same Perswasions to me too, that our Affections might be renew'd, and we might live together in a good understanding as we us'd to do.

I found the Effects of this Treaty presently; my Husband's Conduct was immediately alter'd, and he was quite another Man to me; nothing could be kinder and more obliging than he was to me upon all Occasions; and I could do no less than make some return to it, *which I did as well as I cou'd*; but it was but in an awkward manner at best, for nothing was more frightful to me than his Caresses; and the Apprehensions of being with Child again by him, was ready to throw me into Fits; and this made me see that there was an absolute necessity of breaking the Case to him without any more delay, which however I did with all the caution and reserve imaginable.

He had continued his alter'd Carriage to me near a Month, and we began to live a new kind of Life with one another; and could I have satisfied my self to have gone on with it, I believe it might have continued as long as we had continued alive together. One Evening as we were sitting and talking very friendly together under a little Auning, which serv'd as an Arbour at the entrance from our House into the Garden,[169] he was in a very pleasant agreeable Humour, and

[169]In the light of the earlier garden scenes, Moll's choice of setting for the divisive conversation is interesting. Many seventeenth- and eighteenth-century

said abundance of kind things to me, relating to the Pleasure of our present good Agreement, and the Disorders of our past breach, and what a Satisfaction it was to him, that we had room to hope we should never have any more of it.

I fetch'd a deep Sigh, and told him there was no Body in the World could be more delighted than I was, in the good Agreement we had always kept up, or more afflicted with the Breach of it, and should be so still, but I was sorry to tell him that there was an unhappy Circumstance in our Case, which lay too close to my Heart, and which I knew not how to break to him, that rendred my part of it very miserable, and took from me all the Comfort of the rest.

He importun'd me to tell him what it was; I told him I could not tell how to do it, that while it was conceal'd from him, I alone was unhappy; but if he knew it also, we should be both so, and that therefore to keep him in the dark about it was the kindest thing that I could do, and it was on that account alone that I kept a secret from him, the very keeping of which I thought would first or last be my Destruction.

It is impossible to express his Surprize at this Relation, and the double importunity which he used with me to discover it to him: He told me I could not be call'd kind to him, nay, I could not be faithful to him if I conceal'd it from him; I told him I thought so too, and yet I could not do it. He went back to what I had said before to him, and told me he hoped it did not relate to what I had said in my Passion; and that he had resolv'd to forget all that, as the Effect of a rash provok'd Spirit; I told him I wish'd I could forget it all too, but that it was not to be done, the Impression was too deep, and I cou'd not do it, it was impossible.

He then told me he was resolved not to differ with me in any thing, and that therefore he would importune me no more about it, resolving to acquiesce in whatever I did or said; only begg'd I would then agree, that whatever it was, it should no more interrupt our quiet and our mutual kindness.

This was the most provoking thing he could have said to me, for I really wanted his farther importunities, that I might be prevail'd with to bring out that which indeed it was like Death to me to conceal; so I answer'd him plainly, that I could not say I was glad not to be importuned, tho' I could not tell how to comply; but come, *my Dear, said I*, what Conditions will you make with me upon the opening this Affair to you.

Any Conditions in the World, *said he*, that you can in reason desire

---

writers use the New World symbolically to represent a kind of new Eden of human possibility. Here, Moll seems to invert or complicate the standard symbolism, for she uses the garden setting to explain why she wishes to be expelled from the corrupted family and homestead. Compare Defoe's use of the New World later in the novel. See Starr, pp. 159–60 n.

of me; well, *said I*, come, give it me under your Hand, that if you do not find I am in any fault, or that I am willingly concern'd in the Causes of the Misfortune that is to follow, you will not blame me, use me the worse, do me any Injury, or make me be the Sufferer for that which is not my fault.

That, *says he*, is the most reasonable demand in the World; not to blame you for that which is not your fault; give me a Pen and Ink, *says he*, so I ran in and fetch'd a Pen, Ink, and Paper, and he wrote the Condition down in the very words I had proposed it, and sign'd it with his Name; well, says he, *what is next*, my Dear?

Why, *says I*, the next is, that you will not blame me for not discovering the Secret of it to you before I knew it.

Very just again, *says he*, with all my Heart; so he wrote down that also and sign'd it.

Well, *my Dear*, says I, then I have but one Condition more to make with you, and that is, that as there is no body concern'd in it but you and I, you shall not discover it to any Person in the World, except your own Mother; and that in all the Measures you shall take upon the discovery, as I am equally concern'd in it with you, *tho' as innocent as your self*, you shall do nothing in a Passion, nothing to my Prejudice, or to your Mother's Prejudice, without my knowledge and consent.

This a little amaz'd him, and he wrote down the words distinctly, but read them over and over before he Sign'd them, hesitating at them several times, and repeating them; *my Mother's* Prejudice! *and your Prejudice*! what mysterious thing can this be? however, at last he Sign'd it.

Well, *says I*, my Dear, I'll ask you no more under your Hand, but as you are to bear the most unexpected and surprizing thing that perhaps ever befel any Family in the World, I beg you to promise me you will receive it with Composure and a Presence of Mind suitable to a Man of Sense.

I'll do my utmost, *says he*, upon Condition you will keep me no longer in suspense, for you Terrify me with all these Preliminaries.

Well then, *says I*, it is this, as I told you before in a Heat, that I was not your lawful Wife, and that our Children were not legal Children; so I must let you know now in calmness, and in kindness, but with Affliction enough that *I am* your own Sister, *and you* my own Brother, and that we are both the Children of our Mother now alive, and in the House, who is convinc'd of the Truth of it, in a manner not to be denied or contradicted.

I saw him turn pale, and look wild, and I said, now remember your Promise, and receive it with Presence of mind; for who cou'd have said more to prepare you for it, than I have done? However I call'd a Servant, and got him a little Glass of Rum, which is the usual Dram of the Country, for he was just fainting away.

When he was a little recover'd, *I said to him*, this Story you may be sure requires a long Explanation, and therefore have patience and compose your Mind to hear it out, and I'll make it as short as I can, and with this, I told him what I thought was needful of the Fact, and particularly how my Mother came to discover it to me, as above; and now my Dear, *says I*, you will see Reason for my Capitulations, and that I neither have been the Cause of this Matter, nor could be so, and that I could know nothing of it before now.

I am fully satisfy'd of that, *says he*, but 'tis a dreadful Surprize to me; however, I know a Remedy for it all, and a Remedy that shall put an End to all your Difficulties, without your going to *England*; That would be strange, *said I*, as all the rest; No, No, *says he*, I'll make it easie, there's no Body in the way of it all, but myself: He look'd a little disorder'd, when he said this, but I did not apprehend any thing from it at that time, believing as it us'd to be said, that they who do those things never talk of them; or that they who talk of such things never do them.

But things were not come their height with him, and I observ'd he became Pensive and Melancholly; and in a Word, as I thought, a little Distemper'd in his Head; I endeavour'd to talk him into Temper, and to Reason him into a kind of Scheme for our Government in the Affair, and sometimes he would be well, and talk with some Courage about it; but the Weight of it lay too heavy upon his Thoughts, and in short, it went so far that he made two attempts upon himself, and in one of them had actually strangled[170] himself, and had not his Mother come into the Room in the very Moment, he had died; but with the help of a *Negro* Servant, she cut him down and recover'd him.

Things were now come to a lamentable height in the Family: My pity for him now began to revive that Affection, which at first I really had for him, and I endeavour'd sincerely by all the kind Carriage I could to make up the Breach; but in short, it had gotten too great a Head, it prey'd upon his Spirits, and it threw him into a long ling'ring Consumption, tho' it happen'd not to be Mortal. In this Distress I did not know what to do, as his Life was apparently declining, and I might perhaps have Marry'd again there, very much to my Advantage, had it been certainly my Business to have staid in the Country; but my Mind was restless too, and uneasie; I hanker'd after coming to *England*, and nothing would satisfie me without it.

In short, by an unwearied importunity my Husband who was apparently decaying, as I observ'd, was at last prevail'd with, and so *my own Fate pushing me on*, the way was made clear for me, and *my Mother concurring*, I obtain'd a very good Cargo for my coming to *England*.

When I parted with my Brother, for such I am now to call him; we

[170]I.e., hanged.

agreed that after I arriv'd he should pretend to have an Account that I was Dead in *England*, and so might Marry again when he would; he promis'd, and engag'd to me to Correspond with me as a Sister, and to Assist and Support me as long as I liv'd; and that if he dy'd before me, he would leave sufficient to his Mother to take Care of me still, in the Name of a Sister, and he was in some respect Careful of me, when he heard of me; but it was so oddly mannag'd that I felt the Disappointments very sensibly afterwards, as you shall hear in its time.

I came away for *England* in the Month of *August*, after I had been Eight Years in that Country, and now a new Scene of Misfortunes attended me, which perhaps few Women have gone thro' the like of.

We had an indifferent good[171] Voyage, till we came just upon the Coast of *England*, and where we arriv'd in two and thirty Days, but were then Ruffled with two or three Storms, one of which drove us away to the Coast of *Ireland*, and we put in at *Kinsale*: We remain'd there about thirteen Days, got some Refreshment on Shore, and put to Sea again, tho' we met with very bad Weather again in which the Ship sprung her Main-mast, *as they call'd it, for I knew not what they meant:* But we got at last into *Milford Haven in Wales*, where tho' it was remote from our Port; yet having my Foot safe upon the firm Ground of my Native Country the Isle of *Britain*, I resolv'd to venture it no more upon the Waters, which had been so terrible to me; so getting my Cloths, and Money on Shore with my Bills of Loading, and other Papers, I resolv'd to come for *London*, and leave the Ship to get to her Port as she could; the Port whither she was bound, was to *Bristol*, where my Brothers chief Correspondent liv'd.

I got to *London*, in about three Weeks, where I heard a little while after that the Ship was arriv'd in *Bristol*; but at the same time had the Misfortune to know that by the violent Weather she had been in, and the breaking of her Main-mast, she had great damage on board, and that a great part of her Cargo was spoil'd.

I had now a new Scene of Life upon my Hands, and a dreadful Appearance it had; I was come away with a kind of final Farewel; what I brought with me, was indeed considerable, had it come safe, and by the help of it I might have married again tollerably well; but as it was, I was reduc'd to between two and three Hundred Pounds in the whole, and this without any hope of Recruit: I was entirely without Friends, nay, even so much as without Acquaintance, for I found it was absolutely necessary not to revive former Acquaintances; and as for my subtle Friend that set me up formerly for a Fortune she was Dead, and her Husband also; as I was inform'd upon sending a Person unknown to enquire.

The looking after my Cargo of Goods soon after oblig'd me to take

---

[171]Fairly good.

a Journey to *Bristol*, and during my attendance upon that Affair, I took the Diversion of going to the Bath,[172] for as I was still far from being old, so my Humour, which was always Gay, continu'd so to an Extream; and being now, *as it were*, a Woman of Fortune, tho' I was a Woman without a Fortune, I expected something or other might happen in my way, that might mend my Circumstances as had been my Case before.

The *Bath* is a Place of Gallantry enough; Expensive, and full of Snares; I went thither indeed in the view of taking any thing that might offer; but I must do myself that Justice, as to protest I knew nothing amiss, I meant nothing but in an honest way; nor had I any Thoughts about me at first that look'd the way which afterwards I suffered them to be guided.

Here I stay'd the whole latter Season, *as it is call'd there*, and Contracted some unhappy Acquaintance, which rather prompted the Follies I fell afterwards into, than fortify'd me against them: I liv'd pleasantly enough, kept good Company, *that is to say*, gay fine Company; but had the Discouragement to find this way of Living sunk me exceedingly, and that as I had no settl'd Income, so spending upon the main Stock was but a certain kind of *bleeding to Death*; and this gave me many sad Reflections in the Intervals of my other Thoughts: However I shook them off, and still flatter'd myself that something or other might offer for my Advantage.

But I was in the wrong Place for it; I was not now at *Redriff*, where If I had set myself tollerably up, some honest Sea Captain or other might have talk'd with me upon the honourable terms of Matrimony; but I was at the *Bath* where Men find a Mistress sometimes, but very rarely look for a Wife; and Consequently all the particular Acquaintances a Woman can Expect to make there, must have some Tendency that way.

I had spent the first Season well enough, for tho' I had Contracted some Acquaintance with a Gentleman, who came to the *Bath* for his Diversion, yet I had enter'd into no *felonious Treaty*, as it might be call'd: I had resisted some Casual offers of Gallantry, and had manag'd that way well enough; I was not wicked enough to come into the Crime for the meer Vice of it, and I had no extraordinary Offers made me that tempted me with the main thing which I wanted.

However I went this length the first Season, (*viz.*) I contracted an Acquaintance with a Woman in whose House I Lodg'd, who tho' she did not keep an ill House, *as we call it*, yet had none of the best

---

[172]Bath, or the Bath, was the most famous and most fashionable of English spas. Its waters were considered medicinal to drink or to bathe in, and the city was extremely crowded during the summer, but quite deserted in the winter. Moll, according to the previous chronology, evidently arrived very late in the fall, when the largest tourist rush was already past.

Principles in herself: I had on all Occasions behav'd myself so well as not to get the least Slur upon my Reputation on any Account whatever, and all the Men that I had Convers'd with, were of so good Reputation that I had not given the least Reflection by Conversing with them;[173] nor did any of them seem to think there was room for a wicked Correspondence, if they had any of them offered it; yet there was one Gentleman, *as above*, who always singl'd me out for the Diversion of my Company, as he call'd it, which *as he was pleas'd to say* was very agreeable to him, but at that time there was no more in it.

I had many melancholly Hours at the *Bath* after all the Company was gone, for tho' I went to *Bristol* sometimes for the disposing my Effects, and for Recruits of Money, yet I chose to come back to *Bath* for my Residence, because being on good Terms with the Woman in whose House I lodg'd in the Summer, I found that during the Winter I liv'd rather cheaper there than I could do any where else; here, *I say*, I pass'd the Winter as heavily as I had pass'd the Autumn chearfully; But having contracted a nearer intimacy with the said Woman, in whose House I Lodg'd, I could not avoid communicating to her something of what lay hardest upon my Mind, and particularly the narrowness of my Circumstances, and the loss of my Fortune by the Damage of my Goods by Sea: I told her also that I had a Mother and a Brother in *Virginia* in good Circumstances, and as I had really written back to my Mother in particular to represent my Condition, and the great Loss I had receiv'd, which indeed came to almost 500 *l.*, so I did not fail to let my new Friend know, that I expected a Supply from thence, and so indeed I did; and as the Ships went from *Bristol* to *York* River in *Virginia*, and back again generally in less time than from *London*, and that my Brother Corresponded chiefly at *Bristol*, I thought it was much better for me to wait here for my Returns, than to go to *London*, where also I had not the least Acquaintance.

My new Friend appear'd sensibly affected with my Condition, and indeed was so very kind, as to reduce the Rate of my living with her to so low a Price during the Winter, that she convinced me she got nothing by me; and as for Lodging during the Winter, I paid nothing at all.[174]

When the Spring Season came on, she continu'd to be as kind to me as she could, and I lodg'd with her for a time, till it was found necessary to do otherwise; she had some Persons of Character that frequently lodg'd in her House, and in particular the Gentleman who, as I said, singl'd me out for his Companion the Winter before; and he came down again with another Gentleman in his Company and two Servants, and lodg'd in the same House: I suspected that my Landlady

[173]I.e., Moll's associations did not damage her reputation.
[174]I.e., relatively speaking.

had invited him thither, letting him know that I was still with her, but she deny'd it, and protested to me that she did not, and he said the same.

In a Word, this Gentleman came down and continu'd to single me out for his peculiar Confidence as well as Conversation; he was a compleat Gentleman, *that must be confess'd*, and his Company was very agreeable to me, as mine, *if I might believe him*, was to him; he made no Professions to me but of an extraordinary Respect, and he had such an Opinion of my Virtue, that *as he often profess'd*, he believ'd if he should offer any thing else, I should reject him with Contempt; he soon understood from me that I was a Widow, that I had arriv'd at *Bristol* from *Virginia* by the last Ships; and that I waited at *Bath* till the next *Virginia Fleet* should arrive, by which I expected considerable Effects; I understood by him, and by others of him, that he had a Wife, but that the Lady was distemper'd in her Head, and was under the Conduct of her own Relations, which he consented to, to avoid any Reflections that might, *as was not unusual in such Cases*, be cast on him for mismanaging her Cure; and in the mean time he came to the *Bath* to divert his Thoughts from the Disturbance of such a melancholy Circumstance as that was.

My Landlady, who of her own accord encourag'd the Correspondence on all Occasions, gave me an advantageous Character of him, as of a Man of Honour and of Virtue, as well as of a great Estate; and indeed I had a great deal of Reason to say so of him too; for tho' we lodg'd both on a Floor, and he had frequently come into my Chamber, even when I was in Bed; and I also into his when he was in Bed,[175] yet he never offered any thing to me farther than a kiss, or so much as solicited me to any thing till long after, as you shall hear.

I frequently took notice to my Landlady of his exceeding Modesty, and she again used to tell me, she believ'd it was so from the beginning; however she used to tell me that she thought I ought to expect some Gratification from him for my Company, for indeed he did, as it were, engross me,[176] and I was seldom from him; *I told her* I had not given him the least occasion to think I wanted it, or that I would accept of it from him; *she told me* she would take that part upon her, and she did so, and manag'd it so dextrously, that the first time we were together alone, after she had talk'd with him, he began to enquire a little into my Circumstances, as how I had subsisted myself since I came on shore? and whether I did not want Money? I stood off very boldly, I told him that tho' my Cargo of Tobacco was damag'd, yet that it was not quite lost; that the Merchant I had been consign'd to, had so honestly manag'd for me that I had not wanted; and that I hop'd,

[175]It was not unusual so to entertain guests, levees or morning visits being common in polite company.   [176]Engage my whole time and attention.

with frugal Management, I should make it hold out till more would come, which I expected by the next Fleet; that in the mean time I had retrench'd my Expences, and whereas I kept a Maid last Season, now I liv'd without; and whereas I had a Chamber and a Dining-room then on the first Floor, *as he knew*, I now had but one Room two pair of Stairs,[177] *and the like*; but I live *said I*, as well satisfy'd now as I did then; *adding*, that his Company had been a means to make me live much more chearfully than otherwise I should have done, for which I was much oblig'd to him; and so I put off all room for any offer for the present: However, it was not long before he attack'd me again, and told me he found that I was backward to trust him with the Secret of my Circumstances, *which he was sorry for*; assuring me that he enquir'd into it with no design to satisfie his own Curiosity, but meerly to assist me, if there was any occasion; but since I would not own my self to stand in need of any assistance, he had but one thing more to desire of me, and that was, that I would promise him that when I was any way streighten'd, or like to be so, I would frankly tell him of it, and that I would make use of him with the same freedom that he made the offer, *adding*, that I should always find I had a true Friend, tho' perhaps I was afraid to trust him.

I omitted nothing *that was fit to be said by one infinitely oblig'd*, to let him know, that I had a due Sense of his Kindness; and indeed from that time, I did not appear so much reserv'd to him as I had done before, tho' still within the Bounds of the strictest Virtue on both sides; but how free soever our Conversation was, I cou'd not arrive to that sort of Freedom which he desir'd, (*viz.*) to tell him I wanted Money, tho' I was secretly very glad of his offer.

Some Weeks pass'd after this, and still I never ask'd him for Money; when my Landlady, a cunning Creature, who had often press'd me to it, but found that I cou'd not do it, makes a Story of her own inventing, and comes in bluntly to me when we were together, O Widow, *says she*, I have bad News to tell you this Morning; What is that, said I, are the *Virginia* Ships taken by the *French? for that was my fear*. No, no, *says she*, but the Man you sent to *Bristol* Yesterday for Money is come back, and says he has brought none.

Now I could by no means like her Project; I thought it look'd too much like prompting him, which indeed he did not want,[178] and I saw clearly that I should lose nothing by being backward to ask, so I took her up short; I can't imagine why he should say so to you, *said I*, for I assure you he brought me all the Money I sent him for, and here it is *said I*, (pulling out my Purse with about 12 Guineas in it) and added, I intend you shall have most of it by and by.

[177]A single room on the third floor.
[178]Need.

He seem'd distasted[179] a little at her talking as she did at first, as well as I, taking it as I fancied he would as something forward of her; but when he saw me give such an Answer, he came immediately to himself again: The next Morning we talk'd of it again, when I found he was fully satisfy'd; and smiling said, he hop'd I would not want Money and not tell him of it, and that I had promis'd him otherwise: I told him I had been very much dissatisfy'd at my Landladies talking so publickly the Day before of what she had nothing to do with; but I suppos'd she wanted what I ow'd her, which was about Eight Guineas, which I had resolv'd to give her, and had accordingly given it her the same Night she talk'd so foolishly.

He was in a mighty good Humour, when he heard me say, *I had paid her*, and it went off into some other Discourse at that time; but the next Morning he having heard me up about my Room before him, he call'd to me, *and I answering*, he ask'd me to come into his Chamber; he was in bed when I came in, and he made me come and sit down on his Bed side, *for he said*, he had something to say to me, which was of some Moment: After some very kind Expressions he ask'd me, if I would be very honest to him, and give a sincere Answer to one thing he would desire of me? after some little Cavil with him at the word *Sincere*, and asking him if I had ever given him any Answers which were not Sincere, I promis'd him I would; why then his Request was, *he said*, to let him see my Purse; I immediately put my Hand into my Pocket, *and Laughing at him*, pull'd it out, and there was in it three Guineas and a Half; *then he ask'd me*, if there was all the Money I had? I told him no, *Laughing again*, not by a great deal.

Well then, *he said*, he would have me promise to go and fetch him all the Money I had, every Farthing: *I told him I would*, and I went into my Chamber, and fetch'd him a little private Drawer, where I had about six Guineas more, and some Silver, and threw it all down upon the Bed, and told him there was all my Wealth, honestly to a Shilling: He look'd a little at it, but did not tell[180] it, and Huddled it all into the Drawer again, and reaching his Pocket, pull'd out a Key, and had then me open a little Walnuttree box, he had upon the Table, and bring him such a Drawer, which I did, in which Drawer, there was a great deal of Money in Gold, I believe near 200 Guineas, but I knew not how much: He took the Drawer, and taking my Hand, made me put it in, and take a whole handful; I was backward at that, but he held my Hand hard in his Hand, and put it into the Drawer, and made me take out as many Guineas almost as I could well take up at once.

When I had done so, he made me put them into my Lap, and took my little Drawer, and pour'd out all my own Money among his, and bad me get me gone, and carry it all Home into my own Chamber.

[179]Disgusted, offended.
[180]Count.

I relate this Story the more particularly because of the good Humour there was in it, and to show the temper with which we Convers'd: It was not long after this, but he began every Day to find fault with my Cloths, with my Laces, and Head-dresses; and in a Word, press'd me to buy better, which by the way I was willing enough to do, tho' I did not seem to be so; I lov'd nothing in the World better than fine Clothes, but I told him I must Housewife[181] the Money he had lent me, or else I should not be able to pay him again. He then told me in a few Words, that as he had a sincere Respect for me, and knew my Circumstances, he had not Lent me that Money, but given it me, and that he thought I had merited it from him, by giving him my Company so intirely as I had done: After this, he made me take a Maid, and keep House, and his Friend that came with him to *Bath*, being gone, he oblig'd me to Dyet[182] him, which I did very willingly, believeing *as it appear'd*, that I should lose nothing by it, nor did the Woman of the House fail to find her Account in it too.

We had liv'd thus near three Months, when the Company beginning to wear away at the *Bath*, he talk'd of going away, and fain he would have me to go to *London* with him: I was not very easie in that Proposal, not knowing what Posture I was to live in there, or how he might use me: But while this was in Debate he fell very Sick; he had gone out to a place in *Somersetshire* called *Shepton*, where he had some Business, and was there taken very ill, and so ill that he could not Travel, so he sent his Man back to *Bath* to beg me that I would hire a Coach and come over to him. Before he went, he had left all his Money and other things of Value with me, and what to do with them I did not know, but I secur'd them as well as I could, and Lock'd up the Lodgings and went to him, where I found him very ill indeed; however, I perswaded him to be carry'd in a Litter to the *Bath*, where there was more help and better advice to be had.

He consented, and I brought him to the *Bath*, which was about fifteen Miles, *as I remember*: here he continued very ill of a Fever, and kept his Bed five Weeks, all which time I nurs'd him and tended him my self, as much and as carefully as if I had been his Wife; indeed if I had been his Wife I could not have done more; I sat up with him so much and so often, that at last indeed he would not let me sit up any longer, and then I got a Pallate[183] Bed into his Room, and lay in it just at his Bed's Feet.

I was indeed sensibly affected with his Condition, and with the Apprehension of losing such a Friend as he was, and was like to be to me, and I us'd to sit and Cry by him many Hours together: However at last he grew Better, and gave hopes that he would recover, as indeed he did, tho' very slowly.

[181]Be sparing of.
[182]Board.

[183]I.e., pallet. Defoe may intend a pun here; note the ensuing action.

Were it otherwise than what I am going to say, I should not be backward to disclose it, as it is apparent I have done in other Cases in this Account; but I affirm, that thro' all this Conversation, abating[184] the freedom of coming into the Chamber when I or he was in Bed, and abating the necessary Offices of attending him Night and Day when he was Sick, there had not pass'd the least immodest Word or Action between us. O! that it had been so to the last.

After some time he gathered Strength, and grew well apace, and I would have remov'd my Palate Bed, but he would not let me till he was able to venture himself without any Body to sit up with him, and then I remov'd to my own Chamber.

He took many Occasions to express his Sense of my Tenderness and Concern for him; and when he grew quite well, he made me a Present of Fifty Guineas for my Care, and, as he call'd it, for hazarding my Life to save his.

And now he made deep Protestations of a sincere inviolable Affection for me, but all along attested it to be with the utmost reserve for my Virtue, and his own: I told him I was fully satisfyed of it; he carried it that length that he protested to me, that if he was naked in Bed with me, he would as sacredly preserve my Virtue, as he would defend it if I was assaulted by a Ravisher; I believ'd him, and told him I did so; but this did not satisfie him, he would, *he said*, wait for some opportunity to give me an undoubted Testimony of it.

It was a great while after this that I had Occasion, on my own Business, to go to *Bristol*, upon which he hir'd me a Coach, and would go with me, and did so; and now indeed our intimacy increas'd: From *Bristol* he carry'd me to *Gloucester*, which was meerly a Journey of Pleasure to take the Air; and here it was our hap to have no Lodging in the Inn but in one large Chamber with two beds in it: The Master of the House going up with us to show his Rooms, and coming into that Room, said very frankly to him, Sir, *It is none of my business to enquire whether the Lady be your Spouse or no*, but if not, *you may lie as honestly in these two Beds as if you were in two Chambers*, and with that he pulls a great Curtain which drew quite cross[185] the Room, and effectually divided the Beds; well, *says my Friend*, very readily, these Beds will do, and as for the rest, we are too near a kin to lye together, tho' we may Lodge near one another; and this put an honest Face on the thing too. When he came to go to Bed he decently went out of the Room till I was in Bed, and then went to Bed in the Bed on his own side of the Room, but lay there talking to me a great while.

At last repeating his usual saying, that he could lye naked in the Bed with me and not offer me the least Injury, he starts out of his Bed, and

[184]Omitting.
[185]Across.

now, *my Dear*, *says he*, you shall see how just I will be to you, and that I can keep my word, and away he comes to my Bed.

I resisted a little, but I must confess I should not have resisted him much, if he had not made those Promises at all; so after a little struggle, *as I said*, I lay still and let him come to Bed; when he was there he took me in his Arms, and so I lay all Night with him, but he had no more to do with me, or offer'd any thing to me other than embracing me, as I say, in his Arms, no not the whole Night, but rose up and dress'd him in the Morning, and left me as innocent for him[186] as I was the Day I was born.

This was a surprizing thing to me, and perhaps may be so to others who know how the Laws of Nature work; for he was a strong vigorous brisk Person; nor did he act thus on a principle of Religion at all, *but of meer Affection*; insisting on it, that tho' I was to him the most agreeable Woman in the World, yet because he lov'd me he cou'd not injure me.

I own it was a noble Principle, but as it was what I never understood before, so it was to me perfectly amazing. We Travel'd the rest of the Journey as we did before, and came back to the *Bath*, where, as he had opportunity to come to me when he would, he often repeated the Moderation, and I frequently lay with him, and he with me, and altho' all the familiarities between Man and Wife were common to us, yet he never once offered to go any farther, and he valued himself much upon it; I do not say that I was so wholly pleas'd with it as he thought I was: For I own I was much wickeder than he, *as you shall hear presently*.

We liv'd thus near two Year, only with this exception, that he went three times to *London* in that time, and once he continued there four Months, but, to do him Justice, he always supply'd me with Money to subsist me very handsomly.

Had we continued thus, I confess we had had much to boast of; but as wise Men say, it is ill venturing too near the brink of a Command;[187] so we found it; and here again I must do him the justice to own, that the first Breach was not on his part: It was one Night that we were in Bed together warm and merry, and having drank, I think, a little more Wine that Night, both of us, than usual, tho' not in the least to disorder either of us, when after some other follies which I cannot name, and being clasp'd close in his Arms, *I told him*, (*I repeat it with shame and horror of Soul*) that I cou'd find in my Heart to discharge him of his Engagement for one Night and no more.

He took me at my word immediately, and after that, there was no resisting him; neither indeed had I any mind to resist him any more, let what would come of it.

---

[186]As far as he was concerned; i.e., her innocence had not been violated by him.   [187]Commandment.

Thus the Government of our Virtue was broken, and I exchang'd the Place of Friend, for that unmusical harsh-sounding Title of WHORE. In the Morning we were both at our Penitentials, I cried very heartily, he express'd himself very sorry; but that was all either of us could do at that time; and the way being thus clear'd, and the bars of Virtue and Conscience thus removed, we had the less difficulty afterwards to struggle with.

It was but a dull kind of Conversation that we had together for all the rest of that Week, I look'd on him with Blushes; and every now and then started that melancholy Objection, *what if I should be with Child now? What will become of me then?* He encourag'd me by telling me, that as long as I was true to him he would be so to me; and since it was gone such a length, (which indeed he never intended) yet if I was with Child, he would take care of that, and of me too: This harden'd[188] us both; I assur'd him if I was with Child, I would die for want of a Midwife rather than Name him as the Father of it; and he assur'd me I should never want if I should be with Child: These mutual assurances harden'd us in the thing; and after this we repeated the Crime as often as we pleas'd, till at length, as I had fear'd, so it came to pass, and I was indeed with Child.

After I was sure it was so, and I had satisfied him of it too, we began to think of taking measures for the managing it, and I propos'd trusting the Secret to my Landlady, and asking her Advice, which he agreed to: My Landlady, a Woman (as I found) us'd to such things, made light of it; she said she knew it would come to that at last, and made us very merry about it: As I said above, we found her an Experienc'd old Lady at such Work; she undertook every thing, engag'd to procure a Midwife and a Nurse, to satisfie all Enquiries, and bring us off with Reputation, and she did so very dexterously indeed.

When I grew near my time, she desir'd my Gentleman to go away to *London*, or make as if he did so; when he was gone, she acquainted the Parish Officers that there was a Lady ready to lye in at her House, but that she knew her Husband very well, and gave them, as she pretended, an account of his Name, which she called Sir *Walter Cleave*; telling them he was a very worthy Gentleman, and that she would answer for all Enquiries, and the like: This satisfied the Parish Officers presently,[189] and I lay INN with as much Credit as I could have done

---

[188]For a discussion of the hardening motif, see Starr, chap. 4. In Latin, *mollis* means to soften; "Moll" was, of course, a common nickname for female underworld characters, but Defoe may possibly develop the hardening motif in the light of the ironic resonance of her name.

[189]Parish officers concerned themselves about such information because the parish was financially responsible for indigent children born there; had Moll appeared to be without means, the officers would probably not have allowed her to lie in there.

if I had really been my Lady *Cleave*; and was assisted in my Travel[190] by three or four of the best Citizens Wives of *Bath*, who liv'd in the Neighbourhood, which however made me a little the more expensive to him; I often expressed my concern to him about it, but he bid me not be concern'd at it.

As he had furnish'd me very sufficiently with Money for the extraordinary Expences of my Lying Inn, I had every thing very handsome about me; but did not affect to be Gay or Extravagant neither; besides, knowing my own Circumstances, and knowing the World as I had done, and that such kind of things do not often last long, I took care to lay up as much Money as I could for a wet Day, as I call'd it; making him believe it was all spent upon the extraordinary appearance of things in my Lying Inn.

By this means, and including what he had given me as above, I had at the end of my Lying Inn about 200 Guineas by me, including also what was left of my own.

I was brought to Bed of a fine Boy indeed, and a charming Child it was; and when he heard of it he wrote me a very kind obliging Letter about it, and then told me, he thought it would look better for me to come away for *London* as soon as I was up and well, that he had provided Appartments for me at *Hammersmith*[191] as if I came thither only from *London*, and that after a little while I should go back to the *Bath*, and he would go with me.

I lik'd this offer very well, and accordingly hir'd a Coach on purpose, and taking my Child and a Wet-Nurse to Tend and Suckle it, and a Maid Servant with me, away I went for *London*.

He met me at *Reading* in his own Chariot, and taking me into that, left the Servant and the Child in the hir'd Coach, and so he brought me to my new Lodgings at *Hammersmith*; with which I had abundance of Reason to be very well pleas'd, for they were very handsome Rooms, and I was very well accommodated.

And now I was indeed in the height of what I might call my Prosperity, and I wanted nothing but to be a Wife, which however could not be in this Case, there was no room for it; and therefore on all Occasions I study'd to save what I could, as I have said above, against[192] a time of scarcity; knowing well enough that such things as these do not always continue, that Men that keep Mistresses often change them, grow weary of them, or Jealous of them, or something or other happens to make them withdraw their Bounty; and sometimes the Ladies that are thus well us'd, are not careful by a prudent Conduct to

[190]I.e., travail. In Defoe's time, these words were frequently spelled interchangeably, and writers sometimes exploit the spelling pun to remind their readers that expulsion from Eden, childbirth, and general woe all resulted from the same initial act of disorder.

[191]A parish just west of London, on the north bank of the Thames.

[192]To provide for.

preserve the Esteem of their Persons, or the nice Article of their Fidelity, and then they are justly cast off with Contempt.

But I was secur'd in this Point, for as I had no Inclination to change, so I had no manner of Acquaintance in the whole House, and so no Temptation to look any farther; I kept no Company but in the Family where I Lodg'd, and with a Clergyman's Lady at next Door; so that when he was absent I visited no Body, nor did he ever find me out of my Chamber or Parlor whenever he came down, if I went any where to take the Air it was always with him.

The living in this manner with him, and his with me, was certainly the most undesigned thing in the World; he often protested to me, that when he became first acquainted with me, and even to the very Night when we first broke in upon our Rules, he never had the least Design of lying with me; that he always had a sincere Affection for me, but not the least real inclination to do what he had done; I assur'd him I never suspected him, that if I had, I should not so easily have yielded to the freedoms which brought it on, but that it was all a surprize, and was owing to the Accident of our having yielded too far to our mutual Inclinations that Night; and indeed I have often observ'd since, and leave it as a caution to the Readers of this Story; that we ought to be cautious of gratifying our Inclinations in loose and lewd Freedoms, least we find our Resolutions of Virtue fail us in the juncture when their Assistance should be most necessary.

It is true, *and I have confess'd it before*, that from the first hour I began to converse with him, I resolv'd to let him lye with me, if he offer'd it; but it was because I wanted his help and assistance, and I knew no other way of securing him than that: But when we were that Night together, and, as I have said, had gone such a length, I found my Weakness, the Inclination was not to be resisted, but I was oblig'd to yield up all even before he ask'd it.

However he was so just to me that he never upbraided me with that; nor did he ever express the least dislike of my Conduct on any other Occasion, but always protested he was as much delighted with my Company as he was the first Hour we came together, I mean came together as Bedfellows.

It is true that he had no Wife, that is to say, she was as no Wife to him, and so I was in no Danger that way, but the just Reflections of Conscience oftentimes snatch a Man, especially a Man of Sense, from the Arms of a Mistress, as it did him at last, tho' on another Occasion.

On the other hand, tho' I was not without secret Reproaches of my own Conscience for the Life I led, and that even in the greatest height of the Satisfaction I ever took, yet I had the terrible prospect of Poverty and Starving which lay on me as a frightful Spectre, so that there was no looking behind me: But as Poverty brought me into it, so fear of Poverty kept me in it, and I frequently resolv'd to leave it quite off, if I could but come to lay up Money enough to maintain me: But these were Thoughts of no weight, and whenever he came to me they vanish'd; for his Company was so delightful, that there was no being melancholly when he was there, the Reflections were all the Subject of those Hours when I was alone.

I liv'd six Year in this happy but unhappy[193] Condition, in which time I brought him three Children, but only the first of them liv'd; and tho' I remov'd twice in those six Years, yet I came back the sixth Year to my first Lodgings at *Hammersmith*: Here it was that I was one Morning surpriz'd with a kind, but melancholy Letter from my Gentleman; intimating, that he was very ill, and was afraid he should have another fit of Sickness, but that his Wife's Relations being in the House with him, it would not be practicable to have me with him, which however he express'd his great Dissatisfaction in, and that he wish'd I cou'd be allowed to Tend and Nurse him as I did before.

I was very much concern'd at this Account, and was very impatient to know how it was with him; I waited a Fortnight or thereabouts, and heard nothing, which surpriz'd me, and I began to be very uneasy indeed; I think I may say, that for the next Fortnight I was near to distracted: It was my particular difficulty, that I did not know directly where he was; for I understood at first he was in the Lodgings of his Wive's Mother; but having remov'd my self to *London*, I soon found by the help of the Direction I had for writing my Letters to him, how to enquire after him, and there I found that he was at a House in *Bloomsbury*, whither he had, a little before he fell Sick, remov'd his whole Family; and that his Wife and Wives Mother were in the same House, tho' the Wife was not suffered[194] to know that she was in the same House with her Husband.

Here I also soon understood that he was at the last Extremity, which made me almost at the last Extremity too, to have a true account: One Night I had the Curiosity to disguise my self like a Servant Maid in a Round Cap and Straw Hat, and went to the Door, as[195] sent by a Lady of his Neighbourhood, where he liv'd before, and giving Master and Mistresses Service, I said I was sent to know how Mr. ——— did, and how he had rested that Night; in delivering this Message I got the opportunity I desir'd, for speaking with one of the Maids, I held a long Gossips Tale with her, and had all the Particulars of his Illness, which I found was a Pleurisie attended with a Cough and a Fever; she told me also who was in the House, and how his Wife was, who, by her Relation, they were in some hopes might Recover her Understanding; but as to the Gentleman himself, *in short* she told me the Doctors said there was very little hopes of him, that in the Morning they thought

---

[193]I.e., fortunate, but without pleasure or content of mind.

[194]Allowed.

[195]As if; pretending to be.

he had been dying, and that he was but little better then, for they did not expect that he could live over the next Night.

This was heavy News for me, and I began now to see an end of my Prosperity, and to see also that it was very well I had play'd the good Housewife, and secur'd or saved something while he was alive, for that now I had no view of *my own living* before me.

It lay very heavy upon my Mind too, that I had a Son, a fine lovely Boy, above five Years old, and no Provision made for it, at least that I knew of; with these Considerations, and a sad Heart, I went home that Evening, and began to cast with my self how I should live, and in what manner to bestow my self, for the residue of my Life.

You may be sure I could not rest without enquiring again very quickly what was become of him; and not venturing to go my self, I sent several sham Messengers, till after a Fortnights waiting longer, I found that there was hopes of his Life, tho' he was still very ill; then I abated my sending any more to the House, and in some time after I learnt in the Neighbourhood that he was about House, and then that he was Abroad[196] again.

I made no doubt then but that I shou'd soon hear of him, and began to comfort my self with my Circumstances being, as I thought, recovered; I waited a Week, and two Weeks, and with much surprize and amazement I waited near two Months and heard nothing, but that being recover'd he was gone into the Country for the Air, and for the better Recovery after his Distemper; after this it was yet two Months more, and then I understood he was come to his City-House again, but still I heard nothing from him.

I had written several Letters for him, and Directed them as usual, and found two or three of them had been call'd for, *but not the rest*: I wrote again in a more pressing manner than ever, and in one of them let him know, that I must be forc'd to wait on him myself, Representing my Circumstances, the Rent of Lodgings to pay, and the Provision for the Child wanting, and my own deplorable Condition, destitute of Subsistence after his most solemn Engagement, to take Care of, and Provide for me; I took a Copy of this Letter, and finding it lay at the House, near a Month, and was not call'd for, I found means to have the Copy of it, put into his own Hands at a Coffee-House, where I had by Enquiry found he us'd to go.

This Letter forc'd an Answer from him, by which, tho' I found I was to be abandon'd, yet I found he had sent a Letter to me sometime before, desiring me to go down *to the Bath again*, its Contents I shall come to presently.

It is True that Sick Beds are the times, when such Correspondences as this are look'd on with different Countenance, and seen with other

---

[196]Able to go out of his house.

Eyes then we saw them with, or than they appear'd with before: My Lover had been at the Gates of Death, and at the very brink of Eternity; and it seems had been strook with a due remorse, and with sad Reflections upon his past Life of Gallantry, and Levity; and among the rest, this criminal Correspondence with me, which was neither more or less, than a long continu'd Life of Adultery had represented it self as it really was, not as it had been formerly thought by him to be, and he look'd upon it now with a just, and a religious Aborrence.

I cannot but observe also, and leave it for the Direction of my Sex in such Cases of Pleasure, that when ever sincere Repentance succeeds such a Crime as this, there never fails to attend a Hatred of the Object; and the more the Affection might seem to be before, the Hatred will be the more in Proportion: It will always be so, indeed it can be no otherwise; for there cannot be a true and sincere Abhorrence of the Offence, and the Love to the Cause of it remain; there will with an Abhorrence of the Sin be found a detestation of the fellow Sinner; you can expect no other.

I found it so here, tho' good Manners, and Justice in this Gentleman, kept him from carrying it on to any extream; but the short History of his Part in this Affair was thus; he perceiv'd by my last Letter, and by all the rest, which he went for after,[197] that I was not gone to the *Bath*, that his first Letter had not come to my Hand, upon which he writes me this following,

Madam,
    "I am surpriz'd that my Letter Dated the 8th of last Month did not "come to your Hand, I give you my Word it was deliver'd at your Lodg-"ings, and to the Hands of your Maid.

    "I need not acquaint you with what has been my Condition for some-"time past; and how having been at the Edge of the Grave, I am by the un-"expected and undeserv'd Mercy of Heaven restor'd again: In the "Condition I have been in, it cannot be strange to you that our unhappy "Correspondence has not been the least of the Burthens which lay upon "my Conscience; I need say no more, those things that must be repented "of, must be also reform'd.

    "I wish you would think of going back to the *Bath*, I enclose you here "a Bill for 50 *l.* for clearing your self at your Lodgings, and carrying you "down, and hope it will be no surprize to you to add, that on this account "only, and not for any Offence given me on your side, I can SEE YOU NO "MORE; I will take due care of the Child, leave him where he is, or take "him with you, as you please; I wish you the like Reflections, and that "they may be to your Advantage. I am, &c.

I was struck with this Letter as with a thousand Wounds, such as I cannot describe; the Reproaches of my own Conscience were such as

[197]Which he later called for.

I cannot express, for I was not blind to my own Crime; and I reflected that I might with less Offence have continued with my Brother, and liv'd with him as a Wife, since there was no Crime in our Marriage on that score, neither of us knowing it.

But I never once reflected that I was all this while a marry'd Woman, a Wife to Mr. ——— the Linnen Draper, who tho' he had left me by the Necessity of his Circumstances, had no power to Discharge me from the Marriage Contract which was between us, or to give me a legal liberty to marry again; so that I had been no less than a Whore and an Adultress all this while: I then reproach'd my self with the Liberties I had taken, and how I had been a Snare to this Gentleman, and that indeed I was principal in the Crime; that now he was mercifully snatch'd out of the Gulph[198] by a convincing Work upon his Mind, but that I was left as if I was forsaken of God's Grace, and abandon'd by Heaven to a continuing in my wickedness.

Under these Reflections I continu'd very pensive and sad for near a Month, and did not go down to the *Bath*, having no inclination to be with the Woman who I was with before; least, as I thought, she should prompt me to some wicked course of Life again, as she had done; and besides, I was very loth she should know I was cast off as above.

And now I was greatly perplex'd about my little Boy; it was Death to me to part with the Child, and yet when I consider'd the Danger of being one time or other left with him to keep without a Maintenance to support him, I then resolv'd to leave him where he was; but then I concluded also to be near him my self too, that I might have the satisfaction of seeing him, without the Care of providing for him.

I sent my Gentleman a short Letter therefore, that I had obey'd his Orders in all things, but that of going back to the *Bath*, which I cou'd not think of for many Reasons; that however parting from him was a Wound to me that I could never recover, yet that I was fully satisfied his Reflections were just, and would be very far from desiring to obstruct his Reformation or Repentance.

Then I represented my own Circumstances to him in the most moving Terms that I was able: I told him that those unhappy Distresses which first mov'd him to a generous and an honest Friendship for me, would, I hope, move him to a little concern for me now; tho' the Criminal part of our Correspondence, which I believed neither of us intended to fall into at that time, was broken off; that I desir'd to Repent as sincerely as he had done, but entreated him to put me in some Condition, that I might not be expos'd to the Temptations which the Devil never fails to excite us to from the frightful prospect of Poverty and Distress; and if he had the least Apprehensions of my

---

[198]Gulf; i.e., abyss or whirlpool—hence, metaphorically, damnation.

being troublesome to him, I beg'd he would put me in a Posture to go back to my Mother in *Virginia*, from whence he knew I came, and that would put an end to all his Fears on that account; I concluded, that if he would send me 50 *l.* more to facilitate my going away, I would send him back a general Release, and would promise never to disturb him more with any Importunities; unless it was to hear of the well-doing of the Child, who if I found my Mother living, and my Circumstances able, I would send for to come over to me, and take him also effectually off of his Hands.

This was indeed all a Cheat thus far, *viz.* that I had no intention to go to *Virginia*, as the Account of my former Affairs there may convince any Body of; but the business was to get this last Fifty Pounds of him, if possible, knowing well enough it would be the last Penny I was ever to expect.

However, the Argument I us'd, namely, of giving him a general Release, and never troubling him any more, prevail'd effectually with him, and he sent me a Bill for the Money by a Person who brought with him a general Release for me to sign, and which I frankly[199] sign'd, and receiv'd the Money; and thus, tho' full sore against my will, a final End was put to this Affair.

And here I cannot but reflect upon the unhappy Consequence of too great Freedoms between Persons stated[200] as we were, upon the pretence of innocent intentions, Love of Friendship, *and the like*; for the Flesh has generally so great a share in those Friendships, that it is great odds but inclination prevails at last over the most solemn Resolutions; and that Vice breaks in at the breaches of Decency, which really innocent Friendship ought to preserve with the greatest strictness; but I leave the Readers of these things to their own just Reflections, which they will be more able to make effectual than I, who so soon forgot my self, and am therefore but a very indifferent Monitor.

I was now a single Person again, *as I may call my self*, I was loos'd from all the Obligations either of Wedlock or Mistressship in the World; except my Husband the Linnen Draper, who I having not now heard from in almost Fifteen Year, no Body could blame me for thinking my self entirely freed from; seeing also he had at his going away told me, that if I did not hear frequently from him, I should conclude he was dead, and I might freely marry again to whom I pleas'd.

I now began to cast up my Accounts; I had by many Letters, and much Importunity, and with the Intercession of my Mother too, had a second return of some Goods from my Brother, *as I now call him*, in *Virginia*, to make up the Damage of the Cargo I brought away with me, and this too was upon the Condition of my sealing a general

[199]Unconditionally.   [200]Stationed, situated.

Release to him, and to send it him by his Correspondent at *Bristol*, which though I thought hard of,[201] yet I was oblig'd to promise to do: However, I manag'd so well in this case, that I got my Goods away before the Release was sign'd, and then I always found something or other to say to evade the thing, and to put off the signing it at all; till *at length* I pretended I must write to my Brother, and have his Answer, before I could do it.

Including this Recruit, and before I got the last 50 *l.* I found my strength to amount, put all together, to about 400 *l.* so that with that I had above 450 *l.* I had sav'd above 100 *l.* more, but I met with a Disaster with that, which was this; that a Goldsmith in whose Hands I had trusted it, broke, so I lost 70 *l.* of my Money, the Man's Composition not making above 30 *l.* out of his 100 *l.* I had a little Plate, but not much, and was well enough stock'd with Cloaths and Linnen.

With this Stock I had the World to begin again; but you are to consider, that I was not now the same Woman as when I liv'd at *Redriff*; for first of all I was near 20 Years older, and did not look the better for my Age, nor for my Rambles to *Virginia* and back again; and tho' I omitted nothing that might set me out to Advantage, except Painting, for that I never stoop'd to, and had Pride enough to think I did not want it, yet there would always be some difference seen between Five and Twenty, and Two and Forty.

I cast about innumerable ways for my future State of Life and began to consider very seriously what I should do, *but nothing offer'd*; I took care to make the World take me for something more than I was, and had it given out that I was a Fortune, and that my Estate was in my own Hands, the last of which was very true, the first of it was as above: I had no Acquaintance, which was one of my worst Misfortunes, and the Consequence of that was, I had no adviser, at least who cou'd advise and assist together; and above all, I had no Body to whom I could in confidence commit the Secret of any Circumstances to, and could depend upon for their Secresie and Fidelity; and I found by experience, that to be Friendless is the worst Condition, next to being in want, that a Woman can be reduc'd to: *I say a Woman*, because 'tis evident Men can be their own Advisers, and their own Directors, and know how to work themselves out of Difficulties and into Business better than Women; but if a Woman has no Friend to Communicate her Affairs to, and to advise and assist her, 'tis ten to one but she is undone; nay, and the more Money she has, the more Danger she is in of being wrong'd and deceiv'd; and this was my Case in the Affair of the Hundred Pound which I left in the Hand of the Goldsmith, *as above*, whose Credit, it seems, was upon the Ebb before, but I that had

---

[201]Considered oppressive and difficult to endure.

no knowledge of things, and no Body to consult with, knew nothing of it, and so lost my Money.

In the next place, when a Woman is thus left desolate and void of Council,[202] she is just like a Bag of Money, or a Jewel dropt on the Highway, which is a Prey to the next Comer; if a Man of Virtue and upright Principles happens to find it, he will have it cried,[203] and the Owner may come to hear of it again; but how many times shall such a thing fall into Hands that will make no scruple of siezing it for their own, to once that it shall come into good Hands.

This was evidently my Case, for I was now a loose unguided Creature, and had no Help, no Assistance, no Guide for my Conduct: I knew what I aim'd at, and what I wanted, but knew nothing how to pursue the End by direct means; I wanted to be plac'd in a settled State of Living, and had I happen'd to meet with a sober good Husband, I should have been as faithful and true a Wife to him as Virtue it self could have form'd: If I had been otherwise, the Vice came in always at the Door of Necessity, not at the Door of Inclination; and I understood too well, by the want of it, what the value of a settl'd Life was, to do any thing to forfeit the felicity of it; nay, I should have made the better Wife for all the Difficulties I had pass'd thro', by a greal deal; nor did I in any of the Times that I had been a Wife, give my Husbands the least uneasiness on account of my Behaviour.

But all this was nothing; I found no encouraging Prospect; I waited, I liv'd regularly, and with as much frugality as became my Circumstances, but nothing offer'd; nothing presented, and the main Stock wasted apace; what to do I knew not, the Terror of approaching Poverty lay hard upon my Spirits: I had some Money, but where to place it I knew not, nor would the Interest of it maintain me, at least not in *London*.

At length a new Scene open'd: There was in the House, where I Lodg'd, a North Country Woman that went for a Gentlewoman, and nothing was more frequent in her Discourse, than her account of the cheapness of Provisions, and the easie way of living in her County; how plentiful and how cheap every thing was, what good Company they kept, and the like; till at last I told her she almost tempted me to go and live in her County; for I that was a Widow, tho' I had sufficient to live on, yet had no way of encreasing it, and that *London* was an expensive and extravagant Place; that I found I could not live here under a Hundred Pound a Year, unless I kept no Company, no Servant, made no Appearance, and buried my self in Privacy, as if I was oblig'd to it by Necessity.

I should have observ'd, that she was always made to believe, as

---

[202]Counsel. (R)
[203]Have his discovery announced publicly.

every Body else was, that I was a great Fortune, or at least that I had Three or Four Thousand Pounds, if not more, and all in my own Hands; and she was mighty sweet upon me when she thought me inclin'd in the least to go into her Country; she said she had a Sister liv'd near *Liverpool*, that her Brother was a considerable Gentleman there, and had a great Estate also in *Ireland*; that she would go down there in about two Months, and if I would give her my Company thither, I should be as welcome as her self for a Month or more as I pleas'd, till I should see how I lik'd the Country; and if I thought fit to live there, she would undertake they would take care, tho' they did not entertain Lodgers themselves, they would recommend me to some agreeable Family, where I shou'd be plac'd to my content.

. If this Woman had known my real Circumstances, she would never have laid so many Snares, and taken so many weary steps to catch a poor desolate Creature that was good for little when it was caught; and indeed I, whose case was almost desperate, and thought I cou'd not be much worse, was not very anxious about what might befall me, provided they did me no personal Injury; so I suffered my self, tho' not without a great deal of Invitation, and great Professions of sincere Friendship and real Kindness, *I say* I suffer'd my self to be prevail'd upon to go with her, and accordingly I pack'd up my Baggage, and put my self in a Posture for a Journey, tho' I did not absolutely know whither I was to go.

And now I found my self in great Distress; what little I had in the World was all in Money, except as before, a little Plate, some Linnen, and my Cloaths; as for Houshold stuff I had little or none, for I had liv'd always in Lodgings; but I had not one Friend in the World with whom to trust that little I had, or to direct me how to dispose of it, and this perplex'd me Night and Day; I thought of the Bank, and of the other Companies in *London*, but I had no Friend to commit the Management of it to, and to keep and carry about with me Bank Bills, Talleys,[204] Orders, and such things, I look'd upon it as unsafe; that if they were lost my Money was lost, and then I was undone; and on the other hand I might be robb'd, and perhaps murder'd in a strange place for them; this perplex'd me strangely, and what to do I knew not.

It came in my Thoughts one Morning that I would go to the *Bank* my self, where I had often been to receive the Interest of some Bills I had, which had Interest payable on them, and where I had found the Clark, to whom I applyed my self, very Honest and Just to me, and particularly so fair one time, that when I had miss-told my Money, and taken less than my due, and was coming away, he set me to rights and gave me the rest, which he might have put into his own Pocket.

[204]Financial records of debts and payments.

I went to him, and represented my Case very plainly, *and ask'd if he would trouble himself to be my Adviser, who was a poor friendless Widow, and knew not what to do: He told me*, if I desir'd his Opinion of any thing within the reach of his Business, he would do his Endeavour that I should not be wrong'd, but that he would also help me to a good sober Person who was a grave Man of his Acquaintance, who was a Clark in such business too, tho' not in their House,[205] whose Judgment was good, and whose Honesty I might depend upon, *for*, added he, *I will answer for him, and for every step he takes*; *if he wrongs you*, Madam, *of one Farthing, it shall lye at my door, I will make it good*; and he delights to assist People in such Cases, he does it as an act of Charity.

I was a little at a stand at this Discourse, but after some pause I told him, I had rather have depended upon him because I had found him honest, but if that cou'd not be, I would take his Recommendation sooner than any ones else; *I dare say*, Madam, says he, *that you will be as well satisfied with my Friend as with me, and he is thoroughly able to assist you, which I am not*; it seems he had his Hands full of the Business of the Bank, and had engag'd to meddle with no other Business than that of his Office, which I heard afterwards, but did not understand then: He added, that his Friend should take nothing of me for his Advice or Assistance, and this indeed encourag'd me very much.

He appointed the same Evening after the Bank was shut, and Business over, for me to meet him and his Friend; and indeed as soon as I saw his Friend, and he began but to talk of the Affair, I was fully satisfied that I had a very honest Man to deal with, his Countenance spoke it, and his Character, as I heard afterwards, was every where so good, that I had no room for any more doubts upon me.

After the first meeting, in which I only said what I had said before, we parted, and he appointed me to come the next Day to him, *telling me*, I might in the mean time satisfie my self of him by enquiry, which however I knew not how well to do, having no Acquaintance my self.

Accordingly I met him the next Day, when I entered more freely with him into my Case; *I told him* my Circumstances at large, that I was *a Widow* come over from *America*, perfectly desolate and friendless; that I had a little Money, and but a little, and was almost distracted for fear of losing it, having no Friend in the World to trust with the management of it; that I was going into the North of *England* to live cheap, that[206] my stock might not waste; that I would willingly Lodge my Money in the Bank, but that I durst not carry the Bills about me, and the like, as above; and how to Correspond about it, or with who, I knew not.

He told me I might lodge the Money in the Bank as an Account, and its being entred in the Books would entitle me to the Money at any

---

[205]House of business, firm.   [206]So that.

time, and if I was in the North I might draw Bills on the Cashire and receive it when I would; but that then it would be esteem'd as running Cash, and the Bank would give no Interest for it; that I might buy Stock with it, and so it would lye in store for me, but that then if I wanted to dispose of it, I must come up to Town on purpose to Transfer it, and even it would be with some difficulty I should receive the half yearly Dividend, unless I was here in Person, or had some Friend I could trust with having the Stock in his Name to do it for me, and that would have the same difficulty in it as before; and with that he look'd hard at me *and smil'd a little*; at last, *says he*, why do you not get a head Steward, Madam, that may take you and your Money together into keeping, and then you would have the trouble taken off of your Hands? Ay, Sir, and the Money too it may be, *said I*, for truly *I find the hazard that way is as much as 'tis t'other way*; but I remember, *I said*, secretly to my self, I wish you would ask me the Question fairly, I would consider very seriously on it before I said NO.

He went on a good way with me, and I thought once or twice he was in earnest, but to my real Affliction, I found at last he had a Wife; but when he own'd he had a Wife he shook his Head, and said with some concern, that indeed he had *a Wife*, and *no Wife*: I began to think he had been in the Condition of my late Lover, and that his Wife had been Distemper'd or Lunatick, or some such thing: However, we had not much more Discourse at that time, but he told me he was in too much hurry of business then, but that if I would come home to his House after their Business was over, he would by that time consider what might be done for me, to put my Affairs in a Posture of Security: I told him I would come, and desir'd to know where he liv'd: He gave me a Direction in Writing, and when he gave it me he read it to me, and said, there 'tis, Madam, if you dare trust your self with me: Yes, Sir, *said I*, I believe I may venture to trust you with my self, for you have a Wife you say, and I don't want a Husband; besides, I dare trust you with my Money, which is all I have in the World, and if that were gone, I may trust my self any where.

He said some things in jest that were very handsome and mannerly, and would have pleas'd me very well if they had been in earnest; *but that pass'd over*, I took the Directions, and appointed to attend him at his House at seven a Clock the same Evening.

When I came he made several Proposals for my placing my Money in the Bank, in order to my having Interest for it; but still some difficulty or other came in the way, which he objected as not safe; and I found such a sincere disinterested Honesty in him, that I began to muse with my self, that I had certainly found the honest Man I wanted; and that I could never put my self into better Hands; so I told him with a great deal of frankness that I had never met with Man or Woman yet that I could trust, or in whom I cou'd think my self safe, but that I saw he was so disinterestedly concern'd for my safety; that *I said* I would freely trust him with the management of that little I had, if he would accept to be Steward for a poor Widow that could give him no Salary.

He smil'd, and standing up with great Respect saluted me; he told me he could not but take it very kindly that I had so good an Opinion of him; that he would not deceive me, that he would do any thing in his Power to serve me and expect no Sallary; but that he cou'd not by any means accept of a Trust, that it might bring him to be suspected of Self-interest, and that if I should die he might have Disputes with my Executors, which he should be very loth to encumber himself with.

I told him if those were all his Objections I would soon remove them, and convince him, that there was not the least room for any difficulty; for that *first* as for suspecting him, if ever I should do it now was the time to suspect him, and not put the Trust into his Hands, and whenever I did suspect him, he could but throw it up then and refuse to go any farther; *Then* as to Executors, I assur'd him I had no Heirs, nor any Relations in *England*, and I would have neither Heirs or Executors but himself, unless I should alter my Condition before I died, and then his Trust and Trouble should cease together, which however I had no prospect of yet; but I told him if I died as I was, it should be all his own, and he would deserve it by being so faithful to me as I was satisfied he would be.

He chang'd his Countenance at this Discourse, and ask'd me, how I came to have so much good will for him? and looking very much pleas'd, said, he might very lawfully wish he was a single Man for my sake; I smil'd and told him, that as he was not, my offer could have no design upon him in it, and to wish, as he did, was not to be allow'd, 'twas Criminal to his Wife.

He told me I was wrong; for, *says he*, Madam, as I said before, I have a Wife and no Wife, and 'twould be no Sin to me to wish her hang'd, if that were all; I know nothing of your Circumstances that way, Sir, *said I*; but it cannot be innocent to wish your Wife dead; I tell you, *says he again*, she is a Wife and no Wife; you don't know what I am, or what she is.

That's true, *said I*, Sir, I do not know what you are, but I believe you to be an honest Man, and that's the cause of all my Confidence in you.

Well, well, *says he*, and so I am, *I hope*, too, but I am something else too, Madam; for, *says he*, to be plain with you, I am a *Cuckold*, and she is a *Whore*; he spoke it in a kind of Jest, but it was with such an awkward smile, that I perceiv'd it was what stuck very close to him, and he look'd dismally when he said it.

That alters the case indeed, Sir, *said I*, as to that part you were speaking of; but *a Cuckold* you know may be an honest Man, it does not alter that Case at all; besides I think, *said I*, since your Wife is so dishonest to you, you are too honest to her, to own her for your Wife; but that, *said I*, is what I have nothing to do with.

Nay, *says he*, I do think to clear my Hands of her, for to be plain with you, Madam, *added he*, I am no contented Cuckold neither: *On the other hand*, I assure you it provokes me to the highest degree, but I can't help my self, she that will be *a Whore*, will be a *Whore*.

I wav'd[207] the Discourse, and began to talk of my Business, but I found he could not have done with it, so I let him alone, and he went on to tell me all the Circumstances of his Case, too long to relate here, particularly, that having been out of *England* some time before he came to the Post he was in, she had had two Children in the mean time by an Officer of the Army; and that when he came to *England*, and, upon her Submission, took her again, and maintain'd her very well, yet she run away from him with a Linnen-Draper's Apprentice; robb'd him of what she could come at, and continued to live from him still; so that, Madam, *says he*, she is a Whore not by Necessity, which is the common Bait of your Sex, but by Inclination, and for the sake of the Vice.

Well, I pitied him and wish'd him well rid of her, and still would have talk'd of my Business, but it would not do; at last he looks steadily at me, *look you*, Madam, *says he*, you came to ask Advice of me, and I will serve you as faithfully as if you were my own Sister; but I must turn the Tables, since you oblige me to do it, and are so friendly to me, and I think I must ask advice of you; *tell me what must a poor abus'd Fellow do with* a Whore? *what can I do* to do my self Justice *upon her?*

Alas, *Sir, says I*, 'tis a Case too nice[208] for me to advise in, but it seems she has run away from you, so you are rid of her fairly; what can you desire more? Ay she is gone indeed, *said he*, but I am not clear of her for all that.

That's true, *says I*, she may indeed run you into Debt, but the Law has furnish'd you with Methods to prevent that also, you may Cry her down,[209] *as they call it.*

No, no, *says he*, that is not the Case neither, I have taken care of all that; 'tis not that part that I speak of, but I would be rid of her so that I might marry again.

Well, Sir, *says I*, then you must Divorce her; if you can prove what you say, you may certainly get that done, and then, I suppose, you are free.

That's very tedious and expensive, *says he.*

Why, *says I*, if you can get any Woman you like to take your word,

[207]Waived. (R)
[208]Difficult.

[209]Publicly repudiate financial responsibility for her.

I suppose your Wife would not dispute the Liberty with you that she takes herself.

Ay, *says he*, but 'twou'd be hard to bring an honest Woman to do that; and for the other sort, *says he*, I have had enough of her to meddle with any more Whores.

It occurr'd to me presently, I would have taken your word with all my Heart, if you had but ask'd me the Question, but that was to my self; *to him I reply'd*, why you shut the Door against any honest Woman accepting you, for you condemn all that should venture upon you at once, and conclude, that really a Woman that takes you now, can't be honest.

Why, *says he*, I wish you would satisfie me that an honest Woman would take me, I'd venture it, and then turns short upon me, *will you take me*, Madam?

That's not a fair Question, *says I*, after what you have said; however, least you should think I wait only for a Recantation of it, I shall answer you plainly NO *not I*; my Business is of another kind with you, and I did not expect you would have turn'd my serious Application to you in my own distracted Case, into a Comedy.

Why, Madam, *says he*, my Case is as distracted as yours can be, and I stand in as much need of Advice as you do, for I think if I have not Relief some where, I shall be mad my self, and I know not what course to take, I protest to you.

Why, Sir, *says I*, 'tis easie to give Advice in your Case, much easier than it is in mine; speak then, *says he*, I beg of you, for now you encourage me.

Why, *says I*, if your Case is so plain as you say it is, you may be legally Divorc'd, and then you may find honest Women enough to ask the Question of fairly, the Sex is not so scarce that you can want a Wife.

Well then, *said he*, I am in earnest, I'll take your Advice, but shall I ask you one Question seriously before hand.

Any Question, *said I*, but that you did before.

No, that Answer will not do, *said he*, for, in short, that is the Question I shall ask.

You may ask what Questions you please, but you have my Answer to that already, *said I*; besides Sir, *said I*, can you think so Ill of me as that I would give any Answer to such a Question beforehand? Can any Woman alive believe you in earnest, or think you design any thing but to banter her?

Well, well, *says he*, I do not banter you, I am in earnest, consider of it.

But, SIR, *says I, a little gravely*, I came to you about my own Business, I beg of you let me know, what you will advise me to do?

I will be prepar'd, *says he*, against you come again.

Nay, *says I*, you have forbid my coming any more.

Why so, *said he*, and look'd a little surpriz'd?

Because, *said I*, you can't expect I should visit you on the account you talk of.

Well, *says he*, you shall promise me to come again however, and I will not say any more of it till I have gotten the Divorce, but I desire you will prepare to be better condition'd[210] when that's done, for you shall be the Woman, or I will not be Divorc'd at all: Why I owe it to your unlooked for kindness, if it were to nothing else, but I have other Reasons too.

He could not have said any thing in the World that pleas'd me better; however, I knew that the way to secure him was to stand off while the thing was so remote, as it appear'd to be, and that it was time enough to accept of it when he was able to perform it; so I said very respectfully to him, it was time enough to consider of these things, when he was in a Condition to talk of them; in the mean time I told him, I was going a great way from him, and he would find Objects enough to please him better: We broke off here for the present, and he made me promise him to come again the next Day, for his Resolutions upon my own Business, which after some pressing I did; tho' had he seen farther into me, I wanted no pressing on that Account.

I came the next Evening accordingly, and brought my Maid with me, *to let him see* that I kept a Maid, but I sent her away, as soon as I was gone in: He would have had me let the Maid have staid, but I would not, but order'd her aloud to come for me again about Nine a-Clock, but he forbid that, and told me he would see me safe Home, which by the way I was not very well pleas'd with, supposing he might do that to know where I liv'd, and enquire into my Character, and Circumstances: However, I ventur'd that, for all that the People there, or thereabout knew of me, was to my Advantage; and all the Character he had of me, after he had enquir'd, was, *that I was a Woman of Fortune*, and that I was a very modest sober Body; which whether true or not in the Main, yet you may see how necessary it is, for all Women who expect any thing in the World, to preserve the Character of their Virtue, even when perhaps they may have sacrific'd the Thing itself.

I found, *and was not a little pleas'd with it*, that he had provided a Supper for me: I found also he liv'd very handsomely, and had a House very handsomely furnish'd, all which I was rejoyc'd at indeed, for I look'd upon it as all my own.

We had now a second Conference upon the Subject matter of the last Conference: He laid his business very Home[211] indeed; he protested his Affection to me, and indeed I had no room to doubt it; he declar'd that it began from the first Moment I talk'd with him, and long before I had mention'd leaving my Effects with him; 'tis no

---

[210]I.e., more disposed to hear his proposal.

[211]Literally, attacked at the vital center; i.e., he went to the heart of the matter.

matter when it begun, *thought I*, if it will but hold, 'twill be well enough: *He then told me*, how much the offer I had made of trusting him with my Effects, and leaving them to him, had engag'd him; so I intended it should, *thought I*, but then I thought you had been a single Man too: After we had Supp'd, I observ'd he press'd me very hard to drink two or three Glasses of Wine, which however I declin'd; but Drank one Glass or two: He then told he had a Proposal to make to me, which I should promise him I would not take ill, if I should not grant it: I told him I hop'd he would make no dishonourable Proposal to me, especially in his own House, and that if it was such, I desir'd he would not propose it, that I might not be oblig'd to offer any Resentment to him, that did not become the respect I profess'd for him, and the Trust I had plac'd in him, in coming to his House; and beg'd of him he would give me leave to go away, and accordingly began to put on my Gloves, and prepare to be gone, tho' at the same time I no more intended it, than he intended to let me.

Well, he importun'd me not to talk of going, he assur'd me he had no dishonourable thing in his Thoughts about me, and was very far from offering any thing to me that was dishonourable and if I thought so, he would chuse to say no more of it.

That part I did not relish at all; I told him, I was ready to hear any thing that he had to say, depending that he would say nothing unworthy of himself, or unfit for me to hear; upon this, he told me his Proposal was this, That I would Marry him, tho' he had not yet obtain'd the Divorce from the Whore his Wife; and to satisfie me that he meant honourably, he would promise not to desire me to live with him, or go to Bed to him till the Divorce was obtain'd: My Heart said yes to this offer at first Word, but it was necessary to Play the Hypocrite a little more with him; so I seem'd to decline the Motion with some warmth, and besides a little Condemning the thing as unfair, told him, that such a Proposal could be of no Signification, but to entangle us both in great Difficulties; for if he should not at last obtain the Divorce, yet we could not dissolve the Marriage, neither could we proceed in it; so that if he was disappointed in the Divorce, I left him to consider what a Condition we should both be in.

In short, I carried on the Argument against this so far, that I convinc'd him it was not a Proposal that had any Sense in it: Well then he went from it to another, and that was, that I would Sign and Seal a Contract with him, Conditioning[212] to Marry him as soon as the Divorce was obtain'd, and to be void if he could not obtain it.

I told him such a thing was more Rational than the other; but as this was the first time that ever I could imagine him weak enough to be in

[212]Stipulating; i.e., making her agreement dependent upon a condition to be fulfilled.

earnest in this Affair, I did not use to say YES at first asking, I would consider of it.

I play'd with this Lover, as an Angler does with a Trout: I found I had him fast on the Hook, so I jested with his new Proposal; and put him off: I told him he knew little of me, and bad him enquire about me; I let him also go Home with me to my Lodging, tho' I would not ask him to go in, for I told him it was not Decent.

In short, I ventur'd to avoid Signing a Contract of Marriage, and the Reason why I did it, was because the Lady that had invited me so earnestly to go with her into *Lancashire* insisted so possitively upon it, and promised me such great Fortunes, and such fine things there, that I was tempted to go and try; perhaps, *said I*, I may mend myself[213] very much, and then I made no scruple in my Thoughts, of quitting my honest Citizen, who I was not so much in Love with, as not to leave him for a Richer.

In a Word I avoided a Contract; but told him I would go into the *North*, that he should know where to write to me by the Consequence of the Business I had entrusted with him, that I would give him a sufficient Pledge of my Respect for him; for I would leave almost all I had in the World in his Hands; and I would thus far give him my Word, that as soon as he had su'd out a Divorce from his first Wife, if he would send me an Account of it, I would come up to *London*, and that then we would talk seriously of the Matter.

It was a base Design I went with, *that I must confess*, tho' I was invited thither with a Design much worse than mine was, as the Sequel[214] will discover; well I went with my Friend, *as I call'd her*, into *Lancashire*; all the way we went she Caressed me with the utmost appearance of a sincere undissembled Affection; treated[215] me, except my Coach hire, all the way; and her Brother brought a Gentleman's Coach to *Warrington*, to receive us, and we were carried from thence to *Liverpool* with as much Ceremony as I could desire: We were also entertain'd at a Merchant's House in *Liverpool* three or four Days very handsomely: I forbear to tell his Name, because of what follow'd; then she told me she would carry me to an Uncles House of hers, where we should be nobly entertain'd; she did so; her Uncle, as she call'd him, sent a Coach and four Horses for us, and we were carried near forty Miles, I know not whither.

We came however to a Gentleman's Seat, where was a numerous Family, a large Park, extraordinary Company indeed, and where she was call'd Cousin; I told her if she had resolv'd to bring me into such Company as this, she should have let me have prepar'd my self, and have furnish'd my self with better Cloths; the Ladies took notice of

[213]Improve my financial and social position.

[214]What happens afterward.
[215]Paid expenses for.

that, and told me very genteely, they did not value People in their Country so much by their Cloths, as they did in *London*; that their Cousin had fully inform'd them of my Quality, and that I did not want Cloths to set me off; in short, they entertain'd me not like what I was, but like what they thought I had been, Namely, a Widow Lady of a great Fortune.

The first Discovery I made here was, that the Family were all *Roman Catholicks*, and the Cousin too, who I call'd my Friend; however, *I must say*, that nothing in the World could behave better to me; and I had all the Civility shown me that I could have had, if I had been of their Opinion: The Truth is, I had not so much Principle of any kind, as to be Nice in Point of Religion; and I presently learn'd to speak favourably of the *Romish Church*; particularly I told them I saw little, but the prejudice of Education, in all the Differences that were among Christians about Religion, and if it had so happen'd that my Father had been a *Roman Catholick*, I doubted not but I should have been as well pleas'd with their Religion as my own.

This oblig'd them in the highest Degree, and as I was besieg'd Day and Night with good Company, and pleasant Discourse, so I had two or three old Ladies that lay at me upon the Subject of Religion too; I was so Complaisant that tho' I would not compleatly engage, yet I made no scruple to be present at their Mass, and to conform to all their Gestures as they shew'd me the Pattern, but I would not come too cheap; so that I only in the main encourag'd them to expect that I would turn *Roman Catholick*, if I was instructed in the *Catholick Doctrine* as they call'd it, and so the matter rested.

I stay'd here about six-Weeks; and then my Conducter led me back to a Country Village, about six Miles from *Liverpool*, where her Brother, (as she call'd him) came to Visit me in his own Chariot, and in a very good Figure, with two Footmen in a good Livery; and the next thing was to make Love to me: As it had happen'd to me, one would think I could not have been cheated, and indeed I thought so myself, having a safe Card at home, which I resolv'd not to quit, unless I could mend myself very much: However in all appearance this Brother was a Match worth my lissening to, and the least his Estate was valued at, was a 1000 *l.* a Year, but the Sister said it was worth 1500 *l.* a Year, and lay most of it in *Ireland*.

I that was a great Fortune, and pass'd for such, was above being ask'd how much my Estate was; and my false Friend taking it upon a foolish hearsay had rais'd it from 500 *l.* to 5000 *l.* and by the time she came into the Country she call'd it 15000 *l.* The *Irishman*, for such I understood him to be, was stark Mad at this Bait: In short, he Courted me, made me Presents, and run in Debt like a mad Man for the Expences of his Equipage, and of his Courtship: He had, to give him his due, the Appearance of an extraordinary fine Gentleman; he was Tall, well

Shap'd, and had an extraordinary Address; talk'd as naturally of his Park, and his Stables; of his Horses, his Game-Keepers, his Woods, his Tenants, and his Servants, as if we had been in the Mansion-House, and I had seen them all about me.

He never so much as ask'd me about my Fortune, or Estate; but assur'd me that when we came to *Dublin* he would Joynture me in 600 *l.* a Year good Land; and that he would enter into a Deed of Settlement, or Contract here, for the performance of it.

This was such Language indeed as I had not been us'd to, and I was here beaten out of all my Measures;[216] I had a she Devil in my Bosom, every Hour telling me how great her Brother liv'd: One time she would come for my Orders, how I would have my Coaches painted, and how lin'd; and another time what Cloths my Page should wear: In short, my Eyes were dazl'd, I had now lost my Power of saying No, and to cut the Story short, I consented to be married; but to be the more private we were carried farther into the Country, and married by a Romish Clergyman, which I was assur'd would marry us as effectually as a Church of *England* Parson.

I cannot say but I had some Reflections in this Affair, upon the dishonourable forsaking my faithful Citizen; who lov'd me sincerely, and who was endeavouring to quit himself of a scandalous Whore, by whom he had been indeed barbarously us'd, and promis'd himself infinite Happiness in his new choice; which choice was now giving up her self to another in a manner almost as scandalous as hers could be.

But the glittering show of a great Estate, and of fine Things, which the deceived Creature that was now my Deceiver represented every Hour to my Imagination, hurried me away, and gave me no time to think of *London*, or of any thing there, much less of the Obligation I had to a Person of infinitely more real Merit than what was now before me.

But the thing was done, I was now in the Arms of my new Spouse, who appear'd still the same as before; great even to Magnificence, and nothing less than Thousand Pound a Year could support the ordinary Equipage he appear'd in.

After we had been marry'd about a Month, he began to talk of my going to *West-chester*[217] in order to embark for *Ireland*. However, he did not hurry me, for we staid near three Weeks longer, and then he sent to *Chester* for a Coach to meet us at the *Black Rock*, as they call it, over-against *Liverpool*:[218] Thither we went in a fine Boat they call a Pinnace with six Oars, his Servants, and Horses, and Baggage going in

---

[216]Tricked out of my appropriate restraint; i.e., their clever stratagems lowered Moll's defenses.

[217]The western division of Cheshire, in which the city of Chester is located.

[218]I.e., across the River Mersey, in Cheshire. Liverpool is on the Lancashire side of the Mersey; the Black Rock was north of Chester.

the Ferry Boat. He made his excuse to me, that he had no Acquaintance at *Chester*, but he would go before and get some handsome Apartment for me at a private House; I ask'd him how long we should stay at *Chester*? he said not at all, any longer than one Night or two, but he would immediately hire a Coach to go to *Holyhead*;[219] then I told him he should by no means give himself the trouble to get private Lodgings for one Night or two, for that *Chester* being a great Place, I made no doubt but there would be very good Inns and Accommodation enough; so we lodg'd at an Inn in the West Street, not far from the Cathedral, I forget what Sign it was at.

Here my Spouse talking of my going to *Ireland*, ask'd me if I had no Affairs to settle at *London* before we went off; I told him no not of any great Consequence, but what might be done as well by Letter from *Dublin*: Madam, says he very respectfully, I suppose the greatest part of your Estate, which my Sister tells me is most of it in Money in the Bank of *England*, lies secure enough, but in case it requir'd Transferring, or any way altering its Property, it might be necessary to go up to *London*, and settle those things before we went over.

I seemed to look strange at it, and told him I knew not what he meant; that I had no Effects in the Bank of *England* that I knew of; and I hoped he could not say that I had ever told him I had: No, he said, I had not told him so, but his Sister had said the greatest part of my Estate lay there, and *I only mention'd it my Dear*, said he, *that if there was any occasion to settle it, or order any thing about it, we might not be oblig'd to the hazard and trouble of another Voyage back again*, for, he added, that he did not care to venture me too much upon the Sea.

I was surpriz'd at this talk, and began to consider very seriously, what the meaning of it must be? and it presently occurr'd to me that my Friend, who call'd him Brother, had represented me in Colours which were not my due; and I thought, since it was come to that pitch, that I would know the bottom of it before I went out of *England*, and before I should put my self into I knew not whose Hands, in a strange Country.

Upon this I call'd his Sister into my Chamber the next Morning, and letting her know the Discourse her Brother and I had been upon, the Evening before, I conjur'd her to tell me, what she had said to him, and upon what Foot it was that she had made this Marriage? She own'd that she had told him that I was a great Fortune, and said, that she was told so at *London*: *Told so*, says I warmly, *did I ever tell you so*? No, she said, it was true I did not tell her so, but I had said several times, that what I had, was in my own disposal: I did so, *return'd I very quickly and hastily*, but I never told you I had any thing call'd a Fortune; no not that I had one Hundred Pounds, or the value of an Hundred Pounds in the

[219] A seaport in Anglesey, Wales, from which one could sail to Ireland.

World; and how did it consist with my being a Fortune, *said I*, that I should come here into the North of *England* with you, only upon the account of living cheap? At these words which I spoke warm and sigh'd, my Husband, and her Brother as she call'd him, came into the Room; and I desir'd him to come and sit down, for I had something of moment to say before them both, which it was absolutely necessary he should hear.

He look'd a little disturb'd at the assurance with which I seem'd to speak it, and came and sat down by me, having first shut the Door; upon which I began, for I was very much provok'd, and turning my self to him, I am afraid, says I, *my Dear*, for I spoke with kindness on his side, that you have a very great abuse put upon you, and an Injury done you never to be repair'd in your marrying me, which however as I have had no hand in it, I desire I may be fairly acquitted of it; and that the blame may lie where it ought to lie, and no where else, for I wash my Hands of every part of it.

What Injury can be done me, *my Dear*, says he, in marrying you? I hope it is to my Honour and Advantage every way; I will soon explain it to you, says I, and I fear you will have no reason to think yourself well us'd, but I will convince you, *my Dear, says I again*, that I have had no hand in it, and there I stop'd a while.

He look'd now scar'd and wild, and began, I believ'd, to suspect what follow'd; however, looking towards me, and saying only *go on*, he sat silent, as if to hear what I had more to say; so I went on; I ask'd you last Night, said I, speaking to him, if ever I made any boast to you of my Estate, or ever told you I had any Estate in the Bank of *England*, or any where else, and you own'd I had not, as is most true; and I desire you will tell me here, before your Sister, if ever I gave you any Reason from me to think so, or that ever we had any Discourse about it, and he own'd again I had not; *but said*, I had appeared always as a Woman of Fortune, and he depended on it that I was so, and hoped he was not deceived. I am not enquiring yet whether you have been deceived or not, *said I*, I fear you have, *and I too*; but I am clearing my self from the unjust Charge of being concern'd in deceiving you.

I have been now asking your Sister if ever I told her of any Fortune or Estate I had, or gave her any Particulars of it; and she owns I never did: And pray, Madam, *said I, turning my self to her*, be so just to me, before your Brother, to charge me, if you can, if ever I pretended to you that I had an Estate; and why, if I had, should I come down into this Country with you on purpose to spare *that little I had*, and live cheap? She could not deny one word, but said she had been told in *London* that I had a very great Fortune, and that it lay in the Bank of *England*.

And now, *Dear Sir*, said I, *turning my self to my new Spouse again*, be so just to me as to tell me who has abus'd both you and me so much, as to make you believe I was a Fortune, and prompt you to court me to this Marriage? He cou'd not speak a word, but pointed to her; and after some more pause, flew out in the most serious Passion that ever I saw a Man in my Life; cursing her, and calling her all the Whores and hard Names he could think of; and that she had ruin'd him, declaring that she had told him I had Fifteen Thousand Pounds, and that she was to have Five Hundred Pounds of him for procuring this Match for him: He then added, directing his Speech to me, that she was none of his Sister, but had been his Whore for two Years before, that she had had One Hundred Pound of him in part of this Bargain, and that he was utterly undone if things were as I said; and in his raving *he swore* he would let her Heart's Blood out immediately, which frighted her and me too; *she cried,* said she had been told so in the House where I Lodg'd; but this aggravated him more than before, that she should put so far upon him, and run things such a length upon no other Authority than *a hear-say*; and then turning to me again, said very honestly, he was afraid we were both undone; for to be plain, *my Dear,* I have no Estate, *says he,* what little I had, this Devil has made me run out in waiting on you, and putting me into this Equipage; she took the opportunity of his being earnest in talking with me, and got out of the Room, and I never saw her more.

I was confounded now as much as he, and knew not what to say: I thought many ways that I had the worst of it, but his saying he was undone, and that he had no Estate neither put me into a meer[220] distraction; why, *says I to him,* this has been a hellish Juggle, for we are married here upon the foot of a double Fraud, you are undone by the Disappointment it seems, and if I had had a fortune I had been cheated too, for you say you have nothing.

You would indeed have been cheated, my Dear, *says he,* but you would not have been undone, for Fifteen Thousand Pound would have maintain'd us both very handsomly in this Country; and I assure you, *added he,* I had resolv'd to have dedicated every Groat of it to you; I would not have wrong'd you of a Shilling, and the rest I would have made up in my Affection to you, and Tenderness of you as long as I liv'd.

This was very honest indeed, and I really believe he spoke as he intended, and that he was a Man that was as well qualified to make me happy, as to his Temper and Behaviour, as any Man ever was; but his having no Estate, and being run into Debt on this ridiculous account in the Country, made all the Prospect dismal and dreadful, and I knew not what to say, or what to think of my self.

I told him it was very unhappy, that so much Love, and so much Good-nature, as I discovered in him, should be thus precipitated into

[220]Absolute. (R)

Misery; that I saw nothing before us but Ruin, for as to me, it was my unhappiness, that what little I had was not able to relieve us a Week, and with that I pull'd out a Bank Bill of 20 *l.* and eleven Guineas, which I told him I had saved out of my little Income; and that by the account that Creature had given me of the way of living in that Country, I expected it would maintain me three or four Year; that if it was taken from me I was left destitute, and he knew what the Condition of a Woman among strangers must be, if she had no Money in her Pocket; however, I told him if he would take it, there it was.

He told me with a great concern, and I thought I saw Tears stand in his Eyes, that he would not touch it, that he abhorr'd the thoughts of stripping me, and making me miserable; that on the contrary, he had Fifty Guineas left, which was all he had in the World, and he pull'd it out and threw it down on the Table, bidding me take it, tho' he were to starve for want of it.

I return'd, with the same concern for him, that I could not bear to hear him talk so; that on the contrary, if he could propose any probable method of living, I would do any thing that became me on my part, and that I would live as close and as narrow as he cou'd desire.

He beg'd of me to talk no more at that rate, for it would make him Distracted; he said he was bred a Gentleman, tho' he was reduced to a low Fortune; and that there was but one way left which he cou'd think of, and that would not do, unless I cou'd answer him one Question, which however he said he would not press me to; I told him I would answer it honestly, whether it would be to his Satisfaction or no, that I could not tell.

Why then, My Dear, tell me plainly, *says he* will the little you have keep us together in any Figure, or in any Station or Place, or will it not?

It was my happiness hitherto that I had not discovered myself, or my Circumstances at all; no not so much as my Name; and seeing there was nothing to be expected from him, however good Humoured, and however honest he seem'd to be, but to live on what I knew would soon be wasted, I resolv'd to conceal every thing, but the *Bank Bill*, and the Eleven Guineas, which I had own'd; and I would have been very glad to have lost that, and have been set down where he took me up; I had indeed another *Bank Bill* about me of 30 *l.* which was the whole of what I brought with me, as well to Subsist on in the Country, as not knowing what might offer; because this Creature, the *go-between* that had thus betray'd us both, had made me believe strange things of my Marrying to my Advantage in the Country, and I was not willing to be without Money whatever might happen. This Bill I concealed, and that made me the freer of the rest, in Consideration of his Circumstances, for I really pittied him heartily.

But to return to his Question, I told him I never willingly Deceiv'd

him, and I never would: I was very sorry to tell him that the little I
had would not Subsist us; that it was not sufficient to Subsist me alone
in the *South* Country; and that this was the Reason that made my put
my self into the Hands of that Woman, who call'd him Brother, she
having assur'd me that I might Board very handsomely at a Town
call'd *Manchester*, where I had not yet been, for about six Pound a
Year, and my whole Income not being above 15 *l.* a Year, I thought I
might live easie upon it, and wait for better things.

He shook his Head, and remain'd Silent, and a very melancholly
Evening we had; however we Supped together, and lay together that
Night, and when we had almost Supp'd he look'd a little better and
more chearful, and call'd for a Bottle of Wine; *come* my Dear, *says he*,
tho' the Case is bad, it is to no purpose to be dejected, come be as
easie as you can, I will endeavour to find out some way or other to
live; if you can but Subsist your self, that is better than nothing; I
must try the World again; a Man ought to think like a Man: To be
Discourag'd, is to yield to the Misfortune;[221] with this he fill'd a
Glass, and Drank to me, holding my Hand, and pressing it hard in his
Hand all the while the Wine went down, and Protesting afterward his
main concern was for me.

It was really a truly gallant Spirit he was of, and it was the more
Grievous to me: 'Tis something of Relief even to be undone by a
Man of Honour, rather than by a Scoundrel; but here the greatest
Disappointment was on his side, for he had really spent a great deal of
Money, deluded by this Madam the Procuress; and it was very remark-
able on what poor Terms she proceeded; first the baseness of the
Creature herself is to be observ'd, who for the getting One Hundred
Pound herself, could be content to let him spend Three or Four more,
tho' perhaps it was all he had in the World, and more than all; when
she had not the least Ground, more than a little Tea-Table Chat, to
say that I had any Estate, or was a Fortune, *or the like*: It is true the
Design of deluding a Woman of a Fortune, if I had been so, was base
enough; the putting the Face of great Things upon poor Circumstances was a Fraud, and bad enough; but the Case a little differ'd too,
and that in his Favour, for he was not a Rake that made a Trade to
delude Women, and as some have done get six or seven Fortunes
one after another, and then riffle[222] and run away from them; but
he was really a Gentleman, unfortunate and low, but had liv'd
well; and tho' if I had had a Fortune I should have been enrag'd at
the Slut for betraying me; yet really for the Man, a Fortune would
not have been ill bestow'd on him, for he was a lovely Person in-

---

[221]The vaunting attempt to cheer him-   [222]Rifle.
self up may echo Satan's speeches in Book
I of *Paradise Lost*.

deed; of generous Principles, good Sense, and of abundance of good Humour.

We had a great deal of close Conversation that Night, for we neither of us Slept much; he was as Penitent, for having put all those Cheats upon me as if it had been Felony, and that he was going to Execution; he offer'd me again every Shilling of the Money he had about him, and said, he would go into the Army and seek the World for more.

I ask'd him, why he would be so unkind to carry me into *Ireland*, when I might suppose he cou'd not have Subsisted me there? He took me in his Arms, my Dear, *said he*, depend upon it, I never design'd to go to *Ireland* at all, much less to have carried you thither; but came hither to be out of the Observation of the People, who had heard what I pretended to, and withal, that No Body might ask me for Money before I was furnish'd to supply them.

But where then, *said I*, were we to have gone next?

Why my Dear, *said he*, I'll confess the whole Scheme to you as I had laid it; I purpos'd here to ask you something about your Estate, as you see I did, and when you, as I expected you would, had enter'd into some Account with me of the particular, I would have made an excuse to you, to have put off our Voyage to *Ireland* for some time, and to have gone first towards *London*.

Then my Dear, *said he*, I resolv'd to have confess'd all the Circumstances of my own Affairs to you, and let you know I had indeed made use of these Artifices to obtain your Consent to marry me, but had now nothing to do but to ask you Pardon, and to tell you how abundantly, *as I have said above*, I would endeavour to make you forget what was past, by the felicity of the Days to come.

Truly, *said I to him*, I find you would soon have conquer'd me; and it is my Affliction now, that I am not in a Condition to let you see how easily I should have been reconcil'd to you; and have pass'd by all the Tricks you had put upon me, in Recompence of so much good Humour; but my Dear, *said I*, what can we do now? We are both undone, and what better are we for our being reconcil'd together, seeing we have nothing to live on.

We propos'd a great many things, but nothing could offer, where there was nothing to begin with: He beg'd me at last to talk no more of it, for *he said*, I would break his Heart; so we talked of other things a little, till at last he took a Husbands leave of me, and so we went to Sleep.

He rose before me in the Morning, and indeed having lain Awake almost all Night, I was very sleepy, and lay till near Eleven a-Clock; in this time he took his Horses, and three Servants, and all his Linnen and Bagage, and away he went, leaving a short, but moving Letter for me on the Table, as follows.

My Dear,

I am a Dog; I have abus'd you; but I have been drawn in to do it by a base Creature, contrary to my Principle, and the general Practice of my Life: Forgive me, my Dear! I ask you Pardon with the greatest Sincerity; I am the most miserable of Men, in having deluded you: I have been so happy to Possess you, and am now so wretch'd as to be forc'd to fly from you: Forgive me, My Dear; once more I say forgive me! I am not able to see you Ruin'd by me, and myself unable to Support you: Our Marriage is nothing, I shall never be able to see you again: I here discharge you from it; if you can Marry to your Advantage do not decline it on my Account; I here swear to you on my Faith, and on the Word of a Man of Honour, I will never disturb your Repose if I should know of it, which however is not likely: On the other Hand, if you should not Marry, and if good Fortune should befall me, it shall be all yours where ever you are.

I have put some of the Stock of Money I have left, into your Pocket; take Places for your self and your Maid in the Stage-Coach, and go for London; *I hope it will bear your Charges thither, without breaking into your own: Again I sincerely ask your Pardon, and will do so, as often as I shall ever think of you.*

Adieu my Dear for Ever,

I am yours most Affectionatly,

J. B.

Nothing that ever befel me in my Life, sunk so deep into my Heart as this Farewel: I reproach'd him a Thousand times in my Thoughts for leaving me, for I would have gone with him thro' the World, if I had beg'd my Bread. I felt in my Pocket, and there I found ten Guineas, his Gold Watch, and two little Rings, one a small Diamond Ring, worth only about six Pound, and the other a plain Gold Ring.

I sat me down and look'd upon these Things two Hours together, and scarce spoke a Word, till my Maid interrupted me, by telling me my Dinner was ready: I eat but little, and after Dinner I fell into a vehement Fit of crying, every now and then calling him by his Name, which was *James*, O *Jemy!* said I, *come back, come back*, I'll give you all I have; I'll beg, I'll starve with you, and thus I run Raving about the Room several times, and then sat down between whiles, and then walking about again, call'd upon him to *come back*, and then cry'd again; and thus I pass'd the Afternoon; till about seven a-Clock when it was near Dusk in the Evening, being *August*, when to my unspeakable Surprize he comes back into the Inn, but without a Servant, and comes directly up into my Chamber.

I was in the greatest Confusion imaginable, and so was he too: I could not imagine what should be the Occasion of it; and began to be at odds with myself whether to be glad or sorry; but my Affection byass'd all the rest, and it was impossible to conceal my Joy, which was too great for Smiles, for it burst out into Tears. He was no sooner entered the Room, but he run to me and took me in his Arms, holding me fast and almost stopping my Breath with his Kisses, but spoke not a Word; at length I began, my Dear, *said I*, how could you go away from me? To which he gave no Answer, for it was impossible for him to speak.

When our Extasies were a little over, he told me he was gone about 15 Mile, but it was not in his Power to go any farther, without coming back to see me again, and to take his Leave of me once more.

I told him how I had pass'd my time, and how loud I had call'd him to *come back* again; he told me he heard me very plain upon *Delamere Forest*, at a Place about 12 Miles off: *I smil'd*; *Nay says he*, do not think I am in Jest, for if ever I heard your Voice in my Life, I heard you call me aloud, and sometimes I thought I saw you running after me; why said I, what did I say? for I had not nam'd the Words to him; you call'd aloud, says he, and said, *O Jemy! O Jemy! come back, come back.*

I Laught at him; *my Dear says he*, do not Laugh, for depend upon it, I heard your Voice as plain as you hear mine now; if you please, I'll go before a Magistrate and make Oath of it; I then began to be amaz'd and surpriz'd, and indeed frighted, and told him what I had really done, and how I had call'd after him, as above.

When we had amus'd ourselves a while about this,[223] I said to him, well, you shall go away from me no more, I'll go all over the World with you rather: *He told me*, it would be a very difficult thing for him to leave me, but since it must be, he hoped I would make it as easie to me as I could; but as for him, it would be his Destruction, that he foresaw.

However he told me, that he Consider'd he had left me to Travel to *London* alone, which was too long a Journey; and that as he might as well go that way, as any way else, he was resolv'd to see me safe thither, or near it; and if he did go away then without taking his leave, I should not take it ill of him, and this he made me promise.

He told me how he had dismiss'd his three Servants, sold their Horses, and sent the Fellows away to seek their Fortunes, and all in a little time, at a Town on the Road, I know not where; and *says he*, it cost me some Tears all alone by myself, to think how much happier they were than their Master, for they could go to the next Gentleman's House to see for a Service,[224] whereas, *said he*, I knew not whither to go, or what to do with myself.

I told him, I was so compleatly miserable in parting with him, that I could not be worse; and that now he was come again, I would not go from him, if he would take me with him, let him go whither he

---

[223]Discussed the matter; i.e., concentrated their attention upon it, perhaps with the implication of having beguiled each other.

[224]Look for a position.

would, or do what he would; and in the mean time I agreed that we would go together to *London*; but I could not be brought to Consent he should go away at last, and not take his leave of me, as he propos'd to do; but told him Jesting, that if he did, I would call him back again as loud as I did before; Then I pull'd out his Watch and gave him back, and his two Rings, and his Ten Guineas; but he would not take them, which made me very much suspect that he resolv'd to go off upon the Road, and leave me.

The truth is, the Circumstances he was in, the passionate Expressions of his Letter, the kind Gentlemanly Treatment I had from him in all the Affair, with the Concern he show'd for me in it, his manner of Parting with that large Share which he gave me of his little Stock left; all these had joyn'd to make such Impressions on me, that I really lov'd him most tenderly, and could not bear the Thoughts of parting with him.

Two Days after this we quitted *Chester*, I in the Stage Coach, and he on Horseback; I dismiss'd my Maid at *Chester*; he was very much against my being without a Maid, but she being a Servant hired in the Country, and I resolving to keep no Servant at *London*, I told him it would have been barbarous to have taken the poor Wench, and have turn'd her away as soon as I came to Town; and it would also have been a needless Charge on the Road, so I satisfy'd him, and he was easie enough on that Score.

He came with me as far as *Dunstable*, within 30 Miles of *London*, and then he told me Fate and his own Misfortunes oblig'd him to leave me, and that it was not Convenient for him to go to *London* for Reasons, which it was of no value to me to know, and I saw him preparing to go. The Stage Coach we were in, did not usually stop at *Dunstable*, but I desiring it but for a Quarter of an Hour, they were content to stand at an Inn-Door a while, and we went into the House.

Being in the Inn, I told him I had but one Favour more to ask of him, and that was, that since he could not go any farther, he would give me leave to stay a Week or two in the Town with him, that we might in that time think of something to prevent such a ruinous thing to us both, as a final Separation would be; and that I had something of Moment to offer to him, that I had never said yet, and which perhaps he might find Practicable to our mutual Advantage.

This was too reasonable a Proposal to be denied, so he call'd the Landlady of the House *and told her*, his Wife was taken ill, and so ill that she cou'd not think of going any farther in the Stage Coach, which had tyr'd her almost to Death, and ask'd if she cou'd not get us a Lodging for two or three Days in a private House, where I might rest me a little, for the Journey had been too much for me? The Landlady, a good sort of Woman, well bred, and very obliging, came immediately to see me; *told me*, she had two or three very good Rooms in a part of the House quite out of the noise, and if I saw them, she did not doubt but I would like them, and I should have one of her Maids, that should do nothing else but be appointed to wait on me; this was so very kind, that I could not but accept of it and thank her; so I went to look on the Rooms, and lik'd them very well, and indeed they were extraordinarily Furnish'd, and very pleasant Lodgings; so we paid the Stage Coach, took out our Baggage, and resolv'd to stay here a while.

Here *I told him* I would live with him now till all my Money was spent, but would not let him spend a Shilling of his own: We had some kind squabble about that, but *I told him* it was the last time I was like to enjoy his Company, and I desir'd he would let me be Master in that thing only, and he should govern in every thing else, so he acquiesc'd.

Here one Evening taking a Walk into the Fields, *I told him* I would now make the Proposal to him I had told him of; accordingly I related to him how I had liv'd in *Virginia*, that I had a Mother, I believ'd, was alive there still, tho' my Husband was dead some Years; *I told him*, that had not my Effects miscarry'd, which by the way I magnify'd pretty much, I might have been Fortune good enough to him to have kept us from being parted in this manner: Then I entered into the manner of Peoples going over to those Countries to settle, how they had a quantity of Land given them by the Constitution of the Place: and if not, that it might be purchased at so easie a Rate that it was not worth naming.

I then gave him a full and distinct account of the nature of Planting, how with carrying over but two or three Hundred Pounds value in *English* Goods, with some Servants and Tools, a Man of Application would presently lay a Foundation for a Family, and in a very few Years be certain to raise an Estate.

I let him into the nature of the Product of the Earth, how the Ground was Cur'd and Prepared, and what the usual encrease of it was; and demonstrated to him that in a very few Years, with such a beginning, we should be as certain of being Rich, as we were now certain of being Poor.

He was surpriz'd at my Discourse; for we made it the whole Subject of our Conversation for near a Week together, in which time I laid it down in black and white, *as we say*, that it was morally impossible, with a supposition of any reasonable good Conduct,[225] but that we must thrive there and do very well.

Then I told him what measures I would take to raise such a Sum as 300 *l.* or thereabouts; and I argued with him how good a Method it would be to put an end to our Misfortunes, and restore our Circum-

---

[225]Skill in managing affairs.

stances in the World, to what we had both expected; and I added, that after seven Years, if we liv'd, we might be in a Posture to leave our Plantation in good Hands, and come over again and receive the Income of it, and live here and enjoy it; and I gave him Examples of some that had done so, and liv'd now in very good Circumstances in *London*.

In short, I press'd him so to it, that he almost agreed to it, but still something or other broke it off again; till at last he turn'd the Tables, and he began to talk almost to the same purpose of *Ireland*.

He told me that a Man that could confine himself to a Country Life, and that cou'd but find Stock to enter upon any Land, should have Farms there for 50 *l.* a Year, as good as were here let for 200 *l.* a Year; that the Produce was such, and so Rich the Land, that if much was not laid up, we were sure to live as handsomely upon it as a Gentleman of 3000 *l.* a Year could do in *England*; and that he had laid a Scheme to leave me in *London*, and go over and try; and if he found he could lay a handsome Foundation of living suitable to the Respect he had for me, as he doubted not he should do, he would come over and fetch me.

I was dreadfully afraid that upon such a Proposal he would have taken me at my Word, (*viz.*) to sell my little Income, as I call'd it, and turn it into Money, and let him carry it over into *Ireland* and try his Experiment with it; but he was too just to desire it, or to have accepted it if I had offered it; and he anticipated me in that, for he added, that he would go and try his Fortune that way, and if he found he cou'd do any thing at it to live, then, by adding mine to it when I went over, we should live like our selves; but that he would not hazard a Shilling of mine till he had made the Experiment with a little, and he assur'd me that if he found nothing to be done in *Ireland*, he would then come to me and join in my Project for *Virginia*.

He was so earnest upon his Project being to be try'd first, that I cou'd not withstand him; however, he promis'd to let me hear from him in a very little time after his arriving there, to let me know whether his prospect answer'd his Design, that if there was not a probability of Success, I might take the Occasion to prepare for our other Voyage, and then, he assur'd me, he would go with me to *America* with all his Heart.

I could bring him to nothing farther than this: However, those Consultations entertain'd us near a Month, during which I enjoy'd his Company, which indeed was the most entertaining that ever I met with in my life before. In this time he let me into the whole Story of his own Life, which was indeed surprizing, and full of an infinite Variety sufficient to fill up a much brighter History, for its Adventures and Incidents, than any I ever saw in Print: But I shall have occasion to say more of him hereafter.

We parted at last, tho' with the utmost reluctance on my side, and indeed he took his leave very unwillingly too, but Necessity oblig'd him, for his Reasons were very good why he would not come to *London*, as I understood more fully some time afterwards.

I gave him a Direction how to write to me, tho' still I reserv'd the grand Secret, and never broke my Resolution, which was not to let him ever know my true Name, who I was, or where to be found; he likewise let me know how to write a Letter to him, so that he said he wou'd be sure to receive it.

I came to *London* the next Day after we parted, but did not go directly to my old Lodgings; but for another nameless Reason took a private Lodging in St. *John's-street*, or as it is vulgarly call'd St. *Jones's* near *Clarkenwell*;[226] and here being perfectly alone, I had leisure to sit down and reflect seriously upon the last seven Months Ramble I had made, for I had been abroad no less; the pleasant Hours I had with my last Husband I look'd back on with an infinite deal of Pleasure; but that Pleasure was very much lessen'd, when I found some time after that I was really with Child.

This was a perplexing thing because of the Difficulty which was before me, where I should get leave to Lye Inn;[227] it being one of the nicest[228] things in the World at that time of Day, for a Woman that was a Stranger, and had no Friends, to be entertain'd in that Circumstance without Security,[229] which by the way I had not, neither could I procure any.

I had taken care all this while to preserve a Correspondence with my honest Friend at the Bank, or rather he took care to Correspond with me, for he wrote to me once a Week; and tho' I had not spent my Money so fast as to want any from him, yet I often wrote also to let him know I was alive; I had left Directions in *Lancashire*, so that I had these Letters, which he sent, convey'd to me; and during my Recess at St. *Jones's* I receiv'd a very obliging Letter from him, assuring me that his Process for a Divorce from his Wife went on with Success, tho' he met with some Difficulties in it that he did not expect.

I was not displeas'd with the News, that his Process was more tedious than he expected; for tho' I was in no condition to have had him yet, not being so foolish to marry him when I knew my self to be with Child by another Man, as some I know have ventur'd to do; yet I was not willing to lose him, and in a word, resolv'd to have him if he continu'd in the same mind, as soon as I was up again; for I saw apparently I should hear no more from my other Husband; and as he

---

[226]St. John's Street formerly extended south from Clerkenwell parish into London. Moll evidently stayed within the city.

[227]Lie in.

[228]Most delicate.

[229]I.e., something to satisfy the inquiries of parish officers. See Moll's further explanation on pp. 129–30.

had all along press'd me to Marry, and had assur'd me he would not be at all disgusted at it, or ever offer to claim me again, so I made no scruple to resolve to do it if I could, and if my other Friend stood to his Bargain; and I had a great deal of Reason to be assur'd that he would stand to it, by the Letters he wrote to me, which were the kindest and most obliging that could be.

I now grew Big, and the People where I Lodg'd perceiv'd it, and began to take notice of it to me, and as far as Civility would allow, intimated that I must think of removing; this put me to extreme perplexity, and I grew very melancholy, for indeed I knew not what Course to take, I had Money, but no Friends, and was like now to have a Child upon my Hands to keep, which was a difficulty I had never had upon me yet, as the Particulars of my Story hitherto makes appear.

In the course of this Affair I fell very ill, and my Melancholy really encreas'd my Distemper; my illness prov'd at length to be only an Ague, but my Apprehensions were really that I should Miscarry; I should not say Apprehensions, for indeed I would have been glad to miscarry, but I cou'd never be brought to entertain so much as a thought of endeavouring to Miscarry, or of taking any thing to make me Miscarry, I abhorr'd, I say, so much as the thought of it.

However, speaking of it in the House, the Gentlewoman who kept the House propos'd to me to send for a Midwife; I scrupled it at first, but after some time consented to it, but told her I had no particular Acquaintance with any Midwife, and so left it to her.

It seems the Mistress of the House was not so great a Stranger to such Cases as mine was, as I thought at first she had been, as will appear presently, and she sent for a Midwife of the right sort, that is to say, the right sort for me.

The Woman appear'd to be an experienc'd Woman in her Business, I mean as a Midwife, but she had another Calling too, in which she was as expert as most Women, if not more: My Landlady had told her I was very Melancholy, and that she believ'd that had done me harm; and once, *before me*, said to her, Mrs. B——— *meaning the Midwife*, I believe this Lady's Trouble is of a kind that is pretty much in your way, and therefore if you can do any thing for her, pray do, for she is a very civil Gentlewoman, and so she went out of the Room.

I really did not understand her, but my Mother Midnight[230] began very seriously to explain what she meant, as soon as she was gone: Madam, *says she*, you seem not to understand what your Landlady means, and when you do understand it, you need not let her know at all that you do so.

She means that you are under some Circumstances that may render

---

[230]A slang term for "midwife". Defoe may be further teasing expectation here, for "Mother Midnight" was also cant for "bawd."

your Lying-Inn difficult to you, and that you are not willing to be expos'd; I need say no more, but to tell you, that if you think fit to communicate so much of your Case to me, *if it be so*, as is necessary, for I do not desire to pry into those things, I perhaps may be in a Condition to assist you, and to make you perfectly easie, and remove all your dull Thoughts upon that Subject.

Every word this Creature said was a Cordial to me, and put new Life and new Spirit into my very Heart; my Blood began to circulate immediately, and I was quite another Body; I eat my Victuals again, and grew better presently after it: She said a great deal more to the same purpose, and then having press'd me to be free with her, and promis'd in the solemnest manner to be secret, she stop'd a little, as if waiting to see what Impression it made on me, and what I would say.

I was too sensible of the want I was in of such a Woman, not to accept her offer; *I told her* my Case was partly as she guess'd, and partly not, for I was really married and had a Husband, tho' he was in such Circumstances, and so remote at that time, as that he cou'd not appear publickly.

She took me short, *and told me*, that was none of her Business, all the Ladies that came under her Care were married Women to her; every Woman, *says she*, that is with Child has a Father for it, and whether that Father was a Husband or no Husband, was no Business of hers; her Business was to assist me in my present Circumstances, whether I had a Husband or no; for, *Madam, says she*, to have a Husband that cannot appear, is to have no Husband in the sense of the Case, and therefore whether you are a Wife or a Mistress is all one to me.

I found presently, that whether I was a Whore or a Wife, I was to pass for a Whore here, so I let that go; *I told her*, it was true as she said, but that however, if I must tell her my Case, I must tell it her as it was: So I related it to her as short as I could, and I concluded it to her thus, *I trouble you with all this*, Madam, said I, *not that, as you said before, it is much to the purpose* in your Affair, but this is to the purpose, *namely, that I am not in any pain about being seen, or being publick or conceal'd, for 'tis perfectly indifferent to me; but my difficulty is, that I have no Acquaintance in this part of the Nation.*

I understand you, Madam, *says she*, you have no Security to bring to prevent the Parish Impertinences usual in such Cases; and perhaps, *says she*, do not know very well how to dispose of the Child when it comes; the last, *says I*, is not so much my concern as the first: Well, Madam, *answers the Midwife*, dare you put your self into my Hands, I live in such a place; tho' I do not enquire after you, you may enquire after me, my Name is *B——* I live in such a Street, naming the Street, at the Sign of the *Cradle*, my Profession is a Midwife, and I have many Ladies that come to my House to Lye-Inn; I have given

Security to the Parish in General Terms to secure them from any Charge, from whatsoever shall come into the World under my Roof; I have but one Question to ask in the whole Affair, Madam, *says she*, and if that be answer'd, you shall be entirely easie for all the rest.

I presently understood what she meant, and told her, Madam, *I believe I understand you*; I thank God, *tho' I want Friends in this Part of the World, I do not want Money, so far as may be Necessary, tho' I do not abound in that neither*: This I added, because I would not make her expect great things; well Madam, *says she*, that is the thing indeed, without which nothing can be done in these cases; and yet, *says she*, you shall see that I will not impose upon you, or offer any thing that is unkind to you, and if you desire it, you shall know every thing before hand, that you may suit yourself to the Occasion, and be either costly or sparing as you see fit.

I told her, she seem'd to be so perfectly sensible of my Condition, that I had nothing to ask of her but this, that as I had told her that I had Money sufficient, but not a great Quantity, she would order it so, that I might be at as little superfluous Charge as possible.

She replyed, that she would bring in an Account of the Expences of it, in two or three Shapes, and like a *Bill of Fare*, I should chuse as I pleas'd, and I desir'd her to do so.

The next Day she brought it, and the Copy of her three Bills was as Follow.

		l.	*s.*	*d.*
1.	For Three Months Lodging in her House, including my Diet, at 10s. a Week	06	00	0
2.	For a Nurse for the Month, and Use of Child-bed Linnen	01	10	0
3.	For a Minister to Christen the Child, and to the Godfathers and Clark	01	10	0
4.	For a Supper at the Christening if I had five Friends at it	01	00	0
	For her Fees as a Midwife, and the taking off the Trouble of the Parish	03	03	0
	To her Maid-Servant attending.	00	10	0
		13	13	0

This was the first Bill, the second was in the same Terms.

1.	For Three Months Lodging and Diet, &c. at 20s. per Week	12	00	0
2.	For a Nurse for the Month, and the Use of Linnen and Lace	02	10	0
3.	For the Minister to Christen the Child, &c. as above	02	00	0

4. For a Supper, and for Sweetmeats   03 03 0
    For her Fees, as above   05 05 0
    For a Servant-Maid   01 00 0
            25 18 0

This was the second rate Bill, the third, *she said*, was for a degree Higher, and when the Father, or Friends appeared.

1. For Three Months Lodging and Diet, having two Rooms and a Garret for a Servant   30 00 0
2. For a Nurse for the Month, and the finest Suit of Child-bed Linnen   04 04 0
3. For the Minister to Christen the Child, *&c.*   02 10 0
4. For a Supper, the Gentlemen to send in the Wine   06 00 0
    For my Fees, *&c.*   10 10 0
    The Maid, besides their own Maid only   00 10 0
            53 14 0

I look'd upon all the three Bills, and smil'd, *and told her* I did not see but that she was very reasonable in her Demands, all things Consider'd, and for that I did not doubt but her Accommodations were good.

She told me, I should be Judge of that, when I saw them: *I told her*, I was sorry to tell her that I fear'd I must be her lowest rated Customer, and *perhaps Madam*, said I, *you will make me the less Welcome upon that Account*. No not at all, *said she*, for where I have One of the third Sort, I have Two of the Second, and Four to one of the First, and I get as much by them in Proportion, as by any; but if you doubt my Care of you, I will allow any Friend you have to overlook, and see if you are well waited on, or no.

Then she explain'd the particulars of her Bill; in the first Place, Madam, *said she*, I would have you Observe, that here is three Months Keeping you at but 10 *s.* a Week, I undertake to say you will not complain of my Table: I suppose, *says she*, you do not live Cheaper where you are now; no indeed, *said I*, nor so Cheap, for I give six Shillings *per* Week for my Chamber, and find my own Diet as well as I can, which costs me a great deal more.

Then Madam, *says she*, If the Child should not live, or should be dead Born, as you know sometime happens, then there is the Minister's Article saved; and if you have no Friends to come to you, you may save the Expence of a Supper; so that take those Articles out Madam, *says she*, your Lying-In will not cost you above 5 *l.* 3 *s.* in all, more than your ordinary Charge of Living.

This was the most reasonable thing that I ever heard of; so I smil'd, and told her I would come and be her Customer; but *I told her also*, that as I had two Months, and more to go, I might perhaps be oblig'd to stay longer with her than three Months, and desir'd to know if she would not be oblig'd to remove me before it was proper; no, *she said*, her House was large, and besides, she never put any Body to remove, that had lain Inn, till they were willing to go; and if she had more Ladies offer'd, she was not so ill belov'd among her Neighbours, but she could provide Accommodation for Twenty, if there was occasion.

I found she was an eminent Lady in her way, and *in short*, I agreed to put myself into her Hands, and promis'd her: She then talk'd of other things, look'd about into my Accommodations, where was found fault with my wanting Attendance, and Conveniencies, and that I should not be us'd so at her House: *I told her*, I was shy of speaking, for the Woman of the House look'd stranger, or at least I thought so, since I had been Ill, because I was with Child; and I was afraid she would put some Affront or other upon me, supposing that I had been able to give but a slight Account of myself.

O dear, *said she*, her Ladyship is no stranger to these things; she has try'd to entertain Ladies in your Condition several times, but could not secure the Parish;[231] and besides, she is not such a nice Lady as you take her to be; however, since you are agoing you shall not meddle with her, but I'll see you are a little better look'd after while you are here, than I think you are, and it shall not cost you the more neither.

I did not understand her at all; however I thank'd her, and so we parted; the next Morning she sent me a Chicken roasted and hot, and a pint Bottle of Sherry, and order'd the Maid to tell me that she was to wait on me every Day as long as I stay'd there.

This was surprisingly good and kind, and I accepted it very willingly: At Night she sent to me again, to know if I wanted any thing, and how I did, and to order the Maid to come to her in the morning for my Dinner; the Maid had order to make me some Chocolat in the Morning before she came away, and did so, and at Noon she brought me the Sweetbread of a Breast of Veal whole, and a Dish of Soup for my Dinner, and after this manner she Nurs'd me up at a distance, so that I was mightily well pleas'd and quickly well, for indeed my Dejections before were the principal Part of my Illness.

I expected, as usually is the Case among such People, that the Servant she sent me would have been some impudent brazen Wench of *Drury-Lane*[232] Breeding, and I was very uneasie of having her with

---

[231]I.e., she did not have enough influence with parish authorities, and they refused to accept her assurances about the "ladies."

[232]A district north of the Strand, famous for its theater and prostitutes. For an example of what such breeding might mean, see John Gay, *Trivia: Or, The Art of Walking the Streets of London*, 1716.

me, upon that Account, so I would not let her lie in that House the first Night by any means, but had my Eyes about me as narrowly as if she had been a publick Thief.

My Gentlewoman guess'd presently what was the matter, and sent her back with a short Note, that I might depend upon the honesty of her Maid; that she would be answerable for her upon all Accounts; and that she took no Servants into her House, without very good Security for their Fidelity: I was then perfectly easie, and indeed the Maids behaviour spoke for its self, for a modester, quieter, soberer Girl never came into any bodies Family, and I found her so afterwards.

As soon as I was well enough to go Abroad, I went with the Maid to see the House, and to see the Apartment I was to have; and every thing was so handsome and so clean, and well, that in short, I had nothing to say, but was wonderfully pleas'd, and satisfy'd with what I had met with, which considering the melancholy Circumstances I was in, was far beyond what I look'd for.

It might be expected that I should give some Account of the Nature of the wicked Practice of this Woman, in whose Hands I was now fallen; but it would be but too much Encouragement to the Vice, to let the World see, what easie Measures were here taken to rid the Women's unwelcome Burthen of a Child clandestinely gotten:[233] This grave Matron had several sorts of Practise, and this was one particular, that if a Child was born, tho' not in her House, for she had the occasion to be call'd to many private Labours, she had People at Hand, who for a Peice of Money would take the Child off their Hands, and off from the Hands of the Parish too; and those Children, as she said, were honestly provided for, and taken care of: What should become of them all, Considering so many, as by her Account she was concern'd with, I cannot conceive.

I had many times Discourses upon that Subject with her; but she was full of this Argument, that she sav'd the Life of many an innocent Lamb, as she call'd them, which would otherwise perhaps have been Murder'd; and of many a Woman, who, made Desperate by the Misfortune, would otherwise be tempted to Destroy their Children, and bring themselves to the Gallows: I granted her that this was true, and a very commendable thing, provided the poor Children fell into good Hands afterwards, and were not abus'd, starv'd, and neglected by the Nurses that bred them up; she answer'd, that she always took care of that, and had no Nurses in her Business, but what were very good honest People, and such as might be depended upon.

I cou'd say nothing to the contrary, and so was oblig'd to say, Madam I do not question you do your part honestly, but what those People

---

[233]Begotten, conceived.

do afterwards, is the main Question, and she stop'd my Mouth again with saying, that she took the utmost Care about it.

The only thing I found in all her Conversation on these Subjects, that gave me any distaste, was, that one time in Discoursing about my being so far gone with Child, and the time I expected to come, she said something that look'd as if she could help me off with my Burthen sooner, if I was willing; or in *English*, that she could give me something to make me Miscarry, if I had a desire to put an end to my Troubles that way; but I soon let her see that I abhorr'd the Thoughts of it; and to do her Justice, she put it off so cleverly, that I cou'd not say she really intended it, or whether she only mentioned the practise as a horrible thing; for she couch'd her words so well, and took my meaning so quickly, that she gave her Negative before I could explain my self.

To bring this part into as narrow a Compass as possible, I quitted my Lodging at St. *Jones's* and went to my new Governess, for so they call'd her in the House, and there I was indeed treated with so much Courtesy, so carefully look'd to, so handsomely provided, and every thing so well, that I was surpris'd at it, and cou'd not at first see what Advantage my Governess made of it; but I found afterwards that she profess'd to make no Profit of the Lodgers Diet, nor indeed cou'd she get much by it, but that her Profit lay in the other Articles of her Management, and she made enough that way, I assure you; for 'tis scarce credible what Practice she had, as well Abroad as at Home, and yet all upon the private Account, or in plain *English*, the whoring Account.

While I was in her House, which was near Four Months, she had no less than Twelve Ladies of Pleasure brought to Bed within Doors, and I think she had Two and Thirty, or thereabouts, under her Conduct without Doors, whereof one, as nice as she was with me, was Lodg'd with my old Landlady at St. *Jones's.*

This was a strange Testimony of the growing Vice of the Age, and such a bad one, that as bad as I had been my self, it shock'd my very Senses, I began to nauceate[234] the place I was in, and above all, the wicked Practice; and yet I must say that I never saw, or do I believe there was to be seen, the least indecency in the House the whole time I was there.

Not a Man was ever seen to come up Stairs, except to visit the Lying-Inn Ladies within their Month, nor then without the old Lady with them, who made it a piece of the Honour of her Management, that no Man should touch a Woman, no not his own Wife, within the Month; nor would she permit any Man to lye in the House upon any pretence whatever, no not tho' she was sure it was with his own

[234]Loathe.

Wife, and her general saying for it was, that she car'd not how many Children was born in her House, but she would have none got[235] there if she could help it.

It might perhaps be carried farther than was needful, but it was an Error of the right Hand[236] if it was an Error, for by this she kept up the Reputation, such as it was, of her Business, and obtain'd this Character: that tho' she did take Care of the Women when they were Debauch'd, yet she was not instrumental to their being Debauch'd at all, and yet it was a wicked Trade she drove too.

While I was here, and before I was brought to Bed, I receiv'd a Letter from my Trustee at the Bank full of kind obliging things, and earnestly pressing me to return to *London*: It was near a Fortnight old when it came to me, because it had been first sent into *Lancashire*, and then return'd to me; he concludes with telling me that he had obtain'd a Decree,[237] I think he call'd it, against his Wife, and that he would be ready to make good his Engagement to me, if I would accept of him, adding a great many Protestations of Kindness and Affection, such as he would have been far from offering if he had known the Circumstances I had been in, and which as it was I had been very far from deserving.

I returned an Answer to this Letter, and dated it at *Leverpool*, but sent it by a Messenger, alledging that it came in Cover to a Friend in Town; I gave him Joy of his Deliverance, but rais'd some Scruples at the Lawfulness of his Marrying again, and told him, I suppos'd he would consider very seriously upon that Point before he resolv'd on it, the Consequence being too great for a Man of his Judgment to venture rashly upon a thing of that Nature; so concluded, wishing him very well in whatever he resolv'd, without letting him into any thing of my own Mind, or giving any Answer to his Proposal of my coming to *London* to him, but mention'd at a distance my intention to return the latter end of the Year, this being dated in *April*.

I was brought to Bed about the middle of *May*, and had another brave[238] Boy, and my self in as good Condition as usual on such Occasions: My Governess did her part as a Midwife with the greatest Art and Dexterity imaginable, and far beyond all that ever I had had any Experience of before.

Her Care of me in my Travail, and after in my Lying-Inn, was such, that if she had been my own Mother it cou'd not have been better; let none be encourag'd in their loose Practises from this Dexterous

---

[235]Begotten.

[236]I.e., she erred in the right direction.

[237]A court order declaring the nullity or dissolution of marriage or the separation of parties; the final divorce was yet to be issued.

[238]Excellent. "Brave" often served, in Defoe's time, as a general and indeterminate epithet of admiration and praise.

Lady's Management, for she is gone to her place, and I dare say has left nothing behind her that can or will come up to it.

I think I had been brought to Bed about twenty two Days when I receiv'd another Letter from my Friend at the Bank, with the surprizing News that he had obtain'd a final Sentence of Divorce against his Wife, and had serv'd her with it on such a Day, and that he had such an Answer to give to all my Scruples about his Marrying again, as I could not expect, and as he had no Desire of; for that his Wife, who had been under some Remorse before for her usage of him, as soon as she had the account that he had gain'd his Point, had very unhappily destroy'd her self that same Evening.

He express'd himself very handsomly as to his being concern'd at her Disaster, but clear'd himself of having any hand in it, and that he had only done himself Justice in a Case in which he was notoriously Injur'd and Abus'd: However, he said that he was extremely afflicted at it, and had no view of any Satisfaction left in this World, but only in the hope that I wou'd come and relieve him by my Company; and then he press'd me violently indeed to give him some hopes, that I would at least come up to Town and let him see me, when he would farther enter into Discourse about it.

I was exceedingly surpriz'd at the News, and began now seriously to reflect on my present Circumstances, and the inexpressible Misfortune it was to me to have a Child upon my Hands, and what to do in it I knew not; at last I open'd my Case at a distance to my Governess, I appear'd melancholy and uneasie for several Days, and she lay at me continually to know what troubl'd me; I could not for my life tell her that I had an offer of Marriage, after I had so often told her that I had a Husband, so that I really knew not what to say to her: I own'd I had something which very much troubl'd me, but at the same time told her I cou'd not speak of it to any one alive.

She continued importuning me several Days, but it was impossible, *I told her*, for me to commit the Secret to any Body; this, instead of being an Answer to her, encreas'd her Importunities; she urg'd her having been trusted with the greatest Secrets of this Nature, that it was her business to Conceal every thing, and that to Discover things of that Nature would be her Ruin; she ask'd me if ever I had found her Tatling to her of other Peoples Affairs, and how could I suspect her? *she told me* to unfold my self to her, was telling it to no Body; that she was silent as Death; that it must be a very strange Case indeed, that she could not help me out of; but to conceal it, was to deprive myself of all possible Help, or means of Help, and to deprive her of the Opportunity of Serving me. *In short*, she had such a bewitching Eloquence, and so great a power of Perswasion, that there was no concealing any thing from her.

So I resolv'd to unbosome myself to her, I told her the History of my *Lancashire* Marriage, and how both of us had been Disappointed; how we came together, and how we parted; How he absolutely Discharg'd me, as far as lay in him, and gave me free Liberty to Marry again, protesting that if he knew it he would never Claim me, or Disturb, or Expose me; that I thought I was free, but was dreadfully afraid to venture, for fear of the Consequences that might follow in case of a Discovery.

Then I told her what a good Offer I had; show'd her my Friends two last Letters, inviting me to come to *London*, and let her see with what Affection and Earnestness they were written, but blotted out the Name, and also the Story about the Disaster of his Wife, only that she was dead.

She fell a Laughing at my scruples about marrying, and told me the other was no Marriage, but a Cheat on both Sides; and that as we were parted by mutual Consent, the nature of the Contract was destroy'd, and the Obligation was mutually discharg'd: She had Arguments for this at the tip of her Tongue; and *in short*, reason'd me out of my Reason; not but that it was too by the help of my own Inclination.

But then came the great and main difficulty, and that was the Child; this she told me in so many Words must be remov'd, and that so as that it should never be possible for any one to discover it: I knew there was no Marrying without entirely concealing that I had had a Child, for he would soon have discover'd by the Age of it, that it was born, nay and gotten too, since my Parly with him, and that would have destroy'd all the Affair.

But it touch'd my Heart so forcibly to think of Parting entirely with the Child, and for aught I knew, of having it murther'd, or starv'd by Neglect and Ill-usage, (which was much the same) that I could not think of it, without Horror; I wish all those Women who consent to the disposing their Children out of the way, *as it is call'd* for Decency sake, would consider that 'tis only a contriv'd Method for Murther; that is to say, a killing their Children with safety.

It is manifest to all that understand any thing of Children, that we are born into the World helpless and uncapable, either to supply our own Wants, or so much as make them known; and that without help, we must Perish; and this help requires not only an assisting Hand, whether of the Mother, or some Body else; but there are two Things necessary in that assisting Hand, that is, Care and Skill, without both which, half the Children that are born would die; nay, tho' they were not to be deny'd Food; and one half more of those that remain'd would be Cripples or Fools, lose their Limbs, and perhaps their Sense: I Question not, but that these are partly the Reasons why Affection was plac'd by Nature in the Hearts of Mothers to their Children; without which they would never be able to give themselves up, as 'tis necessary they should, to the Care and waking Pains needful to the Support of their Children.

Since this Care is needful to the Life of Children, to neglect them is to Murther them; again to give them up to be Manag'd by those People, who have none of that needful Affection, plac'd by Nature in them, is to Neglect them in the highest Degree; nay, in some it goes farther, and is a Neglect in order to their being Lost; so that 'tis even an intentional Murther, whether the Child lives or dies.

All those things represented themselves to my View, and that in the blackest and most frightful Form; and as I was very free with my Governness, who I had now learn'd to call Mother; I represented to her all the dark Thoughts which I had upon me about it, and told her what distress I was in: She seem'd graver by much at this Part than at the other; but as she was harden'd in these things beyond all possibility of being touch'd with the Religious part, and the Scruples about the Murther; so she was equally impenetrable in that Part, which related to Affection: She ask'd me if she had not been Careful, and Tender of me in my Lying-Inn, as if I had been her own Child? I told her I own'd she had. Well my Dear, *says she*, and when you are gone, what are you to me? and what would it be to me if you were to be Hang'd? Do you think there are not Women, who as it is their Trade, and they get their Bread by it, value themselves upon their being as careful of Children, as their own Mothers can be, and understand it rather better? Yes, yes, Child, *says she*, fear it not, How were we Nurs'd ourselves? Are you sure, you was Nurs'd up by your own Mother? and yet you look fat, and fair Child, says the old Beldam,[239] and with that she stroak'd me over the Face; never be concern'd Child, *says she*, going on in her drolling way; I have no Murtherers about me, I employ the best, and the honestest Nurses that can be had; and have as few Children miscarry under their Hands, as there would, if they were all Nurs'd by Mothers; we want neither Care nor Skill.

She touch'd me to the Quick, when she ask'd if I was sure that I was Nurs'd by my own Mother; on the contrary I was sure I was not; and I trembled, and look'd pale at the very Expression; sure said I, to myself, this Creature cannot be a Witch, or have any Conversation with a Spirit that can inform her what was done with me before I was able to know it myself;[240] and I look'd at her as if I had been frighted; but reflecting that it cou'd not be possible for her to know any thing about

[239]An aged woman. The term often suggests a hag or witch, and Defoe may be toying with expectation here (see Moll's worries below), but a pejorative connotation is not necessarily implied.

[240]For a discussion of Defoe's interest in the supernatural, see Rodney M. Baine, "Daniel Defoe and *The History and Reality of Apparitions,*" *Proceedings of the American Philosophical Society,* CVI (1962), 335–47, and *Daniel Defoe and the Supernatural.*

me, that Disorder went off, and I began to be easie, but it was not presently.

She perceiv'd the Disorder I was in, but did not know the meaning of it; so she run on in her wild Talk upon the weakness of my supposing that Children were murther'd, because they were not all Nurs'd by the Mother; and to perswade me that the Children she dispos'd of, were as well us'd as if the Mothers had the Nursing of them themselves.

It may be true Mother, *says I*, for aught I know, but my Doubts are very strongly grounded, indeed; come then, *says she*, lets hear some of them: Why first, *says I*, you give a Piece of Money to these People to take the Child off the Parents Hands, and to take Care of it as long as it lives; now we know Mother, *said I*, that those are poor People, and their Gain consists in being quit of the Charge as soon as they can; how can I doubt but that, as it is best for them to have the Child die, they are not over Solicitous about its Life.

This is all Vapours[241] and Fancy,[242] *says the old Woman*, I tell you their Credit depends upon the Child's Life, and they are as careful as any Mother of you all.

O Mother, *says I*, if I was but sure my little Baby would be carefully look'd to, and have Justice done it, I should be happy indeed; but it is impossible I can be satisfy'd in that Point, unless I saw it, and to see it, would be Ruin and Destruction to me, as now my Case stands, so what to do I know not.

A fine Story! *says the Governess*, you would see the Child, and you would not see the Child; you would be Conceal'd and Discover'd both together; these are things impossible my Dear, so you must e'n do as other conscientious Mothers have done before you; and be contented with things as they must be, tho' they are not as you wish them to be.

I understood what she meant by conscientious Mothers, she would have said conscientious Whores; but she was not willing to disoblige me, for really in this Case I was not a Whore, because legally Married, the force of my former Marriage excepted.[243]

However let me be what I would, I was not come up to that pitch of Hardness, common to the Profession; I mean to be unnatural, and regardless of the Safety of my Child, and I preserv'd this honest Affection so long, that I was upon the Point of giving up my Friend at the Bank, who lay so hard at me to come to him, and Marry him, that *in short*, there was hardly any room to deny him.

At last my old Governness came to me, with her usual Assurance. Come my Dear, *says she*, I have found out a way how you shall be at a

---

[241]A frequent eighteenth-century term for a general depression of spirits, supposedly caused by exhalations within bodily organs.

[242]Illusion, imaginary worries.

[243]I.e., except for the validity of Moll's earlier marriage.

certainty, that your Child shall be used well, and yet the People that take Care of it shall never know you, or who the Mother of the Child is.

O Mother, *says I*, If you can do so, you will engage me to you for ever: Well, *says she*, are you willing to be at some small Annual Expence, more than what we usually give to the People we Contract with? Ay, *says I*, with all my Heart, provided I may be conceal'd; as to that, says *the Governness*, you shall be Secure, for the Nurse shall never so much as dare to Enquire about you, and you shall once or twice a Year go with me and see your Child, and see how 'tis used, and be satisfy'd that it is in good Hands, no Body knowing who you are.

Why, *said I*, do you think Mother, that when I come to see my Child, I shall be able to conceal my being the Mother of it, do you think that possible?

Well, well, *says my Governess*, if you discover it, the Nurse shall be never the wiser; for she shall be forbid to ask any Questions about you, or to take any Notice; if she offers it she shall lose the Money which you are to be suppos'd to give her, and the Child be taken from her too.

I was very well pleas'd with this; so the next Week a Country Woman was brought from *Hertford*,[244] or thereabouts, who was to take the Child off our Hands entirely, for 10 *l.* in Money; but if I would allow 5 *l.* a Year more to her, she would be obliged to bring the Child to my Governesses House as often as we desired, or we should come down and look at it, and see how well she us'd it.

The Woman was a very wholesome look'd likely Woman,[245] a Cottager's Wife, but she had very good Cloaths and Linnen, and every thing well about her, and with a heavy Heart and many a Tear I let her have my Child: I had been down at *Hertford* and look'd at her and at her Dwelling, which I lik'd well enough; and I promis'd her great Things if she would be kind to the Child, so she knew at first word that I was the Child's Mother; but she seem'd to be so much out of the way,[246] and to have no room to enquire after me, that I thought I was safe enough, so in short I consented to let her have the Child, and I gave her Ten Pound, that is to say I gave it to my Governess, who gave it the poor Woman before my Face, she agreeing never to return the Child back to me, or to claim any thing more for its keeping or bringing up; only that I promised, if she took a great deal of Care of it, I would give her something more as often as I came to see it; so that I was not bound to pay the Five Pound, only that I promised my Governess I would do it: and thus my great Care was over, after a

---

[244]A town twenty miles north of London.

[245]I.e., she appeared to be mentally and morally healthy.

[246]From an out-of-the-way place, not well acquainted or likely to cause trouble for Moll.

manner, which tho' it did not at all satisfie my Mind, yet was the most convenient for me, as my Affairs then stood, of any that cou'd be thought of at that time.

I then began to write to my Friend at the Bank in a more kindly Style, and particularly about the beginning of *July* I sent him a Letter, that I purpos'd to be in Town sometime in *August*; he return'd me an Answer in the most Passionate Terms imaginable, and desir'd me to let him have timely Notice, and he would come and meet me two Days Journey:[247] This puzzl'd me scurvily, and I did not know what Answer to make to it; once I was resolv'd to take the Stage Coach to *Westchester* on purpose only, to have the satisfaction of coming back, that he might see me really come in the same Coach; for I had a jealous[248] thought, though I had no Ground for it at all, least he should think I was not really in the Country, and it was no ill-grounded Thought, as you shall hear presently.

I endeavour'd to Reason my self out of it, but it was in vain, the Impression lay so strong on my Mind, that it was not to be resisted; at last it came as an Addition to my new Design of going in the Country, that it would be an excellent Blind to my old Governess, and would cover entirely all my other Affairs, for she did not know in the least whether my new Lover liv'd in *London* or in *Lancashire*, and when I told her my Resolution, she was fully perswaded it was in *Lancashire*.

Having taken my Measures for this Journey, I let her know it, and sent the Maid that tended me from the beginning, to take a Place for me in the Coach; she would have had me let the Maid have waited on me down to the last Stage, and come up again in the Waggon,[249] but I convinc'd her it wou'd not be convenient; when I went away she told me, she would enter into no Measures for Correspondence, for she saw evidently that my Affection to my Child would cause me to write to her, and to visit her too when I came to Town again; I assur'd her it would, and so took my leave, well satisfied to have been freed from such a House, however good my Accommodations there had been, as I have related above.

I took the Place in the Coach not to its full Extent, but to a place call'd *Stone*[250] in *Cheshire*, I think it is, where I not only had no manner of Business, but not so much as the least Acquaintance with any

---

[247]A day's journey by stage coach could be up to eighty miles; two days would bring Moll from her presumed Lancashire residence to within easy meeting distance from London.

[248]Apprehensive.

[249]I.e., the governess desired to have the maid attend Moll during her whole journey, then return via waggon, a heavier, cheaper, and less commodious means of transportation, built to carry both passengers and freight.

[250]Stone is actually in Staffordshire, about 140 miles from London. This mistake is probably Moll's, not Defoe's, and is meant to suggest Moll's vagueness.

Person in the Town or near it: But I knew that with Money in the Pocket one is at home any where, so I Lodg'd there two or three Days, till watching my opportunity, I found room in another Stage Coach, and took Passage back again for *London*, sending a Letter to my Gentleman, that I should be such a certain Day at *Stony-Stratford*,[251] where the Coachman told me he was to Lodge.

It happen'd to be a Chance Coach that I had taken up, which having been hired on purpose to carry some Gentlemen to *West Chester* who were going for *Ireland*, was now returning, and did not tye it self up to exact Times or Places as the Stages did, so that having been oblig'd to lye still a *Sunday*, he had time to get himself ready to come out, which otherwise he cou'd not have done.

However, his warning was so short, that he could not reach to *Stony Stratford* time enough to be with me at Night, but he met me at a Place call'd *Brickill*[252] the next Morning, as we were just coming into the Town.

I confess I was very glad to see him, for I had thought my self a little disappointed over Night, seeing I had gone so far to contrive my coming on purpose: He pleas'd me doubly too by the Figure he came in, for he brought a very handsome (Gentleman's) Coach and four Horses with a Servant to attend him.

He took me out of the Stage Coach immediately, which stop'd at an Inn in *Brickill*, and putting in to the same Inn he set up his own Coach, and bespoke his Dinner; I ask'd him what he meant by that, for I was for going forward with the Journey; he said no, I had need of a little Rest upon the Road, and that was a very good sort of a House, tho' it was but a little Town; so we would go no farther that Night, whatever came of it.

I did not press him much, for since he had come so far to meet me, and put himself to so much Expence, it was but reasonable I should oblige him a little too, so I was easy as to that Point.

After Dinner we walk'd to see the Town, to see the Church, and to view the Fields, and the Country as is usual for Strangers to do, and our Landlord was our Guide in going to see the Church; I observ'd my Gentleman enquir'd pretty much about the Parson, and I took the hint immediately, that he certainly would propose to be married; and tho' it was a sudden thought, it follow'd presently, that in short I would not refuse him; for to be plain with my Circumstances, I was in no condition now to say NO, I had no reason now to run any more such hazards.

But while these Thoughts run round in my Head, which was the work but of a few Moments, I observ'd my Landlord took him aside

---

[251] About fifty miles northwest of London, in Buckinghamshire.

[252] Little Brickhill (Buckinghamshire) is on the Great Northern Road, about ten miles closer to London.

and whisper'd to him, tho' not very softly neither, for so much I over-heard, *Sir, if you shall have occasion* — the rest I cou'd not hear, but it seems it was to this purpose, *Sir, if you shall have occasion for a Minister, I have a Friend a little way off that will serve you, and be as private as you please*; my Gentleman answer'd loud enough for me to hear, *very well, I believe I shall*.

I was no sooner come back to the Inn, but he fell upon me with irresistable Words, that since he had had the good Fortune to meet me, and every thing concurr'd, it wou'd be hastening his Felicity if I would put an end to the matter just there; what do you mean, *says I*, colouring a little, what in an Inn, and upon the Road! Bless us all, *said I*, as if I had been surpriz'd, how can you talk so! O I can talk so very well, *says he*, I came a purpose to talk so, and I'll show you that I did, and with that he pulls out a great Bundle of Papers; you fright me, *said I*, what are all these; don't be frighted, my Dear, *said he*, and kiss'd me, *this was the first time that he had been so free to call me my Dear*; then he repeated it, don't be frighted, you shall see what it is all, then he laid them all abroad;[253] there was first the Deed or Sentence of Divorce from his Wife, and the full Evidence of her playing the Whore; then there was the Certificates of the Minister and Church-wardens of the Parish where she liv'd, proving that she was buried, and intimating the manner of her Death; the Copy of the Coroner's Warrant for a Jury to sit upon her, and the Verdict of the Jury, who brought it in *Non Compos Mentis*;[254] all this was indeed to the purpose, and to give me Satisfaction, tho', by the way, I was not so scrupulous, had he known all, but that I might have taken him without it: However, I look'd them all over as well as I cou'd, and told him, that this was all very clear indeed, but that he need not have given himself the Trouble to have brought them out with him, for it was time enough: Well *he said*, it might be time enough for me, but no time but the present time was time enough for him.

There were other Papers roll'd up, and I ask'd him, what they were? Why, Ay, *says he*, that's the Question I wanted to have you ask me; so he unrolls them, and takes out a little Chagreen[255] Case, and gives me out of it a very fine Diamond Ring; I could not refuse it, if I had a mind to do so, for he put it upon my Finger; so I made him a Curtsy, and accepted it; then he takes out another Ring, and this, *says he*, is for another Occasion, so he puts that in his Pocket. Well, but let me see it tho', *says I*, and smil'd, I guess what it is, I think you are Mad: I should have been Mad if I had done less, *says he*, and still he did not show it me, and I had a great mind to see it; so I says, well but let me see it; hold, *says he*, first look here, then he took up the Roll again, and

---

[253]Spread them out.

[254]I.e., their verdict was that she was not of sound mind or discretion.

[255]Shagreen: an untanned rough leather.

read it, and behold! it was a License for us to be married: Why, *says I*, are you Distracted? why you were fully satisfy'd that I would comply, and yield at first Word, or resolved to take no denial; the last is certainly the Case, *said he*; but you may be mistaken, *said I*, no, no, *says he*, how can you think so? I must not be denied, I can't be denied, and with that he fell to Kissing me so violently, I could not get rid of him.

There was a Bed in the Room, and we were walking to and again,[256] eager in the Discourse; at last he takes me by surprize in his Arms, and threw me on the Bed and himself with me, and holding me fast in his Arms, but without the least offer of any Undecency, Courted me to Consent with such repeated Entreaties and Arguments; protesting his Affection and vowing he would not let me go, till I had promised him, that at last I said, why you resolve not to be deny'd indeed, I think: No, no, *says he*, I must not be denyed, I won't be deny'd, I can't be deny'd: Well, well, *said I*, and giving him a slight Kiss, then you shan't be deny'd, *said I*, let me get up.

He was so Transported[257] with my Consent, and the kind manner of it, that I began to think Once, he took it for a Marriage, and would not stay for the Form, but I wrong'd him, for he gave over Kissing me, took me by the Hand, pull'd me up again, and then giving me two or three Kisses again, thank'd me for my kind yielding to him; and was so overcome with the Satisfaction and Joy of it, that I saw Tears stand in his Eyes.

I turn'd from him, for it fill'd my Eyes with Tears too; and I ask'd him leave to retire a little to my Chamber: If ever I had a Grain of true Repentance for a vitious and abominable Life for 24 Years past, it was then. O! what a felicity is it to Mankind, *said I*, to myself, that they cannot see into the Hearts of one another! How happy had it been for me, if I had been Wife to a Man of so much honesty, and so much Affection from the Beginning?

Then it occurr'd to me what an abominable Creature am I! and how is this innocent Gentleman going to be abus'd by me! How little does he think, that having Divorc'd a Whore, he is throwing himself into the Arms of another! that he is going to Marry one that has lain with two Brothers, and has had three Children by her own Brother! one that was born in *Newgate*, whose Mother was a Whore, and is now a transported Thief; one that has lain with thirteen Men,[258] and has had a Child since he saw me! poor Gentleman! *said I*, What is he going to do? After this reproaching myself was over, it followed thus: Well, if I must be his Wife, if it please God to give me Grace, I'll be a true Wife to him, and love him suitably to the strange Excess of his Passion for me; I will make him amends, if possible, by what he shall

---

[256]Back and forth.
[257]Overcome with joy.

[258]Moll has apparently not told us everything.

see, for the Cheats and Abuses I put upon him, which he does not see.

He was impatient for my coming out of my Chamber, but finding me long, he went down Stairs, and talk'd with my Landlord about the Parson.

My Landlord, an Officious, tho' well-meaning Fellow, had sent away for the Neighbouring Clergy Man; and when my Gentleman began to speak of it to him, and talk of sending for him, Sir, says he to him, my Friend is in the House; so without any more words he brought them together: When he came to the Minister, he ask'd him if he would venture to marry a couple of Strangers that were both willing? The Parson said that Mr. —— had said something to him of it; that he hop'd it was no Clandestine Business; that he seem'd to be a grave Gentleman, and he suppos'd Madam was not a Girl, so that the consent of Friends should be wanted; to put you out of doubt of that, says my Gentleman, read this Paper, and out he pulls the License; I am satisfied, says the Minister, where is the Lady? you shall see her presently, says my Gentleman.

When he had said thus, he comes up Stairs, and I was by that time come out of my Room, so he tells me the Minister was below, and that he had talk'd with him, and that upon showing him the License, he was free to marry us with all his Heart, but he asks to see you, so he ask'd if I would let him come up.

'Tis time enough, *said I*, in the Morning, is it not? Why, *said he*, my Dear, he seem'd to scruple whether it was not some young Girl stolen from her Parents, and I assur'd him we were both of Age to command our own Consent; and that made him ask to see you; well, *said I*, do as you please; so up they brings the Parson, and a merry good sort of Gentleman he was; he had been told, it seems, that we had met there by accident, that I came in the *Chester* Coach, and my Gentleman in his own Coach to meet me; that we were to have met last Night at *Stony-Stratford*, but that he could not reach so far: Well, Sir, *says the Parson*, every ill turn has some good in it; the Disappointment, Sir, *says he to my Gentleman*, was yours, and the good Turn is mine, for if you had met at *Stony-Stratford* I had not had the Honour to Marry you: LANDLORD *have you a Common-Prayer Book*.

I started as if I had been frighted, Lord, Sir, *says I*, what do you mean; what, to marry in an Inn, and at Night too: Madam, *says the Minister*, if you will have it be in the Church you shall; but I assure you your Marriage will be as firm here as in the Church; we are not tyed by the Canons to Marry no where but in the Church; and if you will have it in the Church it will be as publick as a Country Fair; and as for the time of Day it does not at all weigh in this Case, our Princes are married in their Chambers, and at Eight or Ten a Clock at Night.

I was a great while before I could be perswaded, and pretended not to be willing at all to be married but in the Church; but it was all

Grimace;[259] so I seem'd at last to be prevail'd on, and my Landlord, and his Wife, and Daughter, were call'd up: My Landlord was Father and Clark and all together, and we were married, and very Merry we were; tho' I confess the self-reproaches which I had upon me before, lay close to me, and extorted every now and then a deep sigh from me, which my Bridegroom took notice of, and endeavour'd to encourage me, thinking, poor Man, that I had some little hesitations at the Step I had taken so hastily.

We enjoy'd our selves that Evening compleatly, and yet all was kept so private in the Inn, that not a Servant in the House knew of it, for my Landlady and her Daughter waited on me, and would not let any of the Maids come up Stairs, except while we were at Supper: My Landlady's Daughter I call'd my Bride-maid, and sending for a Shop-keeper the next Morning, I gave the young Woman a good Suit of Knots,[260] as good as the Town would afford, and finding it was a Lace-making Town, I gave her Mother a piece of Bone-lace[261] for a Head.[262]

One Reason that my Landlord was so close[263] was, that he was unwilling the Minister of the Parish should hear of it; but for all that somebody heard of it, so as that we had the Bells set a Ringing the next Morning early, and the Musick,[264] such as the Town would afford, under our Window; but my Landlord brazen'd it out, that we were marry'd before we came thither, only that being his former Guests, we would have our Wedding Supper at his House.

We cou'd not find in our Hearts to stir the next Day; for in short having been disturb'd by the Bells in the Morning, and having perhaps not slept over much Before, we were so sleepy afterwards that we lay in Bed till almost Twelve a Clock.

I beg'd my Landlady that we might not have any more Musick in the Town, nor Ringing of Bells, and she manag'd it so well that we were very quiet: But an odd Passage interrupted all my Mirth for a good while; the great Room of the House look'd into the Street, and my new Spouse being below Stairs, I had walk'd to the end of the Room, and it being a pleasant warm Day, I had opened the Window, and was standing at it for some Air, when I saw three Gentlemen come by on Horseback and go into an Inn just against[265] us.

It was not to be conceal'd, nor was it so doubtful as to leave me any room to question it, but the second of the three was my *Lancashire* Husband: I was frighted to Death, I never was in such a Consternation

---

[259]Pretense.

[260]A set of ribbons to ornament a dress.

[261]Lace, usually of linen thread, made by knitting upon a pattern marked by pins, with bobbins originally made of bone.

[262]To use in a headdress.

[263]Closemouthed, uncommunicative.

Presumably the parish minister would be offended to have an outsider perform the ceremony, especially if the inkeeper ran a sort of marriage mill.

[264]The customary community serenade of the bride and groom.

[265]Opposite, facing.

in my Life, I thought I should have sunk into the Ground, my Blood
ran Chill in my Veins, and I trembl'd as if I had been in a cold Fit of
an Ague: I say there was no room to question the Truth of it, I knew
his Cloaths, I knew his Horse, and I knew his Face.[266]

The first sensible Reflection I made was, that my Husband was not
by to see my Disorder, and that I was very glad of: The Gentlemen
had not been long in the House but they came to the Window of their
Room, as is usual; but my Window was shut you may be sure: However, I cou'd not keep from peeping at them, and there I saw him
again, heard him call out to one of the Servants of the House for
something he wanted, and receiv'd all the terryfying Confirmations of
its being the same Person, that were possible to be had.

My next concern was to know, if possible, what was his Business
there; but that was impossible; sometimes my Imagination form'd an
Idea of one frightful thing, sometimes of another; sometimes I
thought he had discover'd me, and was come to upbraid me with
Ingratitude and Breach of Honour; and every Moment I fancied he
was coming up the Stairs to Insult me; and innumerable fancies came
into my Head of what was never in his Head, nor ever could be, unless
the Devil had reveal'd it to him.

I remain'd in this fright near two Hours, and scarce ever kept my
Eye from the Window or Door of the Inn, where they were: At last
hearing a great clutter in the Passage of their Inn, I run to the Window,
and, to my great Satisfaction, see them all three go out again and
Travel on Westward; had they gone towards *London*, I should have
been still in a fright, least I should meet him on the Road again, and
that he should know me; but he went the contrary way, and so I was
eas'd of that Disorder.

We resolv'd to be going the next Day, but about six a Clock at
Night we were alarm'd with a great uproar in the Street, and People
riding as if they had been out of their Wits, and what was it but a
Hue and Cry[267] after three Highway Men, that had rob'd two Coaches,
and some other Travellers near *Dunstable* Hill,[268] and notice had, it
seems, been given, that they had been seen at *Brickill* at such a House,
meaning the House where those Gentlemen had been.

The House was immediately beset and search'd, but there were
witnesses enough that the Gentlemen had been gone above three
Hours; the Crowd having gathered about, we had the News presently;
and I was heartily concern'd now another way: I presently told the

---

[266]The coincidence here, like that
elsewhere in Defoe and other eighteenth-
century writers, should probably be
viewed in the light of contemporary accounts of the role of Providence. For a
discussion of "Providence Literature,"
see Hunter, *The Reluctant Pilgrim*,
chap. 3.

[267]A group pursuing felons.

[268]Dunstable, in Bedfordshire, was
about ten miles closer to London.

People of the House, that I durst to say those were not the Persons, for that I knew one of the Gentlemen to be a very honest Person, and of a good Estate in *Lancashire.*

The Constable, who came with the Hue and Cry, was immediately inform'd of this, and came over to me to be satisfy'd from my own Mouth, and I assur'd him that I saw the three Gentlemen as I was at the Window, that I saw them afterwards at the Windows of the Room they din'd in; that I saw them afterwards take Horse, and I could assure him I knew one of them to be such a Man, that he was a Gentleman of a very good Estate, and an undoubted Character in *Lancashire*, from whence I was just now upon my Journey.

The assurance with which I deliver'd this, gave the Mob Gentry a Check, and gave the Constable such Satisfaction, that he immediately sounded a Retreat, told his People these were not the Men, but that he had an account they were very honest Gentlemen, and so they went all back again; what the Truth of the matter was I knew not, but certain it was that the Coaches were rob'd at *Dunstable* Hill, and 560 *l.* in Money taken, besides some of the Lace Merchants that always Travel that way had been visited too; as to the three Gentlemen, that remains to be explain'd hereafter.

Well, this Allarm stop'd us another Day, tho' my Spouse was for Travelling, and told me that it was always safest Travelling after a Robbery, for that the Thieves were sure to be gone far enough off when they had allarm'd the Country; but I was afraid and uneasy, and indeed principally least my old Acquaintance should be upon the Road still, and should chance to see me.

I never liv'd four pleasanter Days together in my life, I was a meer Bride all this while, and my new Spouse strove to make me entirely easie in every thing; O could this State of Life have continued! how had all my past Troubles been forgot, and my future Sorrows been avoided? but I had a past life of a most wretched kind to account for, some of it in this World as well as in another.

We came away the fifth Day; and my Landlord, because he saw me uneasie, mounted himself, his Son, and three honest Country Fellows with good Fire-Arms, and, without telling us of it, follow'd the Coach, and would see us safe into *Dunstable*; we could do no less than treat them very handsomely at *Dunstable*, which Cost my Spouse about Ten or Twelve Shillings, and something he gave the Men for their Time too, but my Landlord would take nothing for himself.

This was the most happy Contrivance for me that could have fallen out, for had I come to *London* unmarried, I must either have come to him for the first Night's Entertainment, or have discovered to him that I had not one Acquaintance in the whole City of *London* that could receive a poor Bride for the first Night's Lodging with her Spouse: But now being an old married Woman, I made no scruple of going directly home with him, and there I took Possession at once of a House well Furnish'd, and a Husband in very good Circumstances, so that I had a prospect of a very happy Life, if I knew how to manage it; and I had leisure to consider of the real Value of the Life I was likely to live; how different it was to be from the loose ungovern'd part I had acted before, and how much happier a Life of Virtue and Sobriety is, than that which we call a Life of Pleasure.

O had this particular Scene of Life lasted, or had I learnt from that time I enjoy'd it, to have tasted the true sweetness of it, and had I not fallen into that Poverty which is the sure Bane of Virtue, how happy had I been, not only here, but perhaps for ever? for while I liv'd thus, I was really a Penitent for all my Life pass'd, I look'd back on it with Abhorrence, and might truly be said to hate my self for it; I often reflected how my Lover at the *Bath*, strook by the Hand of God, repented and abandon'd me, and refus'd to see me any more, tho' he lov'd me to an extreme; but I, prompted by that worst of Devils, Poverty, return'd to the vile Practice, and made the Advantage of what they call a handsome Face, be the Relief to my Necessities, and Beauty be a Pimp to Vice.

Now I seem'd landed in a safe Harbour, after the Stormy Voyage of Life past was at an end; and I began to be thankful for my Deliverance; I sat many an Hour by my self, and wept over the Remembrance of past Follies, and the dreadful Extravagances of a wicked Life, and sometimes I flatter'd my self that I had sincerely repented.

But there are Temptations which it is not in the Power of Human Nature to resist, and few know what would be their Case, if driven to the same Exigences: As Covetousness is the Root of all Evil, so Poverty is, I believe, the worst of all Snares: But I wave that Discourse till I come to the Experiment.[269]

I liv'd with this Husband in the utmost Tranquility; he was a Quiet, Sensible, Sober Man, Virtuous, Modest, Sincere, and in his Business Diligent and Just: His Business was in a narrow Compass, and his Income sufficient to a plentiful way of Living in the ordinary way; I do not say to keep an Equipage,[270] and make a Figure as the World calls it, nor did I expect it, or desire it; for as I abhorr'd the Levity and Extravagance of my former Life, so I chose now to live retir'd, frugal, and within our selves; I kept no Company, made no Visits; minded my Family, and oblig'd my Husband; and this kind of Life became a Pleasure to me.

We liv'd in an uninterrupted course of Ease and Content for Five Years,[271] when a sudden Blow from an almost invisible Hand, blasted

---

[269]Example, trial of the point at issue.

[270]A carriage, horses, and attendant servants—a symbol of rank or social position.

[271]During these five years, according to the chronology Moll later supplies, the monarchy was restored in England; but Moll seems assiduously to avoid mentioning political events, even though she lived during one of the most turbulent times in English history.

all my Happiness, and turn'd me out into the World in a Condition the reverse of all that had been before it.

My Husband having trusted[272] one of his Fellow Clarks with a Sum of Money too much for our Fortunes to bear the Loss of, the Clark Fail'd, and the Loss fell very heavy on my Husband, yet it was not so great neither, but that if he had had Spirit and Courage to have look'd his Misfortunes in the Face, his Credit was so good, that as I told him, he would easily recover it; for to sink under Trouble is to double the Weight, and he that will Die in it shall Die in it.

It was in vain to speak comfortably to him, the Wound had sunk too deep, it was a Stab that touch'd the Vitals, he grew Melancholy and Disconsolate, and from thence Lethargick, and died; I foresaw the Blow, and was extremely oppress'd in my Mind, for I saw evidently that if he died I was undone.

I had two Children by him and no more, for to tell the Truth, it began to be time for me to leave bearing Children, for I was now Eight and Forty, and I suppose if he had liv'd I should have had no more.

I was now left in a dismal and disconsolate Case indeed, and in several things worse than ever: First it was past the flourishing time with me when I might expect to be courted for a Mistress; that agreeable part had declin'd some time, and the Ruins only appear'd of what had been; and that which was worse than all was this, that I was the most dejected, disconsolate Creature alive; I that had encourag'd my Husband, and endeavour'd to support his Spirits under his Trouble, could not support my own; I wanted that Spirit in Trouble which I told him was so necessary to him for bearing the burthen.

But my Case was indeed Deplorable, for I was left perfectly Friendless and Helpless, and the Loss my Husband had sustain'd had reduc'd his Circumstances so low, that tho' indeed I was not in Debt, yet I could easily foresee that what was left would not support me long; that while it wasted[273] daily for Subsistence, I had no way to encrease it one Shilling, so that it would be soon all spent, and then I saw nothing before me but the utmost Distress, and this represented it self so lively to my Thoughts, that it seem'd as if it was come, before it was really very near; also my very Apprehensions doubl'd the Misery, for I fancied every Sixpence that I paid but for a Loaf of Bread, was the last that I had in the World, and that To-morrow I was to fast, and be starv'd to Death.

In this Distress I had no Assistant, no Friend to comfort or advise me, I sat and cried and tormented my self Night and Day; wringing my Hands, and sometimes raving like a distracted Woman; and indeed I have often wonder'd it has not affected my Reason, for I had the

---

[272]I.e., he lent a sum to the clerk.   [273]Was used up.

Vapours to such a degree, that my Understanding was sometimes quite lost in Fancies and Imaginations.

I liv'd Two Years in this dismal Condition, wasting that little I had, weeping continually over my dismal Circumstances, and as it were only bleeding to Death, without the least hope or prospect of help from God or Man; and now I had cried so long, and so often, that Tears were, as I might say, exhausted, and I began to be Desperate, for I grew Poor apace.

For a little Relief I had put off my House and took Lodgings, and as I was reducing my Living so I sold off most of my Goods, which put a little Money in my Pocket, and I liv'd near a Year upon that, spending very sparingly, and eeking things out to the utmost; but still when I look'd before me, my very Heart would sink within me at the inevitable approach of Misery and Want: O let none read this part without seriously reflecting on the Circumstances of a desolate State, and how they would grapple with meer want of Friends and want of Bread; it will certainly make them think not of sparing what they have only, but of looking up to Heaven for support, and of the wise Man's Prayer, *Give me not Poverty least I Steal.*

Let 'em remember that a time of Distress is a time of dreadful Temptation, and all the Strength to resist is taken away; Poverty presses, the Soul is made Desperate by Distress, and what can be done? It was one Evening, when being brought, as I may say, to the last Gasp, I think I may truly say I was Distracted and Raving, when prompted by I know not what Spirit, and as it were, doing I did not know what, or why; I dress'd me, for I had still pretty good Cloaths, and went out: I am very sure I had no manner of Design in my Head, when I went out, I neither knew or considered where to go, or on what Business; but as the Devil carried me out and laid his Bait for me, so he brought me to be sure to the place, for I knew not whither I was going or what I did.

Wandring thus about I knew not whither, I pass'd by an Apothecary's Shop in *Leadenhall-street*,[274] where I saw lye on a Stool just before the Counter a little Bundle wrapt in a white Cloth; beyond it, stood a Maid Servant with her Back to it, looking up towards the top of the Shop, where the Apothecary's Apprentice, as I suppose, was standing up on the Counter, with his Back also to the Door, and a Candle in his Hand, looking and reaching up to the upper Shelf for something he wanted, so that both were engag'd mighty earnestly, and no Body else in the Shop.

This was the Bait; and the Devil who I said laid the Snare, as readily prompted me, as if he had spoke, for I remember, and shall never forget it, 'twas like a Voice spoken to me over my Shoulder, take the

---

[274]The site of a large market.

Bundle; be quick; do it this Moment;[275] it was no sooner said but I step'd into the Shop, and with my Back to the Wench, as if I had stood up for a Cart that was going by,[276] I put my Hand behind me and took the Bundle, and went off with it, the Maid or the Fellow not perceiving me, or any one else.

It is impossible to express the Horror of my Soul all the while I did it: When I went away I had no Heart to run, or scarce to mend my pace; I cross'd the Street indeed, and went down the first turning I came to, and I think it was a Street that went thro' into *Fenchurch-street*, from thence I cross'd and turn'd thro' so many ways and turnings that I could never tell which way it was, nor where I went, for I felt not the Ground I stept on, and the farther I was out of Danger, the faster I went, till tyr'd and out of Breath, I was forc'd to sit down on a little Bench at a Door, and then I began to recover, and found I was got into *Thames-street* near *Billingsgate*:[277] I rested me a little and went on, my Blood was all in a Fire, my Heart beat as if I was in a sudden Fright: In short, I was under such a Surprize that I still knew not whither I was a going, or what to do.

After I had tyr'd my self thus with walking a long way about, and so eagerly, I began to consider and make home to my Lodging, where I came about Nine a Clock at Night.

What the Bundle was made up for, or on what Occasion laid where I found it, I knew not, but when I came to open it I found there was a Suit of Child-bed Linnen in it, very good and almost new, the Lace very fine; there was a Silver Porringer of a Pint, a small Silver Mug and Six Spoons, with some other Linnen, a good Smock, and Three Silk Handkerchiefs, and in the Mug wrap'd up in a Paper Eighteen Shillings and Sixpence in Money.

All the while I was opening these things I was under such dreadful Impressions of Fear, and in such Terror of Mind, tho' I was perfectly safe, that I cannot express the manner of it; I sat me down and cried most vehemently; Lord, *said I*, what am I now? a Thief! why I shall be taken next time and be carry'd to *Newgate* and be Try'd for my Life! and with that I cry'd again a long time, and I am sure, as poor as I was, if I had durst for fear, I would certainly have carried the things back again; but that went off after a while: Well, I went to Bed for that Night, but slept little, the Horror of the Fact was upon my Mind, and I knew not what I said or did all Night, and all the next Day: Then I was impatient to hear some News of the Loss; and would fain know how it was, whether they were a Poor Bodies Goods, or a Rich;

---

[275]Defoe had a good deal to say elsewhere of Satan's machinations; see, e.g., *The Political History of the Devil*, 1726.

[276]London streets were very narrow, and a pedestrian might well have needed to avoid the vehicle itself or avoid being splashed by it, for kennels (containing refuse) flowed down the centers of the streets.

[277]Moll's route is circuitous, but she goes toward the river.

perhaps, *said I*, it may be some poor Widow like me, that had pack'd up these Goods to go and sell them for a little Bread for herself and a poor Child, and are now starving and breaking their Hearts, for want of that little they would have fetch'd, and this Thought tormented me worse than all the rest, for three or four Days time.

But my own Distresses silenc'd all these Reflections, and the prospect of my own Starving, which grew every Day more frightful to me, harden'd my Heart by degrees; it was then particularly heavy upon my Mind, that I had been reform'd, and had, as I hop'd, repented of all my pass'd wickednesses; that I had liv'd a sober, grave, retir'd Life for several Years, but now I should be driven by the dreadful Necessity of my Circumstances to the Gates of Destruction, Soul and Body; and two or three times I fell upon my Knees, praying to God, as well as I could, for Deliverance; but I cannot but say, my Prayers had no hope in them; I knew not what to do, it was all Fear without, and Dark within; and I reflected on my pass'd Life as not sincerely repented of, that Heaven was now beginning to punish me on this side the Grave, and would make me as miserable as I had been wicked.

Had I gone on here I had perhaps been a true Penitent; but I had an evil Counsellor within, and he was continually prompting me to relieve my self by the worst means; so one Evening he tempted me again by the same wicked Impulse that had said, *take that Bundle*, to go out again and seek for what might happen.

I went out now by Day-light, and wandred about I knew not whither, and in search of I knew not what, when the Devil put a Snare in my way of a dreadful Nature indeed, and such a one as I have never had before or since; going thro' *Aldersgate-street* there was a pretty little Child had been at a Dancing-School, and was going home, all alone, and my Prompter, like a true Devil, set me upon this innocent Creature; I talk'd to it, and it prattl'd to me again, and I took it by the Hand and led it along till I came to a pav'd Alley that goes into *Bartholomew Close*,[278] and I led it in there; the Child said that was not its way home; I said, yes, my Dear it is, I'll show you the way home; the Child had a little Necklace on of Gold Beads, and I had my Eye upon that, and in the dark of the Alley I stoop'd, pretending to mend the Child's Clog that was loose, and took off her Necklace and the Child never felt it, and so led the Child on again: Here, I say, the Devil put me upon killing the Child in the dark Alley, that it might not Cry; but the very thought frighted me so that I was ready to drop down, but I turn'd the Child about and bad it go back again, for that was not its way home; the Child said so she would, and I went thro' into *Bartholomew Close*, and then turn'd round to another Passage that goes into *Long-lane*,[279] so away into *Charterhouse-Yard* and out into *St. John's street*, then

[278]The courtyard by the church.
[279]Moll's location is just northwest of the City of London; her escape route may be easily traced on a map of late seventeenth- or early eighteenth-century London.

crossing into *Smithfield*, went down *Chick-lane* and into *Field-lane* to *Holbourn-bridge*, when mixing with the Crowd of People usually passing there, it was not possible to have been found out; and thus I enterpriz'd my second Sally into the World.

The thoughts of this Booty put out all the thoughts of the first, and the Reflections I had made wore quickly off; Poverty, as I have said, harden'd my Heart, and my own Necessities made me regardless of any thing: The last Affair left no great Concern upon me, for as I did the poor Child no harm, I only said to my self, I had given the Parents a just Reproof for their Negligence in leaving the poor little Lamb to come home by it self, and it would teach them to take more Care of it another time.

This String of Beads was worth about Twelve or Fourteen Pounds, I suppose it might have been formerly the Mother's, for it was too big for the Child's wear, but that, perhaps the Vanity of the Mother to have her Child look Fine at the Dancing School, had made her let the Child wear it, and no doubt the Child had a Maid sent to take care of it, but she, like a careless Jade, was taken up perhaps with some Fellow that had met her by the way, and so the poor Baby wandred till it fell into my Hands.

However, I did the Child no harm, I did not so much as fright it, for I had a great many tender Thoughts about me yet, and did nothing but what, as I may say, meer Necessity drove me to.

I had a great many Adventures after this, but I was young in the Business, and did not know how to manage, otherwise than as the Devil put things into my Head; and indeed he was seldom backward to me: One Adventure I had which was very lucky to me; I was going thro' *Lombard-street* in the dusk of the Evening, just by the end of *Three King Court*, when on a sudden comes a Fellow running by me as swift as Lightning, and throws a Bundle that was in his Hand just behind me, as I stood up against the corner of the House at the turning into the Alley; just as he threw it in he said, God bless you Mistress let it lie there a little, and away he runs swift as the Wind: After him comes two more, and immediately a young Fellow without his Hat, crying stop Thief, and after him two or three more, they pursued the two last Fellows so close, that they were forced to drop what they had got, and one of them was taken into the bargain, the other got off free.

I stood stock still all this while till they came back, dragging the poor Fellow they had taken, and luging the things they had found, extremely well satisfied that they had recovered the Booty, and taken the Thief; and thus they pass'd by me, for I look'd only like one who stood up while the Crowd was gone.

Once or twice I ask'd what was the matter, but the People neglected answering me, and I was not very importunate; but after the Crowd was wholly pass'd, I took my opportunity to turn about and take up what was behind me and walk away: This indeed I did with less Disturbance than I had done formerly, for these things I did not steal, but they were stolen to my Hand: I got safe to my Lodgings with this Cargo, which was a Peice of fine black Lustring[280] Silk, and a Peice of Velvet; the latter was but part of a Piece of about 11 Yards; the former was a whole Peice of near 50 Yards; it seems it was a *Mercer's* Shop that they had rifled, I say rifled, because the Goods were so considerable that they had Lost; for the Goods that they Recover'd were pretty many, and I believe came to about six or seven several[281] Peices of Silk: How they came to get so many I could not tell; but as I had only robb'd the Thief I made no scruple at taking these Goods, and being very glad of them too.

I had pretty good Luck thus far, and I made several Adventures more, tho' with but small Purchase,[282] yet with good Success, but I went in daily dread that some mischief would befal me, and that I should certainly come to be hang'd at last: The impression this made on me was too strong to be slighted, and it kept me from making attempts that for aught I know might have been very safely perform'd; but one thing I cannot omit, which was a Bait to me many a Day. I walk'd frequently out into the Villages round the Town to see if nothing would fall in my Way there; and going by a House near *Stepney*, I saw on the Window-board two Rings, one a small Diamond Ring, and the other a plain Gold Ring, to be sure laid there by some thoughtless Lady, that had more Money than Forecast,[283] perhaps only till she wash'd her Hands.

I walk'd several times by the Window to observe if I could see whether there was any Body in the Room or no, and I could see no Body, but still I was not sure; it came presently into my Thoughts to rap at the Glass, as if I wanted to speak with some Body, and if any Body was there they would be sure to come to the Window, and then I would tell them to remove those Rings, for that I had seen two suspicious Fellows take notice of them: This was a ready Thought, I rapt once or twice and no Body came, when seeing the Coast clear, I thrust hard against the Square of Glass, and broke it with very little Noise, and took out the two Rings, and walk'd away with them very safe, the Diamond Ring was worth about 3 *l.* and the other about 9 *s.*

I was now at a loss for a Market for my Goods, and especially for my two Peices of Silk; I was very loth to dispose of them for a Trifle, as the poor unhappy Theives in general do, who after they have ventured their Lives for, perhaps, a thing of Value, are fain[284] to sell it for

---

[280]A glossy silk fabric.
[281]Separate.
[282]Booty, plunder. (R)
[283]Forethought, prudence.

[284]Obliged, or possibly the more common meaning applies here: willing. (The third edition reads "forc'd.")

a Song when they have done; but I was resolv'd I would not do thus whatever shift I made, unless I was driven to the last Extremity; however I did not well know what Course to take: At last I resolv'd to go to my old Governness, and acquaint myself with her again: I had punctually supply'd the 5 *l.* a Year to her for my little Boy as long as I was able; but at last was oblig'd to put a stop to it: However I had written a Letter to her, wherein I had told her that my Circumstances were reduc'd very low; that I had lost my Husband, and that I was not able to do it any longer, and so beg'd that the poor Child might not suffer too much for its Mother's Misfortunes.

I now made her a Visit, and I found that she drove something of the old Trade still, but that she was not in such flourishing Circumstances as before; for she had been Sued by a certain Gentleman, who had had his Daughter stolen from him; and who it seems she had helped to convey away; and it was very narrowly that she escap'd the Gallows; the Expence also had ravag'd her, and she was become very poor; her House was but meanly Furnished, and she was not in such repute for her Practice as before; however she stood upon her Legs, as they say, and as she was a stirring bustling Woman, and had some Stock left, she was turn'd *Pawn Broker, and liv'd pretty well.*

She receiv'd me very civily, and with her usual obliging manner told me, she would not have the less respect for me, for my being reduc'd; that she had taken Care my Boy was very well look'd after, tho' I could not pay for him, and that the Woman that had him was easie, so that I needed not to Trouble myself about him, till I might be better able to do it effectually.

I told her I had not much Money left, but that I had some things that were Monies worth, if she could tell me how I might turn them into Money; she ask'd me what it was I had, I pull'd out the string of gold Beads, and told her it was one of my Husbands Presents to me; then I show'd her the two Parcels of Silk which I told her I had from *Ireland*, and brought up to Town with me; and the little Diamond Ring; as to the small Parcel of Plate and Spoons, I had found means to dispose of them myself before; and as for the Childbed Linnen I had, she offer'd me to take it herself, believing it to have been my own; she told me that she was turn'd *Pawn-Broker*, and that she would sell those things for me as pawn'd to her, and so she sent presently for proper Agents that bought them, being in her Hands, without any scruple, and gave good Prizes[285] too.

I now began to think this necessary Woman[286] might help me a little in my low Condition to some Business; for I would gladly have turn'd my Hand to any honest Employment if I could have got it; but here

[285]A high return, good prices.
[286]Slang term, variously applied, for a woman who renders a useful service.

she was defficient; honest Business did not come within her reach; if I had been younger, perhaps she might have helped me to a Spark,[287] but my Thoughts were off of that kind of Livelihood, as being quite out of the way after 50, which was my Case, and so I told her.

She invited me at last to come, and be at her House till I could find something to do, and it should cost me very little, and this I gladly accepted of, and now living a little easier, I enter'd into some Measures to have my little Son by my last Husband taken off;[288] and this she made easie too, reserving a Payment only of 5 *l.* a Year, if I could pay it. This was such a help to me, that for a good while I left off the wicked Trade that I had so newly taken up; and gladly I would have got my Bread by the help of my Needle if I cou'd have got Work, but that was very hard to do for one that had no manner of Acquaintance in the World.

However at last I got some Quilting-Work for Ladies Beds, Peticoats, and the like; and this I lik'd very well and work'd very hard, and with this I began to live; but the diligent Devil who resolv'd I should continue in his Service, continually prompted me to go out and take a Walk, that is to say, to see if any thing would offer in the old Way.

One Evening I blindly obeyed his Summons and fetch'd a long Circuit thro' the Streets, but met with no purchase and came Home very weary, and empty; but not content with that, I went out the next Evening too, when going by an Alehouse I saw the Door of a little room open, next the very Street, and on the Table a silver Tankard, things much in use in publick Houses at that time; it seems some Company had been drinking there, and the careless Boys had forgot to take it away.

I went into the Box frankly,[289] and setting the silver Tankard on the Corner of the Bench, I sat down before it, and knock'd with my Foot; a Boy came presently, and I bad him fetch me a pint of warm Ale, for it was cold Weather; the Boy run, and I heard him go down the Sellar to draw the Ale; while the Boy was gone, another Boy come into the Room and cried, *d'ye call*, I spoke with a melancholly Air, and said, no Child, the Boy is gone for a Pint of Ale for me.

While I sat here, I heard the Woman in the Bar say, are they all gone in the Five, which was the Box I sat in, and the Boy said *yes*; who fetch'd the Tankard away? *says the Woman*, I did, *says another Boy*, that's it, pointing it seems to another Tankard, which he had fetch'd from another Box by Mistake; or else it must be, that the Rogue forgot that he had not brought it in, which certainly he had not.

I heard all this, much to my satisfaction, for I found plainly that the Tankard was not mist, and yet they concluded it was fetch'd away; so I

---

[287]Gallant.
[288]Moll does not tell us what happened

to her other child (see p. 150).
[289]Ingenuously, undisguisedly.

drank my Ale, call'd to Pay, and as I went away, *I said*, take care of your Plate Child, meaning a silver pint Mug, which he brought me to Drink in; the Boy said, *yes Madam*, *very welcome*, and away I came.

I came Home to my Governness, and now I thought it was a time to try her, that if I might be put to the Necessity of being expos'd, she might offer me some assistance; when I had been at Home some time, and had an opportunity of Talking to her, I told her I had a Secret of the greatest Consequence in the World to commit to her if she had respect enough for me to keep it a Secret: She told me she had kept one of my Secrets faithfully; why should I doubt her keeping another? I told her the strangest thing in the World had befallen me, and that it had made a Thief of me, even without any design; and so told her the whole Story of the Tankard: And have you brought it away with you my Dear, *says she*, to be sure I have, *says I*, and shew'd it her. But what shall I do now, *says I*, must not I carry it again?

Carry it again! *says she*, Ay, if you are minded to be sent to *Newgate* for stealing it; why, *says I*, they can't be so base to stop me, when I carry it to them again? You don't know those Sort of People Child, *says she*, they'll not only carry you to *Newgate*, but hang you too without any regard to the honesty of returning it; or bring in an Account of all the other Tankards they have lost for you to pay for: What must I do then? *says I*; Nay, *says she*, as you have plaid the cunning part and stole it, you must e'n keep it, there's no going back now; besides Child, *says she*, Don't you want it more than they do? I wish you cou'd light of[290] such a Bargain once a Week.

This gave me a new Notion of my *Governess*, and that since she was turn'd *Pawn-Broker*, she had a Sort of People about her, that were none of the honest ones that I had met with there before.

I had not been long there, but I discover'd it more plainly than before, for every now and then I saw Hilts of Swords, Spoons, Forks, Tankards, and all such kind of Ware brought in, not to be Pawn'd, but to be sold down right; and she bought every thing that came without asking any Questions, but had very good Bargains as I found by her Discourse.

I found also that in the following this Trade, she always melted down the Plate she bought, that it might not be challeng'd; and she came to me and told me one Morning that she was going to Melt, and if I would, she would put my Tankard in, that it might not be seen by any Body; I told her with all my Heart; so she weigh'd it, and allow'd me the full value in Silver again; but I found she did not do the same to the rest of her Customers.

Sometime after this, as I was at Work, and very melancholly, she begins to ask me what the Matter was? as she was us'd to do; I told

[290]Upon.

her my Heart was heavy, I had little Work, and nothing to live on, and knew not what Course to take; she Laugh'd and told me I must go out again and try my Fortune; it might be that I might meet with another Peice of Plate. O, Mother! *says I*, that is a Trade I have no skill in, and if I should be taken I am undone at once; *says she*, I cou'd help you to a School-Mistress,[291] that shall make you as dexterous as herself: I trembled at that Proposal for hitherto I had had no Confederates, nor any Acquaintance among that Tribe; but she conquer'd all my Modesty, and all my Fears; and in a little time, by the help of this Confederate I grew as impudent a Thief, and as dexterous as ever *Moll Cut-Purse*[292] was, tho' if Fame does not belie her, not half so Handsome.

The Comrade she helped me to, dealt in three sorts of Craft. (*viz.*) Shop-lifting, stealing of Shop-Books, and Pocket-Books, and taking off Gold Watches from the Ladies Sides, and this last she did so dexteriously that no Woman ever arriv'd to the Perfection of that Art, so as to do it like her: I lik'd the first and the last of these things very well, and I attended her some time in the Practise, just as a Deputy attends a Midwife without any Pay.

At length she put me to Practise, she had shewn me her Art, and I had several times unhook'd a Watch from her own side with great dexterity; at last she show'd me a Prize, and this was a young Lady big with Child who had a charming Watch, the thing was to be done as she came out of Church; she goes on one side of the Lady, and pretends, just as she came to the Steps, to fall, and fell against the Lady with so much violence as put her into a great fright, and both cry'd out terribly; in the very moment that she jostl'd the Lady, I had hold of the Watch, and holding it the right way, the start she gave drew the Hook out and she never felt it; I made off immediately, and left my Schoolmistress to come out of her pretended Fright gradually, and the Lady too; and presently the Watch was miss'd; ay, *says my Comrade*, then it was those Rogues that thrust me down, I warrant ye; I wonder the Gentlewoman did not miss her Watch before, then we might have taken them.

She humour'd[293] the thing so well that no Body suspected her, and I was got home a full Hour before her: This was my first Adventure in Company; the Watch was indeed a very fine one, and had a great many Trinkets about it, and my Governess allow'd us 20 *l.* for it, of which I

---

[291]I.e, someone to teach Moll the skills of a pickpocket and thief.

[292]Mary Frith, a famous criminal, who died nearly penniless at the age of 74 in 1659. During her career, she had tried most varieties of crime, including highway robbery and receiving stolen goods, but she was best known as a pickpocket.

Several legendary exploits of Moll Cut-Purse roughly parallel incidents in *Moll Flanders*; for example, both Molls worked for a time disguised as men. (Cut-purse = pickpocket, the term deriving from the old practice of cutting purses loose from girdles.)

[293]Manipulated delicately.

had half, and thus I was enter'd a compleat Thief, harden'd to a Pitch above all the Reflections of Conscience or Modesty, and to a Degree which I must acknowledge I never thought possible in me.

Thus the Devil who began, by the help of an irresistable Poverty, to push me into this Wickedness, brought me on to a height beyond the common Rate, even when my Necessities were not so great, or the prospect of my Misery so terrifying; for I had now got into a little Vein of Work, and as I was not at a loss to handle my Needle, it was very probable, as Acquaintance came in, I might have got my Bread honestly enough.

I must say, that if such a prospect of Work had presented it self at first, when I began to feel the approach of my miserable Circumstances; I say, had such a prospect of getting my Bread by working presented it self then, I had never fallen into this wicked Trade, or into such a wicked Gang as I was now embark'd with; but practise had hardened me, and I grew audacious to the last degree; and the more so, because I had carried it on so long, and had never been taken; for in a word, my new Partner in Wickedness *and I* went on together so long, without being ever detected, that we not only grew Bold, but we grew Rich, and we had at one time One and Twenty Gold Watches in our Hands.

I remember that one Day being a little more serious than ordinary, and finding I had so good a Stock before-hand as I had, for I had near 200 *l.* in Money for my Share; it came strongly into my Mind, no doubt from some kind Spirit, if such there be; that as at first Poverty excited me, and my Distresses drove me to these dreadful Shifts; so seeing those Distresses were now relieved, and I could also get something towards a Maintenance by working, and had so good a Bank to support me, why should I not now leave off, as they say, while I was well; that I could not expect to go always free; and if I was once surpris'd, and miscarry'd, I was undone.

This was doubtless the happy Minute, when if I had hearken'd to the blessed hint from whatsoever hand it came, I had still a cast for an easie Life; but my Fate was otherwise determin'd, the busie Devil that so industriously drew me in, had too fast hold of me to let me go back; but as Poverty brought me into the Mire, so Avarice kept me in, till there was no going back; as to the Arguments which my Reason dictated for perswading me to lay down, Avarice stept in and said, go on, go on; you have had very good luck, go on till you have gotten Four or Five Hundred Pound, and then you shall leave off, and then you may live easie without working at all.

Thus I that was once in the Devil's Clutches, was held fast there as with a Charm, and had no Power to go without the Circle, till I was ingulph'd in Labyrinths of Trouble too great to get out at all.

However, these Thoughts left some Impression upon me, and made me act with some more caution than before, and more than my Directors us'd for themselves. My Comerade, as I call'd her, but rather she should have been called my Teacher, with another of her Scholars, was the first in the Misfortune, for happening to be upon the hunt for Purchase, they made an attempt upon a Linnen-Draper in *Cheapside*, but were snap'd[294] by a Hawks-ey'd Journey-man,[295] and seiz'd with two pieces of Cambrick, which were taken also upon them.

This was enough to Lodge them both in *Newgate*, where they had the Misfortune to have some of their former Sins brought to remembrance; two other Indictments being brought against them, and the Facts being prov'd upon them, they were both condemned to Die; they both pleaded their Bellies, and were both voted Quick with Child;[296] tho' my Tutress was no more with Child than I was.

I went frequently to see them, and Condole with them, expecting that it would be my turn next; but the place gave me so much Horror, reflecting that it was the place of my unhappy Birth, and of my Mother's Misfortunes, that I could not bear it, so I was forc'd to leave off going to see them.

And O! cou'd I have but taken warning by their Disasters, I had been happy still, for I was yet free, and had nothing brought against me; but it could not be, my Measure was not yet fill'd up.[297]

My Comerade having the Brand of an old Offender, was Executed; the young Offender was spar'd having obtain'd a Reprieve; but lay starving a long while in Prison, till at last she got her Name into what they call a Circuit Pardon,[298] and so came off.

This terrible Example of my Comerade frighted me heartily, and for a good while I made no Excursion; but one Night, in the Neighbourhood of my Governesses House, they cryed Fire; my Governess look'd out, for we were all up, and cryed immediately that such a Gentlewoman's House was all of a light Fire a top, and so indeed it was: Here she gives me a jog, now, Child, says she, there is a rare opportunity, the Fire being so near that you may go to it before the Street is block'd up with the Crowd; she presently gave me my Cue, go, Child, *says she*, to the House, and run in and tell the Lady, or any Body you see, that you come to help them, and that you came from such a Gentlewoman (that is one of her Acquaintance farther up the Street); she gave me the like Cue to the next House, naming another Name that was also an Acquaintance of the Gentlewoman of the House.

Away I went, and coming to the House I found them all in Con-

---

[294]Caught.
[295]A worker, between the levels of apprentice and master, who works for day wages.
[296]Judged to be pregnant.

[297]I.e., the sum of her iniquities was not yet completed (see Matthew 23:32 or Genesis 15:16).
[298]Possibly a general or class pardon.

fusion, you may be sure; I run in, and finding one of the Maids, Lord! Sweetheart, *said I*, how came this dismal Accident? Where is your Mistress? And how does she do? Is she safe? And where are the Children? I came from Madam —— to help you; away runs the Maid, Madam, Madam, *says she*, screaming as loud as she cou'd yell, *here is a Gentlewoman come from Madam* —— *to help us*: The poor Woman half out of her Wits, with a Bundle under her Arm, and two little Children, comes towards me, *Lord, Madam, says I*, let me carry the poor Children to Madam ——, she desires you to send them; she'll take care of the poor Lambs, and immediately I takes one of them out of her Hand, and she lifts the tother up into my Arms; *ay, do; for God sake*, says she, *carry them to her; O thank her for her kindness*: Have you *any thing else to secure*, Madam? says I, *she will take care of it*: O dear! ay, says she, *God bless her, and thank her, take this bundle of Plate and carry it to her too; O she is a good Woman; O Lord, we are utterly ruin'd, utterly undone*; and away she runs from me, out of her Wits, and the Maids after her, and away comes I with the two Children and the Bundle.

I was no sooner got into the Street, but I saw another Woman come to me, O! *says she*, Mistress, in a piteous Tone, you will let fall the Child; come, this is a sad time, let me help you, and immediately lays hold of my Bundle to carry it for me; no, *says I*, if you will help me, take the Child by the Hand, and lead it for me but to the upper end of the Street, I'll go with you and satisfie you for your pains.

She cou'd not avoid going, after what I said, but the Creature, in short, was one of the same Business with me, and wanted nothing but the Bundle; however, she went with me to the Door, for she cou'd not help it; when we were come there I whisper'd her, *go Child*, said I, *I understand your Trade*, you may meet with Purchase enough.

She understood me and walk'd off; I thundered at the Door with the Children, and as the People were rais'd before by the noise of the Fire, I was soon let in, and I said, *is Madam awake, pray tell her* Mrs. —— *desires the favour of her to take the two Children in*; poor Lady, *she will be undone, their House is all of a Flame*; they took the Children in very civily, pitied the Family in Distress, and away came I with my Bundle; one of the Maids ask'd me, if I was not to leave the Bundle too? I said no, Sweetheart, 'tis to go to another place, it does not belong to them.

I was a great way out of the hurry now, and so I went on, clear of any Body's enquiry, and brought the bundle of Plate, which was very considerable, strait home, and gave it to my old Governess; she told me she would not look into it, but bad me go out again to look for more.

She gave me the like Cue to the Gentlewoman of the next House to that which was on Fire, and I did my endeavour to go, but by this time the allarm of Fire was so great, and so many Engines playing,[299] and the Street so throng'd with People, that I cou'd not get near the House, whatever I cou'd do; so I came back again to my Governesses, and taking the Bundle up into my Chamber, I began to examine it: It is with Horror that I tell what a Treasure I found there; 'tis enough to say, that besides most of the Family Plate, which was considerable, I found a Gold Chain, an old fashion'd thing, the Locket of which was broken, so that I suppose it had not been us'd some Years, but the Gold was not the worse for that; also a little Box of burying Rings,[300] the Lady's Wedding-Ring, and some broken bits of old Lockets of Gold, a Gold Watch, and a Purse with about 24 *l.* value in old pieces of Gold Coin, and several other things of Value.

This was the greatest and the worst Prize that ever I was concern'd in, for indeed, tho' as I have said above, I was harden'd now beyond the Power of all Reflection in other Cases, yet it really touch'd me to the very Soul, when I look'd into this Treasure, to think of the poor disconsolate Gentlewoman who had lost so much by the Fire besides; and who would think to be sure that she had sav'd her Plate and best things; how she wou'd be surpriz'd and afflicted when she should find that she had been deceiv'd, and should find that the Person that took her Children and her Goods, had not come, as was pretended, from the Gentlewoman in the next Street, but that the Children had been put upon her without her own knowledge.

I say I confess the inhumanity of this Action mov'd me very much, and made me relent exceedingly, and Tears stood in my Eyes upon that Subject: But with all my Sense of its being cruel and Inhuman, I cou'd never find in my Heart to make any Restitution: The Reflection wore off, and I began quickly to forget the Circumstances that attended the taking them.

Nor was this all, for tho' by this jobb I was become considerably Richer than before, yet the Resolution I had formerly taken of leaving off this horrid Trade, when I had gotten a little more, did not return; but I must still get farther, and more; and the Avarice join'd so with the Success, that I had no more thoughts of coming to a timely Alteration of Life; tho' without it I cou'd expect no Safety, no Tranquility in the Possession of what I had so wickedly gain'd; but a little more, and a little more, was the Case still.

At length yielding to the Importunities of my Crime, I cast off all Remorse and Repentance; and all the Reflections on that Head, turn'd to no more than this, that I might perhaps come to have one Booty more that might compleat my Desires; but tho' I certainly had that one Booty, yet every hit look'd towards another, and was so

[299]Spouting water.
[300]In the eighteenth century, fairly ex-

pensive rings were often given to mourners as a part of the funereal splendor.

couraging to me to go on with the Trade, that I had no Gust to the Thought of laying it down.

In this Condition, harden'd by Success, and resolving to go on, I fell into the Snare in which I was appointed to meet with my last Reward for this kind of Life: But even this was not yet, for I met with several successful Adventures more in this way of being undone.

I remain'd still with my Governess, who was for a while really concern'd for the Misfortune of my Comerade that had been hang'd, and who it seems knew enough of my Governess to have sent her the same way, and which made her very uneasy; indeed she was in a very great fright.

It is true, that when she was gone, and had not open'd her Mouth to tell what she knew, My Governess was easy as to that Point, and perhaps glad she was hang'd; for it was in her power to have obtain'd a Pardon at the Expence of her Friends; But on the other Hand, the loss of her, and the Sense of her Kindness in not making her Market of what she knew,[301] mov'd my Governess to Mourn her very sincerely: I comforted her as well as I cou'd, and she in return harden'd me to Merit more compleatly the same Fate.

However as I have said it made me the more wary, and particularly I was very shie of Shoplifting, especially among the *Mercers*, and *Drapers* who are a Set of Fellows, that have their Eyes very much about them: I made a Venture or two among the Lace Folks, and the Mileners, and particularly at one Shop, where I got Notice of two young Women who were newly set up, and had not been bred to the Trade: There, I think I carried off a Peice of Bonelace, worth six or seven pound, and a Paper of Thread; but this was but once, it was a Trick that would not serve again.

It was always reckon'd a safe Job when we heard of a new Shop, and especially when the People were such as were not bred to Shops; such may depend upon it, that they will be visited once or twice at their beginning, and they must be very Sharp indeed if they can prevent it.

I made another Adventure or two, but they were but Trifles too, tho' sufficient to live on; after this nothing considerable offering for a good while, I began to think that I must give over the Trade in Earnest; but my Governess, who was not willing to lose me, and expected great Things of me, brought me one Day into Company with a young Woman and a Fellow that went for her Husband, tho' as it appear'd afterwards she was not his Wife, but they were Partners it seems in the Trade they carried on; and Partners in something else too. *In short*, they robb'd together, lay together, were taken together, and at last were hang'd together.

[301]I.e., becoming an informer, buying her own freedom by giving information on accomplices.

I came into a kind of League with these two, by the help of my Governess, and they carried me out into three or four Adventures, where I rather saw them commit some Course[302] and unhandy Robberies, in which nothing but a great Stock of impudence on their Side, and gross Negligence on the Peoples Side who were robb'd, could have made them Successful; so I resolv'd from that time forward to be very Cautious how I Adventur'd upon any thing with them; and indeed when two or three unlucky[303] Projects were propos'd by them, I declin'd the offer, and perswaded them against it: One time they particularly propos'd Robbing a Watchmaker of 3 Gold Watches, which they had Ey'd in the Day time, and found the Place where he laid them; one of them had so many Keys of all kinds, that he made no Question to open the Place, where the Watchmaker had laid them; and so we made a kind of an Appointment; but when I came to look narrowly into the Thing, I found they propos'd breaking open the House; and this as a thing out of my Way, I would not Embark in; so they went without me: They did get into the House by main Force, and broke up the lock'd Place where the Watches were, but found but one of the Gold Watches, and a Silver one, which they took, and got out of the House again very clear, but the Family being alarm'd cried out, Thieves, and the Man was pursued and taken; the young Woman had got off, but unhappily was stop'd at a Distance, and the Watches found upon her; and thus I had a second Escape, for they were convicted, and both hang'd, being old Offenders, tho' but young People; as *I said before*, that they robbed together, and lay together, so now they hang'd together, and there ended my new Partnership.

I began now to be very wary, having so narrowly escap'd a Scouring,[304] and having such an Example before me; but I had a new Tempter, who prompted me every Day, I mean my Governess; and now a Prize presented, which as it came by her Management, so she expected a good Share of the Booty; there was a good Quantity of Flanders-Lace Lodg'd in a private House, where she had gotten Intelligence of it; and Flanders-Lace, being then Prohibited, it was a good Booty to any Custom-House Officer that could come at it: I had a full Account from my Governess, as well of the Quantity as of the very Place where it was conceal'd, and I went to a Custom-House Officer, and told him I had such a Discovery to make to him, of such a Quantity of Lace, if he would assure me that I should have my due Share of the Reward: This was so just an offer, that nothing could be fairer; so he agreed, and taking a Constable, and me with him, we beset the House; as I told him, I could go directly to the Place, He left it to me, and the Hole being very dark, I squeez'd myself into it with a

---

[302]Coarse, clumsy.   [304]Chastisement, punishment.
[303]Inauspicious, likely to fail.

Candle in my Hand, and so reach'd the Peices out to him, taking care as I gave him some, so to secure as much about myself as I could conveniently Dispose of: There was near 300 *l.* worth of Lace in the whole; and I secur'd about 50 *l.* worth of it to myself: The People of the House were not owners of the Lace, but a Merchant who had entrusted them with it; so that they were not so surpriz'd as I thought they would be.

I left the Officer overjoy'd with his Prize, and fully satisfy'd with what he had got; and appointed to meet him at a House of his own directing, where I came after I had dispos'd of the Cargo I had about me, of which he had not the least Suspicion; when I came to him, he began to Capitulate[305] with me, believing I did not understand the right I had to a Share in the Prize, and would fain have put me off with Twenty Pound, but I let him know that I was not so ignorant as he suppos'd I was; and yet I was glad too, that he offer'd to bring me to a certainty;[306] I ask'd 100 *l.* and he rise up to 30 *l.* I fell to 80 *l.* and he rise again to 40 *l.* In a Word, he offer'd 50 *l.* and I consented, only demanding a Peice of Lace, which I thought came to about 8 or 9 Pound, as if it had been for my own Wear, and he agreed to it, so I got 50 *l.* in Money paid me that same Night, and made an End of the Bargain; nor did he ever know who I was, or where to enquire for me; so that if it had been discover'd, that part of the Goods were embezzel'd;[307] he could have made no Challenge upon me for it.

I very punctually[308] divided this Spoil with my Governess, and I pass'd with her from this time for a very dexterous Manager in the nicest Cases; I found that this last was the best, and easiest sort of Work that was in my way, and I made it my business to enquire out prohibited Goods; and after buying some usually betray'd them, but none of these Discoveries amounted to any thing Considerable; not like that I related just now; but I was willing to act safe, and was still Cautious of running the great Risques which I found others did, and in which they Miscarried every Day.

The next thing of Moment, was an attempt at a Gentlewoman's gold Watch, it happen'd in a Crowd, at a Meeting-House, where I was in very great Danger of being taken; I had full hold of her Watch, but giving a great Jostle, as if some body had thrust me against her, and in the Juncture giving the Watch a fair pull, I found it would not come, so I let it go that Moment, and cried out as if I had been kill'd, that some body had Trod upon my Foot, and that there was certainly *Pick-pockets* there; for some body or other had given a pull at my Watch, for you are to observe, that on these Adventures we always

---

[305]Bargain.
[306]I.e., Moll was pleased to discover that he offered a specific amount; she could thus bargain with him.

[307]Stolen.
[308]Scrupulously, fairly.

went very well Dress'd, and I had very good Cloaths on, and a Gold Watch by my Side, as like a Lady as other Folks.

I had no sooner said so, but the tother Gentlewoman cried out *a Pick-pocket* too, for some body, *she said,* had try'd to pull her Watch away.

When I touch'd her Watch, I was close to her, but when I cry'd out, I stop'd as it were short, and the Crowd bearing her forward a little, she made a Noise too, but it was at some Distance from me, so that she did not in the least suspect me; but when she cried out *a Pick-pocket,* some body cried Ay, and here has been another, this Gentlewoman has been attempted too.

At that very instant, a little farther in the Crowd, and very Luckily too, they cried out *a Pick-pocket* again, and really seiz'd a young Fellow in the very Fact. This, tho' unhappy for the Wretch was very opportunely for my Case, tho' I had carried it off handsomely enough before, but now it was out of Doubt, and all the loose part of the Crowd run that way, and the poor Boy was deliver'd up to the Rage of the Street, which is a Cruelty I need not describe,[309] and which however they are always glad of, rather than to be sent to *Newgate,* where they lie often a long time, till they are almost perish'd, and sometimes they are hang'd, and the best they can look for, if they are Convicted, is to be Transported.

This was a narrow Escape to me, and I was so frighted, that I ventur'd no more at Gold Watches a great while; there was indeed a great many concurring Circumstances in this Adventure, which assisted to my Escape; but the chief was, that the Woman whose Watch I had pull'd at was a Fool; that is to say, she was Ignorant of the nature of the Attempt, which one would have thought she should not have been, seeing She was wise enough to fasten her Watch, so that it could not be slipt up; but she was in such a Fright, that she had no thought about her proper for the Discovery; for she, when she felt the pull scream'd out, and push'd herself forward, and put all the People about her into disorder, but said not a Word of her Watch, or of a *Pick-pocket,* for at least two Minutes time; which was time enough for me, and to spare, for as I had cried out behind her, *as I have said,* and bore myself back in the Crowd as she bore forward; there were several People, at least seven or eight, the Throng being still moving on, that were got between me and her in that time, and then I crying out *a Pick-pocket,* rather sooner than she, or at least as soon, she might as well be the Person suspected as I, and the People were confus'd in their Enquiry; whereas, had she with a Presence of

---

[309]Later, however, Moll recounts, in a restrained way, how the mob acted in another instance (see p. 194 and note).

Mind needful on such an Occasion, as soon as she felt the pull, not skream'd out as she did, but turn'd immediately round, and seiz'd the next Body that was behind her, she had infallibly taken me.

This is a Direction not of the kindest Sort to the Fraternity; but 'tis certainly a Key to the Clue of *a Pick-pockets* Motions, and whoever can follow it, will as certainly catch the Thief as he will be sure to miss if he does not.

I had another Adventure, which puts this Matter out of doubt, and which may be an Instruction for Posterity in the Case of *a Pickpocket*; my good old Governess, to give a short touch at her History, tho' she had left off the Trade, was as I may say, born *a Pick-pocket*, and as I understood afterward had run thro' all the several Degrees of that Art, and yet had never been taken but once; when she was so grossly detected, that she was convicted and order'd to be Transported; but being a Woman of a rare Tongue, and withal having Money in her Pocket, she found Means, the Ship putting into *Ireland* for Provisions, to get on Shore there, where she liv'd and practis'd her old Trade for some Years; when falling into another sort of bad Company, she turn'd Midwife and Procuress, and play'd a Hundred Pranks there, which she gave me a little History of in Confidence between us as we grew more intimate; and it was to this wicked Creature that I ow'd all the Art and Dexterity I arriv'd to, in which there were few that ever went beyond me, or that practis'd so long without any Misfortune.

It was after those Adventures in *Ireland*, and when she was pretty well known in that Country, that she left *Dublin*, and came over to *England*, where the time of her Transportation being not expir'd, she left her former Trade, for fear of falling into bad Hands again, for then she was sure to have gone to Wreck: Here she set up the same Trade she had followed in *Ireland*, in which she soon by her admirable Management, and a good Tongue, arriv'd to the Height, which I have already describ'd, and indeed began to be Rich tho' her Trade fell off again afterwards; as I have hinted before.

I mention thus much of the History of this Woman here, the better to account for the concern she had in the wicked Life I was now leading; into all the particulars of which she led me as it were by the Hand, and gave me such Directions, and I so well follow'd them, that I grew the greatest Artist of my time, and work'd myself out of every Danger with such Dexterity, that when several more of my Comrades run themselves into *Newgate* presently, and by that time they had been Half a Year at the Trade, I had now Practis'd upwards of five Year, and the People at *Newgate* did not so much as know me; they had heard much of me indeed, and often expected me there; but I always got off, tho' many times in the extreamest Danger.

One of the greatest Dangers I was now in, was that I was too well known among the Trade, and some of them whose hatred was owing rather to Envy, than any Injury I had done them began to be Angry, that I should always Escape when they were always catch'd and hurried to *Newgate*. These were they that gave me the Name of *Moll Flanders*: For it was no more of Affinity with my real Name, or with any of the Names I had ever gone by, than black is of Kin to white, except that once, as before, I call'd my self Mrs. *Flanders*, when I sheltered myself in the *Mint*; but that these Rogues never knew, nor could I ever learn how they came to give me the Name, or what the Occasion of it was.[310]

I was soon inform'd that some of these who were gotten fast into *Newgate*, had vowed to Impeach[311] me; and as I knew that two or three of them were but too able to do it, I was under a great concern about it, and kept within Doors for a good while; but my Governess who I always made Partner in my Success, and who now plaid a sure[312] Game with me, for that she had a Share of the Gain, and no Share in the hazard, *I say*, my Governess was something impatient of my leading such a useless unprofitable Life, as she call'd it; and she laid a new Contrivance for my going Abroad, and this was to Dress me up in Mens Cloths, and so put me into a new kind of Practise.

I was Tall and Personable, but a little too smooth Fac'd for a Man; however as I seldom went Abroad but in the Night it did well enough; but it was a long time before I could behave in my new Cloths: I mean, as to my Craft; it was impossible to be so Nimble, so Ready, so Dexterous at these things, in a Dress so contrary to Nature; and as I did every thing Clumsily, so I had neither the success, or the easiness of Escape that I had before, and I resolv'd to leave it off; but that Resolution was confirm'd soon after by the following Accident.

As my Governess had disguis'd me like a Man, so she joyn'd me with a Man, a young Fellow that was Nimble enough at his Business, and for about three Weeks we did very well together. Our principal Trade was watching Shop-Keepers Compters,[313] and Slipping off any kind of Goods we could see carelessly laid any where, and we made several very good Bargains as we call'd them at this Work: And as we kept always together, so we grew very intimate, yet he never knew that I was not a Man; nay, tho' I several times went home with him to his Lodgings, according as our business directed, and four or five

[310]Criminals usually got their nicknames from a practice or event with which they had been associated, and Moll could well have gotten her name from the episode with contraband Flanders lace (see p. 165). Thus her protestations that she is ignorant of the source of her nickname could be an example of Defoe's deliberate portrait of her mental limitations — a factor that perhaps needs emphasis in the light of her persistent boasting.

[311]Give evidence against, to "peach" on.

[312]Safe.

[313]Counters. [R]

times lay with him all Night: But our Design lay another way, and it
was absolutely necessary to me to conceal my Sex from him, as
appear'd afterwards: The Circumstances of our Living, coming in
late, and having such and such Business to do as requir'd that no
Body should be trusted with coming into our Lodgings, were such as
made it impossible to me to refuse lying with him, unless I would have
own'd my Sex, and as it was I effectually conceal'd my self.

But his ill, and my good Fortune, soon put an end to this Life, which
I must own I was sick of too, on several other Accounts: We had made
several Prizes in this new way of Business, but the last would have
been extraordinary; there was a Shop in a certain Street which had a
Warehouse behind it that look'd into another Street, the House
making the corner of the turning.

Through the Window of the Warehouse we saw lying on the
Counter or Show-board which was just before it, Five pieces of
Silks, besides other Stuffs; and tho' it was almost dark, yet the People
being busie in the fore shop with Customers, had not had time to shut
up those Windows, or else had forgot it.

This the young Fellow was so overjoy'd with that he could not
restrain himself, it lay all within his reach he said, and he swore
violently to me that he would have it, if he broke down the House
for it; I disswaded him a little, but saw there was no remedy, so he
run rashly upon it, slipt out a Square out of the Sash Window dexterously enough, and without noise, and got out four pieces of the
Silks, and came with them towards me, but was immediately pursued
with a terrible Clutter and Noise; we were standing together indeed,
but I had not taken any of the Goods out of his Hand, when I said to
him hastily, you are undone, fly for God sake; he run like Lightning,
and I too, but the pursuit was hotter after him because he had the
Goods, than after me; he dropt two of the Pieces which stop'd them
a little, but the Crowd encreas'd and pursued us both; they took him
soon after with the other two pieces upon him, and then the rest
followed me; I run for it and got into my Governesses House, whither
some quick-eyed People follow'd me so warmly[314] as to fix[315] me there;
they did not immediately knock at the Door, by which I got time to
throw off my Disguise, and dress me in my own Cloths; besides, when
they came there, my Governess, who had her Tale ready, kept her
Door shut, and call'd out to them and told them there was no Man
came in there; the People affirm'd there did a Man come in there, and
swore they would break open the Door.

My Governess, not at all surpriz'd, spoke calmly to them, told
them they should very freely come and search her House, if they
would bring a Constable, and let in none but such as the Constable

---

[314]Closely.   [315]Establish the fact that I was there.

would admit, for it was unreasonable to let in a whole Crowd; this they could not refuse, tho' they were a Crowd; so a Constable was fetch'd immediately, and she very freely open'd the Door, the Constable kept the Door, and the Men he appointed search'd the House, my Governess going with them from Room to Room; when she came to my Room she call'd to me, and said aloud; Cousin, pray open the Door, here's some Gentlemen that must come and look into your Room.

I had a little Girl with me, which was my Governesses Grand-child, as she call'd her; and I bad her open the Door, and there sat I at work with a great litter of things about me, as if I had been at Work all Day, being my self quite undress'd, with only Night-cloaths on my Head, and a loose Morning Gown wrapt about me: My Governess made a kind of excuse for their disturbing me, telling me partly the occasion of it, and that she had no Remedy but to open the Doors to them, and let them satisfie themselves, for all she could say to them would not satisfie them: I sat still, and bid them search the Room if they pleas'd, for if there was any Body in the House, I was sure they was not in my Room; and as for the rest of the House I had nothing to say to that, I did not understand what they look'd for.

Every thing look'd so innocent and so honest about me, that they treated me civiller than I expected, but it was not till they had search'd the Room to a nicety, even under the Bed, in the Bed, and every where else, where it was possible any thing cou'd be hid; when they had done this, and cou'd find nothing, they ask'd my Pardon for troubling me, and went down.

When they had thus searched the House from Bottom to Top, and then from Top to Bottom, and cou'd find nothing, they appeas'd the Mob pretty well; but they carried my Governess before the Justice: Two Men swore that they see the Man, who they pursued, go into her House: My Governess rattled and made a great noise that her House should be insulted, and that she should be used thus for nothing; that if a Man did come in, he might go out again presently for aught she knew, for she was ready to make Oath that no Man had been within her Doors all that Day as she knew of, and that was very true indeed; that it might be indeed that as she was above Stairs, any Fellow in a Fright might find the Door open, and run in for shelter when he was pursued, but that she knew nothing of it; and if it had been so, he certainly went out again, perhaps at the other Door, for she had another Door into an Alley, and so had made his escape and cheated them all.

This was indeed probable enough, and the Justice satisfied himself with giving her an Oath, that she had not receiv'd or admitted any Man into her House to conceal him, or protect or hide him from Justice: This Oath she might justly take, and did so, and so she was dismiss'd.

It is easie to judge what a fright I was in upon this occasion, and it was impossible for my Governess ever to bring me to Dress in that Disguise again; for, as I told her, I should certainly betray my self.

My poor Partner in this Mischief was now in a bad Case, for he was carried away before my Lord Mayor, and by his Worship committed to *Newgate*, and the People that took him were so willing, as well as able, to Prosecute him, that they offer'd themselves to enter into Recognisances[316] to appear at the Sessions, and persue the Charge against them.

However, he got his Indictment deferr'd, upon promise to discover his Accomplices, and particularly, the Man that was concern'd with him in this Robbery, and he fail'd not to do his endeavour, for he gave in my Name who he call'd *Gabriel Spencer*, which was the Name I went by to him, and here appear'd the Wisdom of my concealing my Name and Sex from him, which if he had ever known I had been undone.

He did all he cou'd to discover this *Gabriel Spencer*; he describ'd me, he discover'd the place where he said I Lodg'd, and in a word, all the Particulars that he cou'd of my Dwelling; but having conceal'd the main Circumstances of my Sex from him, I had a vast Advantage, and he never cou'd hear of me; he brought two or three Families into Trouble by his endeavouring to find me out, but they knew nothing of me, any more than that I had a Fellow with me that they had seen, but knew nothing of; and as for my Governess, tho' she was the means of his coming to me, yet it was done at second hand, and he knew nothing of her.

This turn'd to his Disadvantage, for having promis'd Discoveries, but not being able to make it good, it was look'd upon as a trifling with the Justice of the City, and he was the more fiercely persued by the Shopkeepers who took him.

I was however terribly uneasie all this while, and that I might be quite out of the way, I went away from my Governesses for a while; but not knowing whither to wander, I took a Maid Servant with me, and took the Stage Coach to *Dunstable* to my old Landlord and Landlady, where I had liv'd so handsomly with my *Lancashire* Husband: Here I told her a formal Story, that I expected my Husband every Day from *Ireland*, and that I had sent a Letter to him that I would meet him at *Dunstable* at her House, and that he would certainly Land, if the Wind was fair, in a few Days, so that I was come to spend a few Days with them till he should come, for he would either come Post, or in the *West-Chester* Coach, I knew not which, but which soever it was, he would be sure to come to that House to meet me.

My Landlady was mighty glad to see me, and my Landlord made

---

[316]Legally oblige themselves.

such a stir with me, that if I had been a Princess I cou'd not have been better used, and here I might have been welcome a Month or two if I had thought fit.

But my Business was of another Nature, I was very uneasie (tho' so well Disguis'd that it was scarce possible to Detect me) least this Fellow should some how or other find me out; and tho' he cou'd not charge me with this Robbery, having perswaded him not to venture, and having also done nothing in it myself but run away, yet he might have charg'd me with other things, and have bought his own Life at the Expence of mine.

This fill'd me with horrible Apprehensions: I had no Recourse, no Friend, no Confident but my old Governess, and I knew no Remedy but to put my Life in her Hands, and so I did, for I let her know where to send to me, and had several Letters from her while I stayed here, some of them almost scar'd me out of my Wits; but at last she sent me the joyful News that he was hang'd, which was the best News to me that I had heard a great while.

I had stay'd here five Weeks, and liv'd very comfortably indeed, (the secret Anxiety of my Mind excepted) but when I receiv'd this Letter I look'd pleasantly again, and told my Landlady that I had receiv'd a Letter from my Spouse in *Ireland*, that I had the good News of his being very well, but had the bad News that his business would not permit him to come away so soon as he expected, and so I was like to go back again without him.

My Landlady complemented[317] me upon the good News however, that I had heard he was well, for I have observ'd, Madam, *says she*, you han't been so pleasant as you us'd to be; you have been over Head and Ears in Care for him, I dare say, *says the good Woman*; 'tis easie to be seen there's an alteration in you for the better, *says she*: Well, I am sorry the Esquire can't come yet, *says my Landlord*, I should have been heartily glad to have seen him, but I hope, when you have certain News of his coming, you'll take a step hither again, Madam; *says he*, you shall be very welcome whenever you please to come.

With all these fine Complements we parted, and I came merry enough to *London*, and found my Governess as well pleas'd as I was; and now she told me she would never recommend any Partner to me again, for she always found, *she said*, that I had the best luck when I ventur'd by my self; and so indeed I had, for I was seldom in any Danger when I was by myself, or if I was, I got out of it with more Dexterity than when I was entangled with the dull Measures of other People, who had perhaps less forecast, and were more rash and impatient than I; for tho' I had as much courage to venture as any of

---

[317]I.e., complemented. (R)

them, yet I used more caution before I undertook a thing, and had more Presence of Mind when I was to bring my self off.

I have often wondered even at my own hardiness another way, that when all my Companions were surpriz'd, and fell so suddainly into the Hand of Justice, and that I so narrowly escap'd, yet I could not all that while enter into one serious Resolution to leave off this Trade; and especially Considering that I was now very far from being poor, that the Temptation of Necessity, which is generally the Introduction of all such Wickedness, was now remov'd; for I had near 500 *l.* by me in ready Money, on which I might have liv'd very well, if I had thought fit to have retir'd; but *I say,* I had not so much as the least inclination to leave off; no not so much as I had before when I had but 200 *l.* before-hand, and when I had no such frightful Examples before my Eyes as these were; From hence 'tis Evident to me, that when once we are harden'd in Crime, no Fear can affect us, no Example give us any warning.

I had indeed one Comrade, whose Fate went very near me[318] for a good while, tho' I wore it off too in time; that Case was indeed very unhappy; I had made a Prize of a Piece of very good Damask in a *Mercers* Shop, and went clear off myself;[319] but had convey'd the Peice to this Companion of mine, when we went out of the Shop; and she went one way, and I went another: We had not been long out of the Shop, but the *Mercer* mist his Peice of Stuff, and sent his Messengers, one, one way, and one another, and they presently seiz'd her that had the Peice, with the Damask upon her; as for me, I had very Luckily step'd into a House where there was a Lace Chamber, up one Pair of Stairs, and had the Satisfaction, or the Terror indeed of looking out of the Window upon the Noise they made, and seeing the poor Creature drag'd away in Triumph to the Justice, who immediately committed her to *Newgate.*

I was careful to attempt nothing in the Lace-Chamber, but tumbl'd their Goods pretty much to spend time; then bought a few Yards of Edging, and paid for it, and came away very sad Hearted indeed for the poor Woman, who was in Tribulation for what I only had stolen.

Here again my old Caution stood me in good stead; Namely, that tho' I often robb'd with these People, yet I never let them know who I was, or where I Lodg'd; nor could they ever find out my Lodging, tho' they often endeavour'd to Watch me to it. They all knew me by the Name of *Moll Flanders,* tho' even some of them rather believ'd I was she, than knew me to be so; my Name was publick among them indeed; but how to find me out they knew not, nor so much as how to guess at my Quarters, whether they were at the East-End of the Town, or the West; and this wariness was my safety upon all these Occasions.

[318]Depressed my spirits.
[319]I.e., Moll went away "clean," with- out carrying any stolen goods on her person.

I kept close a great while upon the Occasion of this Womans disaster; I knew that if I should do any thing that should Miscarry, and should be carried to Prison she would be there, and ready to Witness against me, and perhaps save her Life at my Expence; I consider'd that I began to be very well known by Name at the *Old Baily*, tho' they did not know my Face; and that if I should fall into their Hands, I should be treated as an old Offender; and for this Reason, I was resolv'd to see what this poor Creatures Fate should be before I stirr'd Abroad, tho' several times in her Distress I convey'd Money to her for her Relief.

At length she came to her Tryal, she pleaded she did not steal the Things; but that one Mrs. *Flanders*, as she heard her call'd, (for she did not know her) gave the Bundle to her after they came out of the Shop, and bad her carry it Home to her Lodging. They ask'd her where this Mrs. *Flanders* was? but she could not produce her, neither could she give the least Account of me; and the *Mercers* Men swearing positively that she was in the Shop when the Goods were stolen; that they immediately miss'd them, and pursu'd her, and found them upon her; Thereupon the Jury brought her in Guilty; but the Court considering that she really was not the Person that stole the Goods, an inferiour Assistant, and that it was very possible she could not find out this Mrs. *Flanders*, *meaning me*, tho' it would save her Life, which indeed was true; I say considering all this, they allow'd her to be Transported, which was the utmost Favour she could obtain, only that the Court told her, that if she could in the mean time produce the said Mrs. *Flanders*, they would intercede for her Pardon, that is to say, if she could find me out, and hang me, she should not be Transported: This I took care to make impossible to her, and so she was Shipp'd off in pursuance of her Sentence a little while after.

I must repeat it again, that the Fate of this poor Woman troubl'd me exceedingly; and I began to be very pensive, knowing that I was really the Instrument of her disaster; but the Preservation of my own Life, which was so evidently in Danger, took off all my tenderness; and seeing she was not put to Death, I was very easie at her Transportation, because she was then out of the way of doing me any Mischief whatever should happen.

The Disaster of this Woman was some Months before that of the last recited Story, and was indeed partly the Occasion of my Governess proposing to Dress me up in Mens Cloths, that I might go about unobserv'd, as indeed I did; but I was soon tir'd of that Disguise, as *I have said*, for indeed it expos'd me to too many Difficulties.

I was now easie, as to all Fear of Witnesses aganst me, for all those, that had either been concern'd with me, or that knew me by the Name of *Moll Flanders*, were either hang'd or Transported; and if I should have had the Misfortune to be taken, I might call myself any thing else, as well as *Moll Flanders*, and no old Sins could be plac'd to my Account; so I began to run a Tick[320] again, with the more freedom, and several successful Adventures I made, tho' not such as I had made before.

We had at that time another Fire happen'd not a great way off from the Place where my Governess liv'd, and I made an attempt there, as before, but as I was not soon enough before the Crowd of People came in, and could not get to the House I aim'd at, instead of a Prize, I got a mischief, which had almost put a Period to my Life, and all my wicked doings together; for the Fire being very furious, and the People in a great Fright in removing their Goods, and throwing them out of Window; a Wench from out of a Window threw a Featherbed just upon me; it is true, the Bed being soft it broke no Bones; but as the weight was great, and made greater by the Fall, it beat me down, and laid me dead[321] for a while; nor did the People concern themselves much to deliver me from it, or to recover me at all; but I lay like one Dead and neglected a good while; till some body going to remove the Bed out of the way, helped me up; it was indeed a wonder the People of the House had not thrown other Goods out after it, and which might have fallen upon it, and then I had been inevitably kill'd; but I was reserved for further Afflictions.

This Accident however spoil'd my Market[322] for that time, and I came Home to my Governess very much hurt, and Bruised, and Frighted to the last degree, and it was a good while before she could set me upon my Feet again.

It was now a Merry time of the Year, and *Bartholomew* Fair[323] was begun; I had never made any Walks that Way, nor was the common Part of the Fair of much Advantage to me; but I took a turn this Year into the Cloisters,[324] and among the rest, I fell into one of the Raffling Shops:[325] It was a thing of no great Consequence to me, nor did I expect to make much of it; but there came a Gentleman extreamly well Dress'd, and very Rich, and as 'tis frequent to talk to every Body in those Shops he singl'd me out, and was very particular

[320]Tab; i.e., she began a new ledger. Typically, Moll uses a trade metaphor to describe the sins and crimes she is accountable for.

[321]Still.

[322]Business.

[323]The largest, oldest, and most famous English fair. It was held in West Smithfield, a three-acre area just northwest of the City of London where the live cattle market was regularly held. The fair began each year on August 24 and lasted fourteen days; it was more distinguished for its varieties of merriment than for its markets.

[324]Arcades, covered walks.

[325]Houses where "raffle" was played. In raffle, three dice are used, and the winner is he who throws all three alike, or the highest pair.

with me; first he told me he would put in for me to Raffle, and did so; and some small matter coming to his Lot, he presented it to me, I think it was a Feather Muff: Then he continu'd to keep talking to me with a more than common Appearance of Respect; but still very civil and much like a Gentleman.

He held me in talk so long till at last he drew me out of the Raffling Place to the Shop-Door, and then to take a walk in the Cloister, still talking of a Thousand things Cursorily without any thing to the purpose; at last he told me that without Complement he was charm'd with my Company, and ask'd me if I durst trust myself in a Coach with him; he told me he was a Man of Honour, and would not offer any thing to me unbecoming him as such: I seem'd to decline it a while, but suffer'd myself to be importun'd a little, and then yielded.

I was at a loss in my Thoughts to conclude at first what this Gentleman design'd; but I found afterward he had had some drink in his Head; and that he was not very unwilling to have some more: He carried me in the Coach to the *Spring-Garden*, at *Knight's-Bridge* where we walk'd in the Gardens, and he Treated me very handsomely; but I found he drank very freely, he press'd me also to drink, but I declin'd it.

Hitherto he kept his Word with me, and offer'd me nothing amiss; we came away in the Coach again, and he brought me into the Streets and by this time it was near Ten a-Clock at Night, and he stop'd the Coach at a House, where it seems he was acquainted, and where they made no scruple to show us up Stairs into a Room with a Bed in it; at first I seem'd to be unwilling to go up, but after a few Words, I yielded to that too, being indeed willing to see the End of it, and in Hopes to make something of it at last; as for the Bed, &c. I was not much concern'd about that Part.

Here he began to be a little freer with me than he had promis'd; and I by little and little yielded to every thing, so that in a Word, he did what he pleas'd with me; I need say no more; all this while he drank freely too, and about One in the Morning we went into the Coach again; the Air, and the shaking of the Coach made the Drink he had get more up in his Head than it was before, and he grew uneasy in the Coach, and was for acting over again, what he had been doing before; but as I thought my Game now secure, I resisted him, and brought him to be a little still, which had not lasted five Minutes, but he fell fast asleep.

I took this opportunity to search him to a Nicety; I took a gold Watch, with a silk Purse of Gold, his fine full bottom Perrewig, and silver fring'd Gloves, his Sword, and fine Snuff-box, and gently opening the Coach-door, stood ready to jump out while the Coach was going on; but the Coach stopping in the narrow Street beyond *Temple-Bar* to let another Coach pass, I got softly out, fasten'd the

Door again, and gave my Gentleman and the Coach the slip both together, and never heard more of them.[326] This was an Adventure indeed unlook'd for, and perfectly undesign'd by me; tho' I was not so past the Merry part of Life, as to forget how to behave, when a Fop so blinded by his Appetite should not know an old Woman from a young: I did not indeed look so old as I was by ten or twelve Year; yet I was not a young Wench of Seventeen, and it was easie enough to be distinguish'd: There is nothing so absurd, so surfeiting, so ridiculous as a Man heated by Wine in his Head, and a wicked Gust in his Inclination together; he is in the possession of two Devils at once, and can no more govern himself by his Reason than a Mill can Grind without Water; His Vice tramples upon all that was in him that had any good in it, if any such thing there was; nay, his very Sense is blinded by its own Rage, and he acts Absurdities even in his View;[327] such is Drinking more, when he is Drunk already; picking up a common Woman, without regard to what she is, or who she is; whether Sound or rotten, Clean or Unclean; whether Ugly or Handsome, whether Old or Young, and so blinded as not really to distinguish; such a Man is worse than Lunatick; prompted by his vicious corrupted Head he no more knows what he is doing, than this Wretch of mine knew when I pick'd his Pocket of his Watch and his Purse of Gold.

These are the Men of whom *Solomon* says, *they go like an Ox to the slaughter, till a Dart strikes through their Liver;*[328] an admirable Description, *by the way,* of the foul Disease,[329] which is a poisonous deadly Contagion mingling with the Blood, whose Center or Fountain is in the Liver; from whence, by the swift Circulation of the whole Mass, that dreadful nauceous Plague strikes immediately thro' his Liver, and his Spirits are infected, his Vitals stab'd thro' as with a Dart.

It is true this poor unguarded Wretch was in no Danger from me, tho' I was greatly apprehensive at first, of what Danger I might be in from him; but he was really to be pityed in one respect, that he seem'd to be a good sort of a Man in himself; a Gentleman that had no harm in his Design; a Man of Sense, and of a fine Behaviour; a comely handsome Person, a sober solid Countenance, a charming beautiful Face, and every thing that cou'd be agreeable; only had unhappily had some Drink the Night before, had not been in Bed, as he told me when we were together, was hot, and his Blood fir'd with Wine, and in that Condition his Reason *as it were* Asleep, had given him up.

---

[326]I.e., she gave them the complete slip. Later, she does hear more of the gentleman.

[327]I.e., even the person himself recognizes that his acts are absurd.

[328]See Proverbs 7:22–23.

[329]Syphilis. The density and complication of the passage derives from the fact that the liver was commonly regarded as the seat of passion.

As for me, my Business was his Money, and what I could make of
him, and after that if I could have found out any way to have done it,
I would have sent him safe home to his House, and to his Family, for
twas ten to one but he had an honest virtuous Wife, and innocent
Children, that were anxious for his Safety, and would have been glad
to have gotten him Home, and have taken care of him, till he was
restor'd to himself; and then with what Shame and Regret would he
look back upon himself? how would he reproach himself with as-
sociating himself with a Whore? pick'd up in the worst of all Holes,
the Cloister, among the Dirt and Filth of all the Town? how would he
be trembling for fear he had not the Pox, for fear a Dart had struck
through his Liver, and hate himself every time he look'd back upon the
Madness and Brutality of his Debauch? how would he, if he had any
Principles of Honour, as I verily believe he had, I say how would
he abhor the Thought of giving any ill Distemper, if he had it, as for
aught he knew he might, to his Modest and Virtuous Wife, and there-
by sowing the Contagion in the Life-blood of his Posterity?

Would such Gentlemen but consider the contemptible Thoughts
which the very Women they are concern'd with, in such Cases as
these, have of them, it wou'd be a surfeit to them: As I said above,
they value not the Pleasure, they are rais'd by no Inclination to the
Man, the passive Jade thinks of no Pleasure but the Money; and when
he is as it were drunk in the Extasies of his wicked Pleasure, her
Hands are in his Pockets searching for what she can find there; and
of which he can no more be sensible in the Moment of his Folly, than
he can fore-think of it when he goes about it.

I knew a Woman that was so dexterous with a Fellow, who indeed
deserv'd no better usage, that while he was busie with her another
way, convey'd his Purse with twenty Guineas in it out of his Fob
Pocket,[330] where he had put it for fear of her, and put another Purse
with guilded Counters[331] in it into the room of it: After he had done,
he says to her, now han't you pick'd my Pocket? she jested with him,
and told him she suppos'd he had not much to lose; he put his Hand
to his Fob, and with his Fingers felt that his Purse was there, which
fully satisfy'd him, and so she brought off his Money; and this was a
Trade with her, she kept a sham Gold Watch, that is a Watch of
Silver Guilt, and a Purse of Counters in her Pocket to be ready on
all such Occasions; and I doubt not practis'd it with Success.

I came home with this last Booty to my Governess, and really
when I told her the Story it so affected her, that she was hardly able to
forbear Tears, to think how such a Gentleman run a daily Risque of
being undone, every time a Glass of Wine got into his Head.

---

[330]A small pocket designed for carrying
watches, money, or other valuables.

[331]Imitation coins of inferior metal,
overlaid with a thin coating of gold.

But as to the Purchase I got, and how entirely I stript him, she told me it pleas'd her wonderfully; nay, Child, *says she*, the usage may, for aught I know, do more to reform him, than all the Sermons that ever he will hear in his Life, and if the remainder of the Story be true, so it did.

I found the next Day she was wonderful inquisitive about this Gentleman; the description I had given her of him, his Dress, his Person, his Face, every thing concur'd to make her think of a Gentleman whose Character she knew, and Family too; she mus'd a while, and I going still on with the Particulars, she starts up, *says she*, I'll lay a Hundred Pound I know the Gentleman.

I am sorry you do, *says I*, for I would not have him expos'd on any account in the World; he has had injury enough already by me, and I would not be instrumental to do him any more: No, no *says she*, I will do him no Injury, I assure you, but you may let me satisfie my Curiosity a little, for if it is he, I warrant you I find it out: I was a little startled at that, and told her with an apparent concern in my Face, that by the same Rule he might find me out, and then I was undone: *she return'd warmly*, why, do you think I will betray you, Child? No, no, *says she*, not for all he is worth in the World; I have kept your Counsel in worse things than these, sure you may trust me in this: So I said no more at that time.

She laid her Scheme another way, and without acquainting me of it, but she was resolv'd to find it out, if possible; so she goes to a certain friend of hers who was acquainted in the Family, that she guess'd at, and told her Friend she had some extraordinary business with such a Gentleman (who by the way was no less than a Baronet, and of a very good Family) and that she knew not how to come at him without somebody to introduce her: Her Friend promis'd her very readily to do it, and accordingly goes to the House to see if the Gentleman was in Town.

The next Day she comes to my Governess and tells her, that Sir —— was at Home, but that he had met with a Disaster and was very ill, and there was no speaking with him; what Disaster, *says my Governess hastily*, as if she was surpriz'd at it? Why, *says her Friend*, he had been at *Hampstead*[332] to Visit a Gentleman of his Acquaintance, and as he came back again he was set upon and Robb'd; and having got a little Drink too, as they suppose, the Rogues abus'd him, and he is very ill: Robb'd, *says my Governess*, and what did they take from him; why, *says her Friend*, they took his Gold Watch, and his Gold Snuffbox, his fine Perriwig, and what Money he had in his Pocket, which

[332] A fashionable spa northwest of London, some miles from Knightsbridge, where Moll's encounter occurred.

was considerable to be sure, for Sir ———— never goes without a Purse of Guineas about him.

Pshaw! says my old Governess jeering, I warrant you he has got drunk now and got a Whore, and she has pick'd his Pocket, and so he comes home to his Wife and tells her he has been Robb'd; that's an old sham, a thousand such tricks are put upon the poor Women every Day.

Fye, *says her Friend*, I find you don't know Sir ————, why he is as Civil a Gentleman, there is not a finer Man, nor a soberer grave modester Person in the whole City; he abhors such things, there's no Body that knows him will think such a thing of him: Well, well, *says my Governess*, that's none of my Business; if it was, I warrant I should find there was something of that kind in it; your Modest Men in common Opinion are sometimes no better than other People, only they keep a better Character, or if you please, are the better Hypocrites.

No, no, *says her Friend*, I can assure you Sir ———— is no Hypocrite, he is really an honest sober Gentleman, and he has certainly been Robb'd: Nay, *says my Governess*, it may be he has, it is no Business of mine I tell you; I only want to speak with him, my Business is of another Nature; but, *says her Friend*, let your Business be of what nature it will, you cannot see him yet, for he is not fit to be seen, for he is very ill, and bruis'd very much: Ay, *says my Governess*, nay then he has fallen into bad Hands to be sure; and then she ask'd gravely, pray where is he bruised? Why in his Head, *says her Friend*, and one of his Hands, and his Face, for they us'd him barbarously. Poor Gentleman, *says my Governess*, I must wait then till he recovers, and adds, I hope it will not be long, for I want very much to speak with him.

Away she comes to me and tells me this Story, I have found out your fine Gentleman, and a fine Gentleman he was, *says she*, but Mercy on him, he is in a sad pickle now, I wonder what the D——l you have done to him; why you have almost kill'd him: I look'd at her with disorder enough; I kill'd him! *says I*, you must mistake the Person, I am sure I did nothing to him, he was very well when I left him, *said I*, only drunk and fast asleep; I know nothing of that, *says she*, but he is in a sad pickle now, and so she told me all that her Friend had said to her: Well then, *says I*, he fell into bad Hands after I left him, for I am sure I left him safe enough.

About ten Days after, or a little more, my Governess goes again to her Friend, to introduce her to this Gentleman; she had enquir'd other ways in the mean time, and found that he was about again, if not abroad again, so she got leave to speak with him.

She was a Woman of an admirable Address, and wanted no Body to introduce her; she told her Tale much better than I shall be able to tell it for her, for she was a Mistress of her Tongue, as I have said

already: She told him that she came, tho' a Stranger, with a single
design of doing him a Service, and he should find she had no other
End in it; that as she came purely on so Friendly an account, she beg'd
a promise from him, that if he did not accept what she should offi-
ciously[333] propose, he would not take ill that she meddl'd with what
was not her Business; she assur'd him that as what she had to say was a
Secret that belong'd to him only, so whether he accepted her offer or
not, it should remain a Secret to all the World, unless he expos'd it
himself; nor should his refusing her Service in it, make her so little
show her Respect, as to do him the least Injury, so that he should be
entirely at liberty to act as he thought fit.

He look'd very shy at first, and said he knew nothing that related to
him that requir'd much secresie; that he had never done any Man any
wrong, and car'd not what any Body might say of him; that it was no
part of his Character to be unjust to any Body, nor could he imagine
in what any Man cou'd render him any Service; but that if it was so
disinterested a Service as she said, he could not take it ill from any
one that they should endeavour to serve him; and so, as it were, left
her at liberty either to tell him, or not to tell him, as she thought fit.

She found him so perfectly indifferent, that she was almost afraid to
enter into the point with him; but however, after some other Circum-
locutions, she told him, that by a strange and unaccountable Accident
she came to have a particular knowledge of the late unhappy Adventure he had fallen into; and that in such a manner, that there was no
Body in the World but herself and him that were acquainted with it,
no not the very Person that was with him.

He look'd a little angrily at first, what Adventure? *said he*; why, Sir,
said she, of your being Robb'd coming from *Knightsbr*—, *Hampstead*,
Sir, I should say, *says she*; be not surpris'd, Sir, *says she*, that I am able
to tell you every step you took that Day from the *Cloyster* in *Smithfield*, to the *Spring-Garden* at *Knightsbridge*, and thence to the —— in
the *Strand*, and how you were left asleep in the Coach afterwards;
I say let not this surprize you, for Sir I do not come to make a Booty
of[334] you, I ask nothing of you, and I assure you the Woman that was
with you knows nothing who you are, and never shall; and yet perhaps
I may serve you farther still, for I did not come barely to let you know,
that I was inform'd of these things, as if I wanted a Bribe to conceal
them; assure your self, Sir, *said she*, that whatever you think fit to do or
say to me, it shall be all a secret as it is, as much as if I were in my
Grave.

He was astonish'd at her Discourse, and said gravely to her, Madam,
you are a Stranger to me, but it is very unfortunate, that you should

[333]Obligingly, with eagerness to serve;
in the eighteenth century the term was
sometimes pejorative, as elsewhere in
Moll Flanders, but not always so.
[334]Extort money from.

be let into the Secret of the worst action of my Life, and a thing that I am so justly asham'd of, that the only satisfaction of it to me was, that I thought it was known only to God and my own Conscience: Pray, Sir, *says she*, do not reckon the Discovery of it to me, to be any part of your Misfortune; it was a thing, I believe, you were surprised into, and perhaps the Woman us'd some Art to prompt you to it; however, you will never find any just Cause, *said she*, to repent that I came to hear of it; nor can your own Mouth be more silent in it than I have been, and ever shall be.

Well, *says he*, but let me do some Justice to the Woman too, who-ever she is, I do assure you she prompted me to nothing, she rather declin'd me, it was my own Folly and Madness that brought me into it all, ay and brought her into it too; I must give her her due so far, as to what she took from me, I cou'd expect no less from her in the condi-tion I was in, and to this Hour I know not whether she Robb'd me or the Coachman; if she did it I forgive her, and I think all Gentlemen that do so, should be us'd in the same manner; but I am more concern'd for some other things than I am for all that she took from me.

My Governess now began to come into the whole matter, and he open'd himself freely to her; first, she said to him, in answer to what he had said about me, I am glad Sir you are so just to the Person that you were with; I assure you she is a Gentlewoman, and no Woman of the Town; and however you prevail'd with her so far as you did, I am sure 'tis not her Practise; you run a great venture[335] indeed, Sir, but if that be any part of your Care, I am perswaded you may be perfectly easie, for I dare assure you no Man has touch'd her, before you, since her Husband, and he has been dead now almost eight Year.

It appear'd that this was his Grievance,[336] and that he was in a very great fright about it; however, when my Governess said this to him he appeared very well pleased; and said, well, Madam, to be plain with you, if I was satisfy'd of that, I should not so much value what I lost; for as to that, the Temptation was great, and perhaps she was poor and wanted it: If she had not been poor Sir ———, *says my Governess*, I assure you she would never have yielded to you, and as her Poverty first prevailed with her to let you do as you did, so the same Poverty prevail'd with her to pay her self at last, when she saw you was in such a Condition, that if she had not done it, perhaps the next Coach-man or Chair-man[337] might have done it.

Well, *says he*, much good may it do her; I say again, all the Gentle-men that do so, ought to be us'd in the same manner, and then they would be cautious of themselves; I have no more concern about it, but on the score which you hinted at before, Madam: Here he entred

---

[335]Took a big risk.
[336]Distress, worry.

[337]The bearer of a sedan chair.

into some freedoms with her on the Subject of what pass'd between us, which are not so proper for a Woman to write, and the great Terror that was upon his Mind with relation to his Wife, for fear he should have receiv'd any Injury from me, and should communicate it farther; and ask'd her at last if she cou'd not procure him an opportunity to speak with me; my Governess gave him farther assurances of my being a Woman clear from any such thing, and that he was as entirely safe in that respect, as he was with his own Lady; but as for seeing me, she said it might be of dangerous consequence; but however, that she would talk with me, and let him know my Answer; using at the same time some Arguments to perswade him not to desire it, and that it cou'd be of no Service to him; seeing she hop'd he had no desire to renew a Correspondence with me, and that on my account it was a kind of putting my Life in his Hands.

He told her, he had a great desire to see me, that he would give her any assurances that were in his Power, not to take any Advantages of me, and that in the first place he would give me a general release from all Demands of any kind; she insisted how it might tend to a farther divulging the Secret, and might in the end be injurious to him, entreating him not to press for it, so at length he desisted.

They had some Discourse upon the Subject of the things he had lost, and he seem'd to be very desirous of his Gold Watch, and told her if she cou'd procure that for him, he would willingly give as much for it, as it was worth; she told him she would endeavour to procure it for him and leave the valuing it to himself.

Accordingly the next Day she carried the Watch, and he gave her 30 Guineas for it, which was more than I should have been able to make of it, tho' it seems it cost much more; he spoke something of his Perriwig, which it seems cost him threescore Guineas, and his Snuff-box, and in a few Days more, she carried them too; which oblig'd him very much, and he gave her Thirty more; the next Day I sent him his fine Sword, and Cane *Gratis*, and demanded nothing of him, but I had no mind to see him, unless it had been so that he might be satisfy'd I knew who he was, which he was not willing to.

Then he entered into a long Tale with her of the manner how she came to know all this matter; she form'd a long Talk of that part; how she had it from one, that I had told the whole Story to, and that was to help me dispose of the Goods, and this Confident brought the Things to her, she being by Profession a *Pawn-Broker*; and she hearing of his Worship's dissaster, guess'd at the thing in general; that having gotten the Things into her Hands, she had resolv'd to come and try as she had done: She then gave him repeated Assurances that it should never go out of her Mouth, and tho' she knew the Woman very well, yet she had not let her know, *meaning me*, any thing of it; *that is to say*, who the Person was, which by the way was false; but however it was not to his Damage, for I never open'd my Mouth of it to any Body. I had a great many Thoughts in my Head about my seeing him again, and was often sorry that I had refus'd it; I was perswaded that if I had seen him, and let him know that I knew him, I should have made some Advantage of him, and perhaps have had some Maintenance from him; and tho' it was a Life wicked enough, yet it was not so full of Danger as this I was engag'd in. However those Thoughts wore off, and I declin'd seeing him again, for that time; but my Governess saw him often, and he was very kind to her, giving her something almost every time he saw her; one time in particular she found him very Merry, and as she thought he had some Wine in his Head, and he press'd her again very earnestly to let him see that Woman, that *as he said*, had Betwitch'd him so that Night; my Governess, who was from the beginning for my seeing him, told him, he was so desirous of it, that she could almost yield to it, if she cou'd prevail upon me; adding that if he would please to come to her House in the Evening she would endeavour it, upon his repeated Assurances of forgetting what was pass'd.

Accordingly she came to me and told me all the Discourse; *in short*, she soon byass'd me to consent, in a Case which I had some regret in my mind for declining before: so I prepar'd to see him: I dress'd me to all the Advantage possible I assure you, and for the first time us'd a little Art; I say for the first time, for I had never yielded to the baseness of Paint before, having always had vanity enough to believe I had no need of it.

At the Hour appointed he came; and as she observ'd before, so it was plain still, that he had been drinking, tho' very far from what we call being in drink: He appear'd exceeding pleas'd to see me, and enter'd into a long Discourse with me, upon the old Affair; I beg'd his pardon very often, for my share of it; protested I had not any such design when first I met him; that I had not gone out with him, but that I took him for a very civil Gentleman; and that he made me so many promises of offering no uncivility to me.

He alledg'd the Wine he drank, and that he scarce knew what he did, and that if it had not been so, I should never have let him take the freedom with me that he had done: He protested to me that he never touch'd any Woman but me since he was married to his Wife, and it was a surprise upon him; Complimented me upon being so particularly agreeable to him, and the like, and talk'd so much of that kind, till I found he had talk'd himself almost into a temper to do the same thing over again: But I took him up short, I protested I had never suffer'd any Man to touch me since my Husband died, which was near eight Year; he said he believed it to be so truly; and added that Madam had intimated as much to him, and that it was his Opinion of that part which made him desire to see me again; and that since he had once broke in upon his Vertue with me, and found no ill Consequences, he cou'd be safe in venturing there again; and so in short it went on to what I expected, and to what will not bear relating.

My old Governess had foreseen it, as well as I, and therefore led him into a Room which had not a Bed in it, and yet had a Chamber within it, which had a Bed, whither we withdrew for the rest of the Night, and in short, after some time being together, he went to Bed, and lay there all Night; I withdrew, but came again undress'd in the Morning before it was Day, and lay with him the rest of the time.

Thus you see having committed a Crime once, is a sad Handle to the committing of it again; whereas all the Regret, and Reflections wear off when the Temptation renews it self; had I not yielded to see him again, the Corrupt desire in him had worn off, and 'tis very probable he had never fallen into it, with any Body else, as I really believe he had not done before.

When he went away, I told him I hop'd he was satisfy'd he had not been robb'd again; he told me he was satisfy'd in that Point, and cou'd trust me again; and putting his Hand in his Pocket gave me five Guineas, which was the first Money I had gain'd that way for many Years.

I had several Visits of the like kind from him, but he never came into a settled way of Maintenance, which was what I would have been best pleas'd with: Once indeed he ask'd me how I did to live, I answer'd him pretty quick, that I assur'd him I had never taken that Course that I took with him; but that indeed I work'd at my Needle, and could just Maintain myself, that sometimes it was as much as I was able to do, and I shifted hard enough.[338]

He seem'd to reflect upon himself, that he should be the first Person to lead me into that, which he assur'd me he never intended to do himself, and it touch'd him a little, *he said*, that he should be the Cause of his own Sin, and mine too: He would often make just Reflections also upon the Crime itself, and upon the particular Circumstances of it, with respect to himself; how Wine introduc'd the Inclinations, how the Devil led him to the Place, and found out an Object to tempt him, and he made the Moral always himself.

When these thoughts were upon him he would go away, and perhaps not come again in a Months time or longer; but then as the serious part wore off, the lewd Part would wear in, and then he came prepar'd for the wick'd Part; thus we liv'd for sometime; tho' he did not KEEP,[339] as they call it, yet he never fail'd doing things that were Handsome, and sufficient to Maintain me without working, and which was better, without following my old Trade.

[338]Had difficulty making a living.
[339]I.e., he did not maintain Moll as a kept mistress.

But this Affair had its End too; for after about a Year, I found that he did not come so often as usual, and at last he left it off altogether without any dislike,[340] or bidding adieu; and so there was an End of that short Scene of Life, which added no great Store to me, only to make more Work for Repentance.

However during this interval, I confin'd my self pretty much at Home; at least being thus provided for, I made no Adventures, no not for a Quarter of a Year after he left me; but then finding the Fund fail, and being loth to spend upon the main Stock, I began to think of my old Trade, and to look Abroad into the Street again; and my first Step was lucky enough.

I had dress'd myself up in a very mean Habit, for as I had several Shapes to appear in I was now in an ordinary Stuff-Gown, a blue Apron and a Straw-Hat; and I plac'd myself at the Door of the three Cups-Inn in St. *John Street*: There were several Carriers us'd the Inn, and the Stage Coaches for *Barnet*, for *Toteridge*, and other Towns that way, stood always in the Street, in the Evening, when they prepar'd to set out; so that I was ready for any thing that offer'd for either one or other: The meaning was this, People come frequently with Bundles and small Parcels to those Inns, and call for such Carriers, or Coaches as they want, to carry them into the Country; and there generally attends Women, Porters Wives, or Daughters, ready to take in such things for their respective People that employ them.

It happen'd very oddly that I was standing at the Inn-Gate, and a Woman that had stood there before, and which was the Porter's Wife belonging to the *Barnet* Stage Coach, having observ'd me, ask'd if I waited for any of the Coaches; I told her yes, I waited for my Mistress, that was coming to go to *Barnet*; she ask'd me who was my Mistress, and I told her any Madam's Name that came next me;[341] but as it seem'd I happen'd upon a Name, a Family of which Name liv'd at *Hadly* just beyond *Barnet*.

I said no more to her, or she to me a good while, but by and by, some body calling her at a Door a little way off, she desir'd me that if any body call'd for the *Barnet* Coach, I would step and call her at the House, which it seems was an Ale-house; I said yes very readily, and away she went.

She was no sooner gone; but comes a Wench and a Child, puffing and sweating, and asks for the *Barnet* Coach, I answer'd presently *Here*; do you belong to the *Barnet* Coach, *says she*? yes Sweetheart, *said I*, what do ye want? I want Room, for two Passengers *says she*; Where are they Sweetheart, *said I*? Here's this Girl, pray let her go into the Coach, *says she*, and I'll go and fetch my Mistress; make hast then Sweetheart, *says I*, for we may be full else; the Maid had a great

---

[340]Disagreement, quarrel.　　　　　[341]I.e., the first name she thought of.

Bundle under Arm; so she put the Child into the Coach, and *I said*, you had best put your Bundle into the Coach too; No, *says she*, I am afraid some body should slip it away from the Child; give it me then, *said I*, and I'll take care of it; do then, *says she*, and be sure you take care of it; I'll answer for it, *said I*, if it were for Twenty Pound value. There take it then, *says she*, and away she goes.

As soon as I had got the Bundle, and the Maid was out of Sight, I goes on towards the Ale-house, where the Porter's Wife was, so that if I had met her, I had then only been going to give her the Bundle, and to call her to her Business, as if I was going away, and cou'd stay no longer; but as I did not meet her I walk'd away, and turning into *Charter-house-Lane*, made off thro' *Charter-house-Yard*, into *Long-Lane*, then cross'd into *Bartholomew-Close*, so into *Little-Britain*, and thro' the *Blue-Coat-Hospital* into *Newgate-Street*.[342]

To prevent my being known, I pull'd off my blue Apron, and wrapt the Bundle in it, which before was made up in a Piece of painted Callico, and very Remarkable; I also wrapt up my Straw-Hat in it, and so put the Bundle upon my Head; and it was very well, that I did thus, for coming thro' the *Blue-Coat-Hospital*, who should I meet but the Wench, that had given me the Bundle to hold; it seems she was going with her Mistress, who she had been gone to fetch to the *Barnet* Coaches.

I saw she was in hast, and I had no Business to stop her; so away she went, and I brought my Bundle safe Home to my Governess; there was no Money, nor Plate, or Jewels in the Bundle; but a very good Suit of *Indian* Damask, a Gown and Petticoat, a lac'd Head and Ruffles of very good Flanders-Lace, and some Linnen, and other things, such as I knew very well the value of.

This was not indeed my own Invention, but was given me by one that had practis'd it with Success, and my Governess lik'd it extreamly; and indeed I try'd it again several times, tho' never twice near the same Place; for the next time I try'd it in *White-Chappel* just by the Corner of *Petty-Coat-Lane*, where the Coaches stand that go out to *Stratford* and *Bow*, and that Side of the Country, and another time at the *Flying-Horse*, without *Bishops-gate*, where the *Cheston* Coaches then lay, and I had always the good Luck to come off with some Booty.

Another time I plac'd myself at a Warehouse by the Waterside, where the Coasting Vessels[343] from the *North* come, such as from *New-Castle* upon *Tyne*, *Sunderland*, and other Places; here, the Warehouse being shut, comes a young Fellow with a Letter; and he wanted a Box, and a Hamper[344] that was come from *New-Castle* upon

---

[342]Moll's windings here are in the same general area as her theft of the child's gold necklace.

[343]Ships which traded at ports within England.

[344]A wicker packing case.

Tyne, I ask'd him if he had the Marks[345] of it, so he shows me the Letter, by Vertue of which he was to ask for it, and which gave an Account of the Contents, the Box being full of Linnen, and the Hamper full of Glass-Ware; I read the Letter, and took care to see the Name, and the Marks, the Name of the Person that sent the Goods, the Name of the Person that they were sent to, then I bad the Messenger come in the Morning, for that the Warehouse Keeper, would not be there any more that Night.

Away went I, and getting Materials in a publick House, I wrote a Letter from Mr. *John Richardson* of *New-Castle* to his Dear Cousin *Jemey Cole,* in *London,* with an Account that he had sent by such a Vessel, (for I remember'd all the Particulars to a tittle,) so many pieces of Huckaback Linnen, so many Ells of *Dutch* Holland and the like, in a Box, and a Hamper of Flint Glasses[346] from Mr. *Henzill*'s Glass-house, and that the Box was mark'd I C. No 1. and the Hamper was directed[347] by a Label on the Cording.

About an Hour after, I came to the Warehouse, found the Warehouse-keeper, and had the Goods deliver'd me without any scruple; the value of the Linnen being about 22 Pound.

I could fill up this whole Discourse with the variety of such Adventures which daily Invention directed to, and which I manag'd with the utmost Dexterity, and always with Success.

At length, as when does the Pitcher come safe home that goes so very often to the Well, I fell into some small Broils,[348] which tho' they cou'd not affect me fatally, yet made me known, which was the worst thing next to being found Guilty, that cou'd befall me.

I had taken up the Disguise of a Widow's Dress; it was without any real design in view, but only waiting for any thing that might offer, as I often did: It happen'd that while I was going along the Street in *Covent-Garden,* there was a great Cry of stop Thief, stop Thief; some Artists had it seems put a trick upon a Shop-keeper, and being pursued, some of them fled one way, and some another; and one of them was, they said, dress'd up in Widow's Weeds, upon which the Mob gathered about me, and some said I was the Person, others said no; immediately came the Mercer's Journeyman, and he swore aloud I was the Person, and so seiz'd on me; however, when I was brought back by the Mob to the Mercer's Shop, the Master of the House said freely that I was not the Woman that was in his Shop, and would have let me go immediately; but another Fellow said gravely, pray stay till Mr. ———,

[345]Devices stamped upon an object to indicate ownership. Moll asks whether the youth knows what mark the packages bear, and the youth assumes that Moll wants to see proof of his right to claim the packages.

[346]Lustrous glasses originally made with ground flint or pebbles.

[347]Addressed.

[348]Disturbances, difficulties.

meaning the Journeyman, comes back, for he knows her; so they kept me by force near half an Hour; they had call'd a Constable, and he stood in the Shop as my Jayler; and in talking with the Constable I enquir'd where he liv'd, and what Trade he was; the Man not apprehending in the least what happened afterwards, readily told me his Name, and Trade, and where he liv'd; and told me as a Jest, that I might be sure to hear of his Name when I came to the *Old Bayley*.

Some of the Servants likewise us'd me saucily, and had much ado to keep their Hands off of me, the Master indeed was civiler to me than they; but he would not yet let me go, tho' he owned he could not say I was in his Shop before.

I began to be a little surly with him, and told him I hop'd he would not take it ill, if I made my self amends upon him in a more legal way another time; and desir'd I might send for Friends to see me have right done me: No, *he said*, he could give no such liberty, I might ask it when I came before the Justice of Peace, and seeing I threaten'd him, he would take care of me in the mean time, and would lodge me safe in *Newgate*: I told him it was his time now, but it would be mine by and by, and govern'd my Passion as well as I was able; however, I spoke to the Constable to call me a Porter, which he did, and then I call'd for Pen, Ink, and Paper, but they would let me have none; I ask'd the Porter his Name, and where he liv'd, and the poor Man told it me very willingly; I bad him observe and remember how I was treated there; that he saw I was detain'd there by Force; I told him I should want his Evidence in another place, and it should not be the worse for him to speak; the Porter said he would serve me with all his Heart; but, Madam, *says he*, let me hear them refuse to let you go, then I may be able to speak the plainer.

With that I spoke aloud to the Master of the Shop, and said, Sir, you know in your own Conscience that I am not the Person you look for, and that I was not in your Shop before, therefore I demand that you detain me here no longer, or tell me the reason of your stopping me; the Fellow grew surlier upon this than before, and said he would do neither till he thought fit; very well, said I to the Constable and to the Porter, you will be pleas'd to remember this, Gentlemen, another time; the Porter said, *yes, Madam*, and the Constable began not to like it, and would have perswaded the Mercer to dismiss him, and let me go, since, as he said, he own'd I was not the Person; Good Sir, *says the Mercer to him Tauntingly*, are you a Justice of Peace, or a Constable? I charg'd you with her, pray do you do your Duty: The Constable told him, a little mov'd, but very handsomely, *I know my Duty, and what I am, Sir, I doubt you hardly know what you are doing*; they had some other hard words, and in the mean time the Journeymen, impudent and unmanly to the last degree, used me barbarously, and one of them, the same that first seized upon me, pretended he would search me, and began to lay Hands on me: I spit in his Face, call'd out to the Constable, and had him take notice of my usage; and pray, Mr. Constable, *said I*, ask that Villain's Name, pointing to the Man; the Constable reprov'd him decently, told him that he did not know what he did, for he knew that his Master acknowledg'd I was not the Person that was in his Shop; and, says the Constable, I am afraid your Master is bringing himself and me too into Trouble, if this Gentlewoman comes to prove who she is, and where she was, and it appears that she is not the Woman you pretend to; Dam her, *says the Fellow again*, with an impudent harden'd Face, she is the Lady you may depend upon it, I'll swear she is the same Body that was in the Shop, and that I gave the pieces of Satin that is lost into her own hand, you shall hear more of it when Mr. *William* and *Anthony, those were other Journeymen*, come back, they will know her again as well as I.

Just as the insolent Rogue was talking thus to the Constable, comes back Mr. *William* and Mr. *Anthony*, as he call'd them, and a great Rabble with them, bringing along with them the true Widow that I was pretended to be; and they came sweating and blowing into the Shop, and with a great deal of Triumph dragging the poor Creature in a most butcherly manner up towards their Master, who was in the back Shop, and cryed out aloud, here's the Widow, Sir, we have catch'd her at last; what do ye mean by that, *says the Master*, why we have her already, there she sits, *says he*, and Mr. ——— *says he*, can swear this is she: The other Man who they call'd Mr. *Anthony* replyed, Mr. ——— may say what he will, and swear what he will, but this is the Woman, and there's the Remnant of Sattin she stole, I took it out of her Cloaths with my own Hand.

I sat still now, and began to take a better Heart, but smil'd and said nothing; the Master look'd Pale; the Constable turn'd about and look'd at me; *let 'em alone Mr. Constable*, said I, *let 'em go on*; the Case was plain and could not be denied, so the Constable was charg'd with the right Thief, and the Mercer told me very civilly he was sorry for the mistake, and hoped I would not take it ill; that they had so many things of this nature put upon them every Day, that they cou'd not be blam'd for being very sharp in doing themselves Justice: Not take it ill, Sir! *said I*, how can I take it well? if you had dismiss'd me when your insolent Fellow seiz'd on me in the Street, and brought me to you; and when you your self acknowledg'd I was not the Person, I would have put it by, and not taken it ill, because of the many ill things I believe you have put upon you daily; but your Treatment of me since has been unsufferable, and especially that of your Servant, I must and will have Reparation for that.

Then be began to parly with me, said he would make me any reasonable Satisfaction, and would fain have had me told him what it was I expected; I told him I should not be my own Judge, the Law should decide it for me, and as I was to be carried before a Magistrate, I should let him hear there what I had to say; he told me there was no occasion to go before the Justice now, I was at liberty to go where I pleased, and so calling to the Constable told him, he might let me go, for I was discharg'd; the Constable said calmly to him, Sir, you ask'd me just now, if I knew whether I was a Constable or a Justice, and bad me do my Duty, and charg'd me with this Gentlewoman as a Prisoner; now, Sir, I find you do not understand what is my Duty, for you would make me a Justice indeed; but I must tell you it is not in my Power: I may keep a Prisoner when I am charg'd with him, but 'tis the Law and the Magistrate alone that can discharge that Prisoner; therefore 'tis a mistake, Sir, I must carry her before a Justice now, whether you think well of it or not: The Mercer was very high with the Constable at first; but the Constable happening to be not a hir'd Officer, but a good Substantial kind of Man,[349] I think he was a Corn-chandler, and a Man of good Sense, stood to his Business, would not discharge me without going to a Justice of the Peace; and I insisted upon it too: When the Mercer see that; well, *says he to the Constable*, you may carry her where you please, I have nothing to say to her; but Sir, *says the Constable*, you will go with us, I hope, for 'tis you that charg'd me with her; no not I, *says the Mercer*, I tell you I have nothing to say to her: But pray Sir do, *says the Constable*, I desire it of you for your own sake, for the Justice can do nothing without you: Prithee Fellow, *says the Mercer*, go about your Business, I tell you I have nothing to say to the Gentlewoman, I charge you in the King's Name to dismiss her: Sir, *says the Constable*, I find you don't know what it is to be a Constable, I beg of you don't oblige me to be rude to you; I think I need not, you are rude enough already, *says the Mercer*: No, Sir, *says the Constable*, I am not rude, you have broken the Peace in bringing an honest Woman out of the Street, when she was about her lawful Occasion, confining her in your Shop, and ill using her here by your Servants; and now can you say I am rude to you? I think I am civil to you in not commanding or charging you in the King's Name to go with me, and charging every Man I see, that passes your Door, to aid and assist me in carrying you by Force; this you cannot but know I have power to do, and yet I forbear it, and once more entreat you to go with me: Well, he would not for all this, and gave the Constable ill Language: However, the Constable kept his Temper, and would not be provoked; and then I put in and said, come, Mr. Constable, let him alone, I shall find ways enough to fetch him before a Magistrate, I don't fear that; but there's the Fellow, *says I*, he was the Man that seized on me, as I was innocently going along the Street, and you are a Witness of his Violence with me since, give me

---

[349]Many constables were of none too lustrous a reputation. London then had no paid police force, and constables were sometimes men of substance, sometimes men who took the job for its opportunities to make devious gain.

leave to charge you with him, and carry him before the Justice; yes, Madam, *says the Constable*; and turning to the Fellow, come young Gentleman, *says he to the Journey man*, you must go along with us, I hope you are not above the Constable's Power, tho' your Master is.

The Fellow look'd like a condemn'd Thief, and hung back, then look'd at his Master, as if he cou'd help him; and he, like a Fool, encourag'd the Fellow to be rude, and he truly resisted the Constable, and push'd him back with a good Force when he went to lay hold on him, at which the Constable knock'd him down, and call'd out for help, and immediately the Shop was fill'd with People, and the Constable seiz'd the Master and Man, and all his Servants.

The first ill Consequence of this Fray was, that the Woman they had taken, who was really the Thief, made off, and got clear away in the Crowd; and two others that they had stop'd also, whether they were really Guilty or not, that I can say nothing to.

By this time some of his Neighbours having come in, and, upon inquiry, seeing how things went, had endeavour'd to bring the hot-brain'd Mercer to his Senses; and he began to be convinc'd that he was in the wrong; and so at length we went all very quietly before the Justice, with a Mob of about 500 People at our Heels; and all the way I went I could hear the People ask what was the matter? and others reply and say, a Mercer had stop'd a Gentlewoman instead of a Thief, and had afterwards taken the Thief, and now the Gentlewoman had taken the Mercer, and was carrying him before the Justice; this pleas'd the People strangely, and made the Crowd encrease, and they cry'd out as they went, which is the Rogue? which is the Mercer? and especially the Women, then when they saw him they cryed out, *that's he*, *that's he*; and every now and then came a good dab of Dirt at him; and thus we march'd a good while, till the Mercer thought fit to desire the Constable to call a Coach to protect himself from the Rabble; so we Rode the rest of the way, the Constable and I, and the Mercer and his Man.

When we came to the Justice, which was an ancient Gentleman in *Bloomsbury*, the Constable giving first a summary account of the Matter the Justice bad me speak, and tell what I had to say; and first he asked my Name, which I was very loath to give, but there was no remedy, so I told him my Name was *Mary Flanders*, that I was a Widow, my Husband being a Sea Captain, dyed on a Voyage to *Virginia*; and some other Circumstances I told, which he cou'd never contradict, and that I lodg'd at present in Town with such a Person, naming my Governess, but that I was preparing to go over to *America*, where my Husband's Effects lay, and that I was going that Day to buy some Cloaths to put my self into second Mourning, but had not yet been in any Shop, when that Fellow, pointing to the Mercer's Journeyman came rushing upon me with such fury, as very much frighted me, and carried me

back to his Masters Shop; where tho' his Master acknowledg'd I was
not the Person; yet he would not dismiss me, but charg'd a Constable
with me.

Then I proceeded to tell how the Journeyman treated me; how they
would not suffer me to send for any of my Friends; how afterwards
they found the real Thief, and took the very Goods they had Lost
upon her, and all the particulars as before.

Then the Constable related his Case; his Dialogue with the *Mercer*
about Discharging me, and at last his Servants refusing to go with
him, when he had Charg'd him with him, and his Master encouraging
him to do so; and at last his striking the Constable, and the like, all as I
have told it already.

The Justice then heard the *Mercer* and his Man; the *Mercer* indeed
made a long Harangue of the great loss they have daily by Lifters and
Thieves; that it was easy for them to Mistake, and that when he found
it, he would have dismiss'd me, &c. as above; as to the Journeyman
he had very little to say, but that he pretended other of the Servants
told him, that I was really the Person.

Upon the whole, the Justice first of all told me very courteously I
was Discharg'd; that he was very sorry that the *Mercers* Man should in
his eager pursuit have so little Discretion, as to take up an innocent
Person for a guilty Person; that if he had not been so unjust as to
detain me afterward, he believ'd I would have forgiven the first
Affront; that however it was not in his Power to award me any
Reparation for any thing, other than by openly reproving them, which
he should do; but he suppos'd I would apply to such Methods as the
Law directed; in the mean time he would bind him over.

But as to the Breach of the Peace committed by the Journeyman,
he told me he should give me some satisfaction for that, for he should
commit him to *Newgate* for Assaulting the Constable, and for Assaulting of me also.

Accordingly he sent the Fellow to *Newgate*, for that Assault, and his
Master gave Bail, and so we came away; but I had the satisfaction of
seeing the Mob wait upon them both, as they came out, Holooing,
and throwing Stones and Dirt at the Coaches they rode in, and so I
came home to my Governess.[350]

After this hustle, coming home, and telling my Governess the Story,
she falls a Laughing at me; Why are you merry, *says I*? the Story has

[350]Watching criminals in their discom-
fort was a favorite eighteenth-century
sport, and London mobs tended to be
rather enthusiastic in greeting individuals
who encountered, in one manner or
another, the law. Executions were
especially colorful, and the pillory also
stimulated the wit and brutality of
crowds; there are even recorded instances
of prisoners being killed by the flingings
of the mob. The conduct of the mob here
is not especially surprising, and part of
Moll's enthusiasm derives from the fact
that the activity is directed at someone
other than herself.

not so much Laughing room in it, as you imagine; I am sure I have had a great deal of Hurry and Fright too, with a Pack of ugly Rogues. *Laugh*, says my Governess, I laugh Child to see what a lucky Creature you are; why this Jobb will be the best Bargain to you, that ever you made in your Life, if you manage it well: I warrant you, *says she*, you shall make the *Mercer* pay you 500 *l.* for Damages, besides what you shall get of the Journeyman.

I had other Thoughts of the Matter than she had; and especially, because I had given in my Name to the Justice of Peace; and I knew that my Name was so well known among the People at *Hick's-Hall*,[351] the *Old Baily*, and such Places, that if this Cause came to be tryed openly, and my Name came to be enquir'd into, no Court would give much Damages for the Reputation of a Person of such a Character; however, I was oblig'd to begin a Prosecution in Form, and accordingly my Governess found me out a very creditable sort of a Man to manage it, being an Attorney of very good Business, and of good Reputation, and she was certainly in the right of this; for had she employ'd a petty Fogging hedge Soliciter,[352] or a Man not known, and not in good Reputation, I should have brought it to but little.

I met this Attorney, and gave him all the particulars at large, as they are recited above; and he assur'd me, it was a Case, *as he said*, that would very well support itself, and that he did not Question, but that a Jury would give very considerable Damages on such an Occasion; so taking his full Instructions, he began the Prosecution, and the *Mercer* being Arrested, gave Bail; a few Days after his giving Bail, he Comes with his Attorney to my Attorney, to let him know, that he desir'd to Accommodate the matter; that it was all carried on in the heat of an unhappy Passion; that his Client, *meaning me*, had a sharp provoking Tongue, that I us'd them ill, gibbing at them, and jeering them, even while they believed me to be the very Person, and that I had provok'd them, and the like.

My Attorney manag'd as well on my Side; made them believe I was a Widow of Fortune, that I was able to do myself Justice, and had great Friends to stand by me too, who had all made me promise to Sue to the utmost, and that if it cost me a Thousand Pound, I would be sure to have satisfaction, for that the Affronts I had receiv'd were unsufferable.

However they brought my Attorney to this, that he promis'd he would not blow the Coals, that if I enclin'd to an Accommodation, he would not hinder me, and that he would rather perswade me to Peace than to War; for which they told him he should be no loser, all which he told me very honestly, and told me that if they offer'd him any Bribe, I should certainly know it; but upon the whole he told me very honestly that if I would take his Opinion, he would Advise me to make it up with them; for that as they were in a great Fright, and were desirous above all things to make it up, and knew that let it be what it would, they would be alotted to bear all the Costs of the Suit; he believ'd they would give me freely more than any Jury or Court of Justice would give upon a Trial: I ask'd him what he thought they would be brought to; he told me he could not tell, as to that; but he would tell me more when I saw him again.

Some time after this, they came again to know if he had talk'd with me: He told them he had, that he found me not so Averse to an Accommodation as some of my Friends were, who resented the Disgrace offer'd me, and set me on; that they blow'd the Coals in secret, prompting me to Revenge, or to do myself Justice, as they call'd it; so that he could not tell what to say to it; he told them he would do his endeavour to persuade me, but he ought to be able to tell me what Proposal they made: They pretended they could not make any Proposal, because it might be made use of against them; and he told them, that by the same Rule he could not make any offers, for that might be pleaded in Abatement of what Damages a Jury might be inclin'd to give: However after some Discourse and mutual Promises that no Advantage should be taken on either Side, by what was transacted then, or at any other of those Meetings, they came to a kind of a Treaty; but so remote, and so wide from one another, that nothing could be expected from it; for my Attorney demmanded 500 *l.* and Charges, and they offer'd 50 *l.* without Charges; so they broke off, and the *Mercer* propos'd to have a Meeting with me myself; and my Attorney agreed to that very readily.

My Attorney gave me Notice to come to this Meeting in good Cloaths, and with some State,[353] that the *Mercer* might see I was something more than I seem'd to be that time they had me: Accordingly I came in a new Suit of second Mourning, according to what I had said at the Justices; I set myself out[354] too, as well as a Widows dress in second Mourning would admit; my Governess also furnish'd me with a good Pearl Neck-lace, that shut in behind with a Locket of Diamonds, which she had in Pawn; and I had a very good gold Watch by my Side; so that in a Word, I made a very good Figure,[355] and as I stay'd, till I was sure they were come, I came in a Coach to the Door with my Maid with me.

When I came into the Room, the *Mercer* was surpriz'd, he stood up and made his Bow, which I took a little Notice of, and but a little, and went and Sat down, where my own Attorney had pointed to me to sit, for it was his House; after a little while, the *Mercer* said, he did not

---

[353]Stateliness, splendor.
[354]I.e., ornamented, accessoried herself.
[355]Impressive appearance.

know me again, and began to make some Compliments his way; I told him, I believe he did not know me at first, and that if he had, I believ'd he would not have treated me as he did.

He told me was very sorry for what had happen'd, and that it was to testifie the willingness he had to make all possible Reparation, that he had appointed this Meeting; that he hop'd I would not carry things to extremity, which might be not only too great a Loss to him, but might be the ruin of his Business and Shop, in which Case I might have the satisfaction of repaying an Injury with an Injury ten times greater; but that I would then get nothing, whereas he was willing to do me any Justice that was in his Power, without putting himself, or me to the Trouble or Charge of a Suit at Law.

I told him I was glad to hear him talk so much more like a Man of Sense than he did before; that it was true, acknowledgement in most Cases of Affronts was counted Reparation sufficient; but this had gone too far to be made up so; that I was not Revengeful, nor did I seek his Ruin, or any Mans else, but that all my Friends were unanimous not to let me so far neglect my Character, as to adjust a thing of this kind without a sufficient Reparation of Honour: That to be taken up for a Thief was such an Indignity as could not be put up, that my Character was above being treated so by any that knew me; but because in my Condition of a Widow, I had been for sometime Careless of myself, and Negligent of myself, I might be taken for such a Creature, but that for the particular usage I had from him afterward; and then I repeated all as before, it was so provoking I had scarce Patience to repeat it.

Well he acknowledg'd all, and was mighty humble indeed; he made Proposals very handsome; he came up to a Hundred Pounds, and to pay all the Law Charges, and added that he would make me a Present of a very good Suit of Cloths; I came down to three Hundred Pounds, and I demanded that I should publish an Advertisement of the particulars in the common News Papers.

This was a Clause he never could comply with; however at last he came up by good Management of my Attorney to 150 *l.* and a Suit of black silk Cloaths and there, I agreed, and as it were at my Attornies request, complied with it; he paying my Attornies Bill and Charges, and gave us a good Supper into the Bargain.

When I came to receive the Money, I brought my Governess with me, dress'd like an old Dutchess, and a Gentleman very well dress'd, who we pretended Courted me, but I call'd him Cousin, and the Lawyer was only to hint privately to him, that this Gentleman Courted the Widow.

He treated us handsomely indeed, and paid the Money chearfully enough; so that it cost him 200 *l.* in all, or rather more: At our last Meeting when all was agreed, the Case of the Journeyman came up,

and the *Mercer* beg'd very hard for him, told me he was a Man that
had kept a Shop of his own, and been in good Business, had a Wife and
several Children, and was very poor, that he had nothing to make
satisfaction with, but he should come to beg my pardon on his Knees,
if I desir'd it, as openly as I pleas'd: I had no Spleen at the sawcy Rogue,
nor were his Submissions any thing to me, since there was nothing to
be got by him; so I thought it was as good to throw that in generously
as not, so I told him I did not desire the Ruin of any Man, and therefore at his Request I would forgive the Wretch, it was below me to
seek any Revenge.

When we were at Supper he brought the poor Fellow in to make
acknowledgement, which he would have done with as much mean
Humility, as his Offence was with insulting Haughtiness and Pride,
in which he was an Instance of a compleat baseness of Spirit, imperious, cruel, and relentless when Uppermost, and in Prosperity;
abject and low Spirited when Down in Affliction: However I abated
his Cringes, told him I forgave him, and desir'd he might withdraw, as
if I did not care for the sight of him, tho' I had forgiven him.

I was now in good Circumstances indeed, if I could have known my
time for leaving off, and my Governess often said I was the richest of
the Trade in *England*, and so I believe I was; for I had 700 *l.* by me in
Money, besides Cloaths, Rings, some Plate, and two gold Watches, and
all of them stol'n, for I had innumerable Jobbs, besides these I have
mention'd; O! had I even now had the Grace of Repentance, I had
still leisure to have look'd back upon my Follies, and have made some
Reparation; but the satisfaction I was to make for the publick Mischiefs I had done, was yet left behind; and I could not forbear going
Abroad again, *as I call'd it now*, any more than I could when my
Extremity really drove me out for Bread.

It was not long after the Affair with the *Mercer* was made up, that
I went out in an Equipage[356] quite different from any I had ever
appear'd in before; I dress'd myself like a Beggar Woman, in the
coursest and most despicable Rags I could get, and I walk'd about
peering, and peeping into every Door and Window I came near; and
indeed I was in such a Plight[357] now, that I knew as ill how to behave
in as ever I did in any; I naturally abhorr'd Dirt and Rags; I had been
bred up Tite[358] and Cleanly, and could be no other, whatever Condition I was in; so that this was the most uneasie Disguise to me that
ever I put on: I said presently to myself that this would not do, for
this was a Dress that every body was shy, and afraid of; and I thought
every body look'd at me, as if they were afraid I should come near
them, least I should take something from them, or afraid to come

---

[356]Attire.
[357]Posture, or (possibly) attire; Moll finds her unfamiliar role to be uncomfortable.

[358]Reared to be neat in appearance.

near me, least they should get something from me: I wandered about all the Evening the first time I went out, and made nothing of it, but came home again wet, draggl'd and tired; However I went out again, the next Night, and then I met with a little Adventure, which had like to have cost me dear; as I was standing near a Tavern Door, there comes a Gentleman on Horse back, and lights at the Door, and want-ing to go into the Tavern, he calls one of the Drawers to hold his Horse; he stay'd prety long in the Tavern, and the Drawer heard his Master call, and thought he would be angry with him; seeing me stand by him, when[359] he call'd to me, here Woman, *says he*, hold this Horse a while, till I go in, if the Gentleman comes, he'll give you something; *yes says I*, and takes the Horse, and walks off with him very soberly, and carri'd him to my Governess.

This had been a Booty to those that had understood it; but never was poor Thief more at a loss to know what to do with any thing that was stolen; for when I came home, my Governess was quite con-founded, and what to do with the Creature, we neither of us knew; to send him to a Stable was doing nothing, for it was certain that publick Notice would be given in the *Gazette*, and the Horse describ'd, so that we durst not go to fetch it again.

All the remedy we had for this unlucky Adventure was to go and set up the Horse at an Inn, and send a Note by a Porter to the Tavern, that the Gentleman's Horse that was lost such a time, was left at such an Inn, and that he might be had there; that the poor Woman that held him, having led him about the Street, not being able to lead him back again, had left him there; we might have waited till the owner had publish'd, and offer'd a Reward, but we did not care to venture the receiving the Reward.

So this was a Robbery and no Robbery, for little was lost by it, and I was quite Sick of going out in a Beggar's dress; it did not answer at all, and besides I thought it was Ominous and Threatning.

While I was in this Disguise, I fell in with a parcel of Folks of a worse kind than any I ever sorted[360] with, and I saw a little into their ways too, these were Coiners of Money, and they made some very good offers to me, as to profit; but the part they would have had me have embark'd in, was the most dangerous Part; I mean that of the very working the Dye, as they call it, which had I been taken, had been certain Death, and that at a Stake, *I say*, to be burnt to Death at a Stake;[361] so that tho' I was to Appearance, but a Beggar; and they

---

[359]Then.

[360]Consorted, associated.

[361]Moll's life is at stake in several senses, and though she may not be famous for her sense of humor, she shows in this paragraph that she can detachedly play with words, even (or perhaps especially) on a very serious subject.

The stake metaphor may relate to Moll's frequent toying with "cast" and her attention to gaming activities, and her references to the fatality of her moves. The puns on "die" also involve her prospective new job: Dye = device for impressing a design on a coin.

promis'd Mountains of Gold and Silver to me, to engage; yet it would not do; it is True if I had been really a Beggar, or had been desperate as when I began, I might perhaps have clos'd with it, for what care they to Die, that can't tell how to Live? But at present this was not my Condition, at least I was for no such terrible Risques as those; besides the very Thoughts of being burnt at a Stake, struck terror into my very Soul, chill'd my Blood, and gave me the Vapours to such a degree as I could not think of it without trembling.

This put an End to my Disguise too, for as I did not like the Proposal, so I did not tell them so; but seem'd to relish it, and promis'd to meet again; but I durst see them no more; for if I had seen them, and not complied, tho' I had declin'd it with the greatest assurances of Secresy in the World, they would have gone near to have murther'd me to make sure Work, and make themselves easy, *as they call it*; what kind of easiness that is, they may best Judge that understand how easy Men are, that can Murther People to prevent Danger.

This and Horse stealing were things quite out of my way, and I might easily resolve I would have no more to say to them; my business seem'd to lye another way, and tho' it had hazard enough in it too, yet it was more suitable to me, and what had more of Art in it, more room to Escape, and more Chances for a coming off, if a Surprize should happen.

I had several Proposals made also to me about that time, to come into a Gang of House-Breakers;[362] but that was a thing I had no mind to venture at neither, any more than I had at the Coining Trade; I offer'd to go along with two Men, and a Woman, that made it their Business to get into Houses by Stratagem, and with them I was willing enough to venture; but there was three of them already, and they did not care to part,[363] nor I to have too many in a Gang, so I did not close with them, but declin'd them, and they paid dear for their next Attempt.

But at length I met with a Woman that had often told me what Adventures she had made, and with Success at the Water-side, and I clos'd with her, and we drove on our Business pretty well: One Day we came among some *Dutch* People at St. *Catherines*,[364] where we went on pretence to buy Goods that were privately got on Shore: I was two or three times in a House, where we saw a good Quantity of prohibited Goods, and my Companion once brought away three Peices of *Dutch* black Silk that turn'd to good Account, and I had my Share of it; but in all the Journeys I made by myself, I could not get an Opportunity to do any thing, so I laid it aside; for I had

---

[362]Burglars.
[363]Separate, or (possibly) divide the spoils into more shares.

[364]The river area just east of the Tower.

been so often, that they began to suspect something, and were so shy, that I saw nothing was to be done.

This baulk'd me a little, and I resolv'd to push at something or other, for I was not us'd to come back so often without Purchase; so the next Day I dress'd myself up fine, and took a Walk to the other End of the Town, I pass'd thro' the *Exchange*[365] in the *Strand*, but had no Notion of finding any thing to do there, when on a sudden I saw a great Clutter in the Place, and all the People, Shop-keepers as well as others, standing up, and staring, and what should it be? but some great Dutchess come into the *Exchange*; and they said the Queen was coming; I set myself close up to a Shop-side with my back to the Compter, as if to let the Crowd pass by, when keeping my Eye upon a parcel of Lace, which the Shop-keeper was showing to some Ladies that stood by me; the Shop-keeper and her Maid were so taken up with looking to see who was a coming, and what Shop they would go to, that I found means to slip a Paper[366] of Lace into my Pocket, and come clear off with it, so the Lady Millener paid dear enough for her gaping after the Queen.

I went off from the Shop, as if driven along by the Throng, and mingling myself with the Crowd, went out at the other Door of the *Exchange*, and so got away before they miss'd their Lace; and because I would not be follow'd, I call'd a Coach and shut myself up in it; I had scarse shut the Coach Doors up, but I saw the Milleners Maid, and five or six more come running out into the Street, and crying out as if they were frighted; they did not cry stop Thief, because no body ran away, but I cou'd hear the Word robb'd, and Lace, two or three times, and saw the Wench wringing her Hands, and run staring, to, and again, like one scar'd; the Coachman that had taken me up, was getting up into the Box, but was not quite up, so that the Horses had not begun to move, so that I was terrible uneasy; and I took the Packet of Lace and laid it ready to have dropt it out at the Flap of the Coach, which opens before just behind the Coachman;[367] but to my great satisfaction in less then a Minute the Coach began to move, that is to say, as soon as the Coachman had got up, and spoken to his Horses; so he drove away without any interruption, and I brought off my Purchase, which was worth near twenty Pound.

The next Day I dress'd me up again, but in quite different Cloths, and walk'd the same way again; but nothing offer'd till I came into St. *James's Park*,[368] where I saw abundance of fine Ladies in the *Park*,

---

[365]The Royal Exchange, a center of shops and offices. In *Tour* Defoe called it "the greatest and finest of the Kind in the World."

[366]Parcel.

[367]I.e., a slot in front of Moll and behind the coachman.

[368]A fashionable place to walk, especially between noon and 2:00 P.M. and again after 7:00. A favorite diversion was watching for the King to pass by.

walking in the *Mall*, and among the rest, there was a little Miss, a young Lady of about 12 or 13 Years old, and she had a Sister, as I suppose it was, with her, that might be about Nine Year old: I observ'd the biggest had a fine gold Watch on, and a good Necklace of Pearl, and they had a Footman in Livery with them; but as it is not usual for the Footman to go behind the Ladies in the *Mall*, so I observ'd the Footman stop'd at their going into the *Mall*, and the biggest of the Sisters spoke to him, which I perceiv'd was to bid him be just there when they came back.

When I heard her dismiss the Footman, I step'd up to him, and ask'd him, what little Lady that was? and held a little Chat with him, about what a pretty Child it was with her, and how Genteel, and well Carriag'd a Lady the eldest would be; how Womanish, and how Grave; and the Fool of a Fellow told me presently who she was, that she was Sir *Thomas* ———'s eldest Daughter of *Essex*, and that she was a great Fortune, that her Mother was not come to Town yet; but she was with Sir *William* ———'s Lady of *Suffolk*, at her Lodgings in *Suffolk-Street*, and a great deal more; that they had a Maid and a Woman to wait on them, besides Sir *Thomas's* Coach, the Coachman and himself and that young Lady was governess to the whole Family as well here, as at Home too; and in short, told me abundance of things enough for my business.

I was very well dress'd, and had my gold Watch, as well as she; so I left the Footman, and I puts myself in a Rank with[369] this young Lady, having stay'd till she had taken one double Turn in the *Mall*, and was going forward again; by and by, I saluted her by her Name, with the Title of Lady *Betty*: I ask'd her when she heard from her Father? when my Lady her Mother would be in Town and how she did?

I talk'd so familiarly to her of her whole Family that she cou'd not suspect, but that I knew them all intimately: I ask'd her why she would come Abroad without Mrs. *Chime* with her (that was the Name of her Woman) to take care of Mrs. *Judith* that was her Sister. Then I enter'd into a long Chat with her about her Sister, what a fine little Lady she was, and ask'd her if she had learn'd *French*, and a Thousand such little things to entertain her, when on a sudden we see the Guards come, and the Crowd run to see the King go by to the Parliament-House.

The Ladies run all to the Side of the *Mall*, and I help'd my Lady to stand upon the edge of the Boards on the side of the *Mall*, that she might be high enough to see; and took the little one and lifted her quite up; during which, I took care to convey the gold Watch so clean away from the Lady *Betty*, that she never felt it, nor miss'd it, till

---

[369]Abreast of.

all the Crowd was gone, and she was gotten into the middle of the *Mall* among the other Ladies.

I took my leave of her in the very Crowd, and said to her, as if in hast, dear Lady *Betty* take care of your little Sister, and so the Crowd did, as it were, Thrust me away from her, and that I was oblig'd unwillingly³⁷⁰ to take my leave.

The hurry in such Cases is immediately over, and the Place clear as soon as the King is gone by; but as there is always a great running and clutter just as the King passes; so having drop'd the two little Ladies, and done my Business with them, without any Miscarriage, I kept hurrying on among the Crowd, as if I run to see the King, and so I got before the Crowd and kept so, till I came to the End of the *Mall*; when the King going on toward the Horse-Guards, I went forward to the Passage, which went then thro' against the lower End of the *Hay-Market*, and there I bestow'd a Coach upon myself, and made off; and I confess I have not yet been so good as my word (*viz.*) to go and visit my Lady *Betty*.

I was once of the mind to venture staying with Lady *Betty*, till she mist the Watch, and so have made a great Out-cry about it with her, and have got her into her Coach, and put myself in the Coach with her, and have gone Home with her; for she appear'd so fond of me, and so perfectly deceiv'd by my so readily talking to her of all her Relations and Family, that I thought it was very easy to push the thing farther, and to have got at least the Neck-lace of Pearl; but when I consider'd that tho' the Child would not perhaps have suspected me, other People might, and that if I was search'd I should be discover'd; I thought it was best to go off with what I had got, and be satisfy'd.

I came accidentally afterwards to hear, that when the young Lady miss'd her Watch, she made a great Out-cry in the *Park*, and sent her Footman up and down, to see if he could find me out, she having describ'd me so perfectly, that he knew presently that it was the same Person that had stood and talked so long with him, and ask'd him so many Questions about them; but I was gone far enough out of their reach before she could come at her Footman to tell him the Story.

I made another Adventure after this, of a Nature different from all I had been concern'd in yet, and this was at a Gaming-House near *Covent-Garden*.

I saw several People go in and out; and I stood in the Passage a good while with another Woman with me, and seeing a Gentleman go up that seem'd to be of more than ordinary Fashion, I said to him, Sir, pray don't they give Women leave to go up? *yes Madam, says he*, and to play too if they please; I mean so Sir, *said I*; and with that, he said he would introduce me if I had a mind; so I follow'd him to the Door,

³⁷⁰I.e., Moll contrives to make it seem
as if she is thrust away unwillingly.

and he looking in, there, Madam, *says he*, are the Gamesters, if you have a mind to venture; I look'd in and said to my Comrade, aloud, here's nothing but Men, I won't venture among them; at which one of the Gentlemen cry'd out, you need not be afraid Madam, here's none but fair Gamesters, you are very welcome to come and Set[371] what you please; so I went a little nearer and look'd on, and some of them brought me a Chair, and I sat down and see the Box and Dice go round a pace;[372] then I said to my Comrade, the Gentlemen play too high for us, come let us go.

The People were all very civil, and one Gentleman in particular encourag'd me, and said, come Madam, if you please to Venture, if you dare Trust me I'll answer for it; you shall have nothing put upon you here; no Sir, *said I*, smiling, I hope the Gentlemen wou'd not Cheat a Woman; but still I declin'd venturing, tho' I pull'd out a Purse with Money in it, that they might see I did not want Money.

After I had sat a while, one Gentleman said to me Jeering, come Madam, I see you are afraid to venture for yourself; I always had good luck with the Ladies, you shall Set for me, if you won't Set for yourself; I told him, Sir I should be very loth to lose your Money, tho' I added, I am pretty lucky too, but the Gentlemen play so high, that I dare not indeed venture my own.

Well well, *says he*, there's ten Guineas Madam, Set them for me; so I took his Money and set, himself looking on; I run out Nine of the Guineas by One and Two at a Time, and then the Box coming to the next Man to me, my Gentleman gave me Ten Guineas more, and made me Set Five of them at once, and the Gentleman who had the Box threw out,[373] so there was five Guineas of his Money again; he was encourag'd at this, and made me take the Box, which was a bold Venture: However, I held the box so long that I had gain'd him his whole Money, and had a good handful of Guineas in my Lap, and which was the better Luck, when I threw out, I threw but at One or Two of those that had Set me, and so went off easie.

When I was come this length, I offer'd the Gentleman all the Gold, for it was his own; and so would have had him play for himself, pretending I did not understand the Game well enough: He laugh'd, and said if I had but good Luck, it was no matter whether I understood the Game or no; but I should not leave off: However he took out the 15 Guineas that he had put in at first, and bad me play with the rest: I would have told them to see how much I had got, but he said no, no, don't tell them, I believe you are very honest, and 'tis bad Luck to tell them, so I play'd on.

[371]Wager.

[372]I.e., apace, speedily.

[373]Made a losing throw; the game is apparently Hazard, a game in which three dice are used and bets are placed on the total roll. With rules varying from place to place, the game is now sometimes called Chuck-a-luck or Birdcage.

I understood the Game well enough, tho' I pretended I did not, and play'd cautiously; it[374] was to keep a good Stock in my Lap, out of which I every now and then convey'd some into my Pocket; but in such a manner, and at such convenient times, as I was sure he cou'd not see it.

I play'd a great while, and had very good Luck for him, but the last time I held the Box, they Set me high, and I threw boldly at all; I held the Box till I gain'd near Fourscore Guineas, but lost above half of it back at the last throw; so I got up, for I was afraid I should lose it all back again, and said to him, pray come Sir now and take it and play for your self, I think I have done pretty well for you; he would have had me play'd on, but it grew late, and I desir'd to be excus'd. When I gave it up to him, I told him I hop'd he would give me leave to tell it now, that I might see what I had gain'd, and how lucky I had been for him; when I told them, there was Threescore, and Three Guineas. Ay, *says I*, if it had not been for that unlucky Throw I had got you a Hundred Guineas; so I gave him all the Money, but he would not take it till I had put my Hand into it, and taken some for myself, and bid me please myself; I refus'd it, and was positive I would not take it myself; if he had a mind to any thing of that kind it should be all his own doings.

The rest of the Gentlemen seeing us striving, cry'd give it her all; but I absolutely refus'd that; then one of them said, D——n ye *Jack*, half it with her, don't you know you should be always upon even Terms with the Ladies; so in short, he divided it with me, and I brought away 30 Guineas, besides about 43, which I had stole privately, which I was sorry for afterwards, because he was so generous.

Thus I brought Home 73 Guineas, and let my old Governess see what good Luck I had at Play: However, it was her Advice that I should not venture again, and I took her Council, for I never went there any more; for I knew as well as she, if the Itch[375] of Play came in, I might soon lose that, and all the rest of what I had got.

Fortune had smil'd upon me to that degree, and I had Thriven so much, and my Governess too, for she always had a Share with me, that really the old Gentlewoman began to talk of leaving off while we were well, and being satisfy'd with what we had got; but, I know not what Fate guided me, I was as backward to it now as she was when I propos'd it to her before, and so in an ill Hour we gave over the Thoughts of it for the present, and in a Word, I grew more hardn'd and audacious than ever, and the Success I had, made my Name as famous as any Thief of my sort ever had been at *Newgate*, and in the *Old-Bayly*.

[374]I.e., the "game" Moll understood.
[375]Restless desire; Moll's worry is that she will become addicted to gaming.

I had sometimes taken the liberty to Play the same Game over again, which is not according to Practice, which however succeeded not amiss; but generally I took up new Figures, and contriv'd to appear in new Shapes every time I went abroad.

It was now a rumbling[376] time of the year, and the Gentlemen being most of them gone out of Town, *Tunbridge*, and *Epsom*,[377] and such Places were full of People, but the City was Thin, and I thought our Trade felt it a little, as well as others; so that at the latter End of the Year I joyn'd myself with a Gang, who usually go every Year to *Sturbridge* Fair, and from thence to *Bury* Fair,[378] in *Suffolk*: We promis'd our selves great things here, but when I came to see how things were, I was weary of it presently; for except meer Picking of Pockets, there was little worth meddling with; neither if a Booty had been made, was it so easy carrying it off, nor was there such a variety of occasion for Business in our way, as in *London*; all that I made of the whole Journey, was a gold Watch at *Bury* Fair, and a small parcel of Linnen at *Cambridge*, which gave me an occasion to take leave of the Place: It was an old Bite,[379] and I thought might do with a Country Shop keeper, tho' in *London* it would not.

I bought at a Linnen Draper's Shop, not in the Fair, but in the Town of *Cambridge*, as much fine Holland and other things as came to about seven Pound; when I had done, I bad them be sent to such an Inn, where I had purposely taken up my being[380] the same Morning, as if I was to Lodge there that Night.

I order'd the Draper to send them Home to me, about such an Hour to the Inn where I lay, and I would pay him his Money; at the time appointed the Draper sends the Goods, and I plac'd one of our Gang at the Chamber Door, and when the Innkeeper's Maid brought the Messenger to the Door, who was a young Fellow, an Apprentice, almost a Man; she tells him her Mistress was a sleep, but if he would leave the things, and call in about an Hour, I should be awake, and he might have the Money; he left the Parcel very readily, and goes his way, and in about half an Hour my Maid and I walk'd off, and that very Evening I hired a Horse, and a Man to ride before me, and went to *Newmarket*, and from thence got my Passage in a Coach that was not quite full to St. *Edmund's Bury*; Where as I told you I could make but little of my Trade, only at a little Country *Opera*-House, made a shift to carry off a gold Watch from a Ladies side, who was not only intollerably Merry, but as I thought a little Fuddled,[381] which made my Work much easier.

---

[376]Rambling.
[377]Famous and fashionable spas.
[378]Famous autumn fairs, north and east of London. In *Tour* Defoe called Sturbridge Fair "not only the greatest in the whole Nation, but in the World."
[379]Trick, hoax.
[380]Residence.
[381]Tipsy.

I made off with this little Booty to *Ipswich*, and from thence to *Harwich*;[382] where I went into an Inn, as if I had newly arriv'd from *Holland*, not doubting but I should make some Purchase[383] among the Foreigners that came on shore there; but I found them generally empty of things of value, except what was in their Portmanteuas,[384] and *Dutch* Hampers, which were generally guarded by Footmen; however, I fairly got one of their Portmanteuas one Evening out of the Chamber where the Gentleman lay, the Footman being fast asleep on the Bed, and I suppose very Drunk.

The Room in which I Lodg'd, lay next to the *Dutchman's*, and having dragg'd the heavy thing with much a-do out of the Chamber into mine; I went out into the Street, to see if I could find any possibility of carrying it off; I walk'd about a great while but could see no probability, either of getting out the thing, or of conveying away the Goods that was in it if I had open'd it, the Town being so small, and I a perfect Stranger in it; so I was returning with a resolution to carry it back again, and leave it where I found it: Just in that very Moment I heard a Man make a Noise to some People to make hast, for the Boat was going to put off, and the Tide would be spent; I call'd to the Fellow, What Boat is it Friend, *says I*, that you belong to? the *Ipswich* Wherry, Madam, *says he*: When do you go off, *says I*? this Moment Madam, *says he*, do you want to go thither? yes, *said I*, if you can stay till I fetch my things: Where are your things Madam, *says he*? At such an Inn, *said I*: Well I'll go with you Madam, *says he*, very civilly, and bring them for you; come away then, *says I*, and takes him with me.

The People of the Inn were in great hurry, the Packet-Boat[385] from *Holland* being just come in, and two Coaches just come also with Passengers from *London* for another Packet-Boat that was going off for *Holland*, which Coaches were to go back next Day with the Passengers that were just Landed: In this hurry it was not much minded,[386] that I came to the Bar,[387] and paid my Reckoning, telling my Landlady I had gotten my Passage by Sea in a Wherry.

These Wherries are large Vessels, with good Accommodation for carrying Passengers from *Harwich* to *London*; and tho' they are call'd Wherries, which is a word us'd in the *Thames* for a small Boat, Row'd with one or two Men; yet these are Vessels able to carry twenty Passengers, and ten or fifteen Ton of Goods, and fitted to bear the Sea;[388] all this I had found out by enquiring the Night before into the several ways of going to *London*.

[382]On the east coast, at the mouth of the rivers Stour and Orwell.

[383]Steal some booty.

[384]Portmanteaus, suitcases.

[385]A mail and passenger boat plying regularly between two ports.

[386]Little attention was paid to the fact.

[387]Counter.

[388]I.e., sturdy enough for use in open seas.

My Landlady was very Courteous, took my Money for my Reckoning, but was call'd away, all the House being in a hurry; so I left her, took the Fellow up to my Chamber, gave him the Trunk, or Portmanteua, for it was like a Trunk, and wrapt it about with an old Apron, and he went directly to his Boat with it, and I after him, no Body asking us the least Question about it; as for the drunken *Dutch* Footman he was still asleep, and his Master with other Foreign Gentlemen at Supper, and very Merry below; so I went clean off with it to *Ipswich*, and going in the Night, the People of the House knew nothing, but that I was gone to *London*, by the *Harwich* Wherry as I had told my Landlady.

I was plagu'd at *Ipswich* with the Custom-House Officers, who stopt my Trunk, *as I call'd it*, and would open, and search it; I was willing I told them, they should search it, but my Husband had the Key, and he was not yet come from *Harwich*; this I said, that if upon searching it they should find all the things be such, as properly belong'd to a Man rather than a Woman, it should not seem strange to them; however, they being possitive to open the Trunk, I consented to have it be broken open, that is to say, to have the Lock taken off, which was not difficult.

They found nothing for their turn, for the Trunk had been search'd before, but they discover'd several things very much to my satisfaction, as particularly a parcel of Money in *French* Pistoles,[389] and some *Dutch* Ducatoons, or *Rix* Dollars,[390] and the rest was chiefly two Perriwigs, wearing Linnen, and Razors, Wash-balls,[391] Perfumes and other useful things, Necessaries for a Gentleman; which all pass'd for my Husband's, and so I was quit of them.[392]

It was now very early in the Morning, and not Light, and I knew not well what Course to take; for I made no doubt but I should be pursued in the Morning, and perhaps be taken with the things about me; so I resolv'd upon taking new Measures; I went publickly to an Inn in the Town with my Trunk, *as I call'd it*, and having taken the Substance out, I did not think the Lumber[393] of it worth my concern; however, I gave it the Landlady of the House with a Charge to take great Care of it, and lay it up safe till I should come again, and away I walk'd into the Street.

When I was got into the Town a great way from the Inn, I met with an antient Woman who had just open'd her Door, and I fell into Chat with her, and ask'd her a great many wild Questions of things all

---

[389]Gold coins whose English value was fixed in 1717 at seventeen shillings.

[390]Silver coins of less value than pistoles.

[391]Balls of soap, often perfumed and medicated, and relatively expensive.

[392]Satisfied the officers' enquiries.

[393]The material of which it was made, not necessarily wood.

remote to my Purpose and Design, but in my Discourse I found by her how the Town was situated, that I was in a Street which went out towards *Hadly*; but that such a Street went towards the Water-side, such a Street went into the Heart of the Town; and at last such a Street went towards *Colchester*, and so the *London* Road lay there.[394]

I had soon my Ends of[395] this old Woman; for I only wanted to know which was *London* Road, and away I walk'd as fast as I could; not that I intended to go on Foot, either to *London* or to *Colchester*, but I wanted to get quietly away from *Ipswich*.

I walk'd about two or three Mile, and then I met a plain Countryman, who was busy about some Husbandry work I did not know what; and I ask'd him a great many Questions first, not much to the purpose; but at last told him I was going for *London*, and the Coach was full, and I cou'd not get a Passage, and ask'd him if he cou'd not tell me where to hire a Horse that would carry double, and an honest Man to ride before me to *Colchester*, so that I might get a Place there in the Coaches; the honest Clown[396] look'd earnestly at me, and said nothing for above half a Minute; when scratching his Pole,[397] a Horse say you, and to *Colchester* to carry double; why yes Mistress, alack-a-day, you may have Horses enough for Money; well Friend, *says I*, that I take for granted, I don't expect it without Money: Why but Mistress, *says he*, how much are you willing to give; nay, says I again, Friend, I don't know what your Rates are in the Country here, for I am a Stranger; but if you can get one for me, get it as Cheap as you can, and I'll give you somewhat for your Pains.

Why that's honestly said too, says the Countryman; *not so honest neither*, said I, to myself, *if thou knewest all*; why Mistress, *says he*, I have a Horse that will carry Double, and I don't much care if I go myself with you, *an you like*;[398] Will you, *says I*? well I believe you are an honest Man, if you will, I shall be glad of it, I'll pay you in Reason; why look ye Mistress, *says he*, I won't be out of Reason with you then; if I carry you to *Colechester*, it will be worth five Shillings for myself and my Horse, for I shall hardly come back to Night.

In short, I hir'd the honest Man and his Horse; but when we came to a Town upon the Road, I do not remember the Name of it; but it stands upon a River, I pretended myself very ill, and I could go no farther that Night, but if he would stay there with me, because I was a Stranger, I would pay him for himself, and his Horse with all my Heart.

This I did because I knew the *Dutch* Gentlemen and their Servants

---

[394]Colchester is about 20 miles from Harwich, west and a bit south, and on the main road to London, 50 miles farther away.

[395]I.e., got what she wanted from.

[396]Countryman, rustic.

[397]Poll; i.e., head.

[398]If you wish.

would be upon the Road that Day, either in the Stage Coaches, or riding Post, and I did not know but the drunken Fellow, or some body else that might have seen me at *Harwich*, might see me again, and so I thought that in one Days stop they would be all gone by.

We lay all that Night there, and the next Morning it was not very early when I set out, so that it was near Ten a-Clock by the time I got to *Colechester*: It was no little Pleasure that I saw the Town, where I had so many pleasant Days, and I made many Enquiries after the good old Friends, I had once had there, but could make little out, they were all dead or remov'd: The young Ladies had been all married or gone to *London*; the old Gentleman and the old Lady, that had been my early Benefactress all dead; and which troubled me most the young Gentleman my first Lover, and afterwards my Brother-in-Law was dead; but two Sons Men grown, were left of him, but they too were Transplanted to *London*.

I dismiss'd my old Man here, and stay'd incognito for three or four Days in *Colechester*, and then took a Passage in a Waggon, because I would not venture being seen in the *Harwich* Coaches; but I needed not have used so much Caution, for there was no Body in *Harwich* but the Woman of the House, could have known me; nor was it rational to think that she, considering the hurry she was in, and that she never saw me but once, and that by Candle light, should have ever discover'd me.

I was now return'd to *London*, and tho' by the Accident of the last Adventure, I got something considerable, yet I was not fond of any more Country rambles, nor should I have ventur'd Abroad again if I had carried the Trade on to the End of my Days; I gave my Governess a History of my Travels, she lik'd the *Harwich* Journey well enough, and in Discoursing of these things between ourselves she observ'd, that a Theif being a Creature that Watches the Advantages of other Peoples mistakes, 'tis impossible but that to one that is vigilant and industrious many Opportunities must happen, and therefore she thought that one so exquisitely keen in the Trade as I was, would scarce fail of something extraordinary where ever I went.

On the other hand, every Branch of my Story, if duly consider'd, may be useful to honest People, and afford a due Caution to People of some sort, or other to Guard against the like Surprizes, and to have their Eyes about them when they have to do with Strangers of any kind, for 'tis seldom that some Snare or other is not in their way. The Moral indeed of all my History is left to be gather'd by the Senses[399] and Judgment of the Reader; I am not Qualified to preach to them, let the Experience of one Creature compleatly Wicked, and

[399]The faculties of perception conceived generally and distinguished from the critical faculty (judgment).

compleatly Miserable be a Storehouse of useful warning to those that read.

I am drawing now towards a new Variety of the Scenes of Life: Upon my return, being hardened by a long Race of Crime, and Success unparalell'd, at least in the reach of my own Knowledge, I had, as I have said, no thoughts of laying down a Trade, which if I was to judge by the Example of others, must however End at last in Misery and Sorrow.

It was on the *Christmas-day* following in the Evening that, to finish a long Train of Wickedness, I went Abroad to see what might offer in my way; when going by a Working Silver-Smiths in *Foster-lane*, I saw a tempting Bait indeed, and not to be resisted by one of my Occupation; for the Shop had no Body in it, as I could see, and a great deal of loose Plate lay in the Window, and at the Seat of the Man, who usually as I suppose Work'd at one side of the Shop.

I went boldly in and was just going to lay my Hand upon a peice of Plate, and might have done it, and carried it clear off, for any care that the Men who belong'd to the Shop had taken of it; but an officious Fellow in a House, not a Shop, on the other side of the Way, seeing me go in, and observing that there was no Body in the shop, comes running over the Street, and into the Shop, and without asking me what I was, or who, seizes upon me, and cries out for the People of the House.

I had not as I said above, touch'd any thing in the Shop, and seeing a glimpse of some Body running over to the Shop, I had so much presence of Mind, as to knock very hard with my Foot on the Floor of the House, and was just calling out too, when the Fellow laid Hands on me.

However as I had always most Courage, when I was in most danger; so when the Fellow laid Hands on me, I stood very high upon it, that I came in, to buy half a Dozen of silver Spoons, and to my good Fortune, it was a Silver-smith's that sold Plate, as well as work'd Plate, for other Shops: The Fellow laugh'd at that Part, and put such a value upon the Service that he had done his Neighbour, that he would have it be that I came not to buy, but to steal, and raising a great Crowd, I said to the Master of the Shop, who by this time was fetch'd Home from some Neighbouring Place, that it was in vain to make Noise, and enter into Talk there of the Case; the Fellow had insisted, that I came to steal, and he must prove it, and I desir'd we might go before a Magistrate without any more Words; for I began to see I should be too hard for[400] the Man that had seiz'd me.

The Master and Mistress of the Shop were really not so violent, as

---

[400]Too much for; i.e., Moll saw that she could maneuver so that he could not prove his charges.

the Man from tother side of the Way, and the Man said, Mistress you might come into the Shop with a good Design for aught I know, but it seem'd a dangerous thing for you to come into such a Shop as mine is, when you see no Body there, and I cannot do so little Justice to my Neighbour, who was so kind to me, as not to acknowledge he had reason on his Side; tho' upon the whole I do not find you attemp'd to take any thing, and I really know not what to do in it: I press'd him to go before a Magistrate with me, and if any thing cou'd be prov'd on me, that was like a design of Robbery, I should willingly submit, but if not I expected reparation.

Just while we were in this Debate, and a Crowd of People gather'd about the Door, came by Sir. *T. B.* an Alderman of the City, and Justice of the Peace, and the Goldsmith hearing of it goes out, and entreated his Worship to come in and decide the Case.

Give the Goldsmith his due, he told his Story with a great deal of Justice and Moderation, and the Fellow that had come over, and seiz'd upon me, told his with as much Heat, and foolish Passion, which did me good still, rather than Harm: It came then to my turn to speak, and I told his Worship that I was a Stranger in *London*, being newly come out of the *North*, that I Lodg'd in such a Place, that I was passing this Street, and went into the Goldsmiths Shop to buy half a Dozen of Spoons; by great good Luck I had an old silver Spoon in my Pocket, which I pull'd out, and told him I had carried that Spoon to match it with half a Dozen of new ones, that it might match some I had in the Country.

That seeing no Body in the Shop, I knock'd with my Foot very hard to make the People hear, and had also call'd aloud with my Voice: Tis true, there was loose Plate in the Shop, but that no Body cou'd say I had touch'd any of it, or gone near it; that a Fellow came running into the Shop out of the Street, and laid Hands on me in a furious manner, in the very Moments, while I was calling, for the People of the House; that if he had really had a mind to have done his Neighbour any Service, he should have stood at a distance, and silently watch'd to see whether I had touch'd any thing, or no, and then have clap'd in upon me, and taken me in the Fact: That is very true, *says Mr. Alderman*, and turning to the Fellow that stopt me, he ask'd him if it was true that I knock'd with my Foot; he said yes I had knock'd, but that might be because of his coming; Nay, says *the Alderman*, taking him short, now you contradict yourself, for just now you said, she was in the Shop with her back to you, and did not see you till you came upon her; now it was true, that my back was partly to the Street, but yet as my Business was of a kind that requir'd me to have my Eyes every way, so I really had a glance of him running over, as I said before, tho' he did not perceive it.

After a full Hearing, the Alderman gave it as his Opinion, that his

Neighbour was under a mistake, and that I was Innocent, and the Goldsmith acquiesc'd in it too, and his Wife, and so I was dismiss'd; but as I was going to depart, Mr. *Alderman* said, but *hold Madam*, if you were designing to buy Spoons I hope you will not let my Friend here lose his Customer by the Mistake: I readily answer'd, no Sir, I'll buy the Spoons still if he can Match my odd Spoon, which I brought for a Pattern, and the Goldsmith shew'd me some of the very same Fashion; so he weigh'd the Spoons, and they came to five and thirty Shillings, so I pulls out my Purse to pay him, in which I had near 20 Guineas, for I never went without such a Sum about me, what ever might happen, and I found it of use at other times as well as now.

When Mr. *Alderman* saw my Money, *he said*, well Madam, now I am satisfy'd you were wrong'd, and it was for this Reason, that I mov'd you should buy the Spoons, and staid till you had bought them, for if you had not had Money to pay for them, I should have suspected that you did not come into the Shop with an intent to buy, for indeed the sort of People who come upon those Designs that you have been Charg'd with, are seldom troubl'd with much Gold in their Pockets, as I see you are.

I smil'd, and told his Worship, that then I ow'd something of his Favour to my Money, but I hop'd he saw reason also in the Justice he had done me before; he said, yes he had, but this had confirm'd his Opinion, and he was fully satisfy'd now of my having been injur'd; so I came off with flying Colours, tho' from an Affair, in which I was at the very brink of Destruction.

It was but three Days after this that, not at all made Cautious by my former Danger as I us'd to be, and still pursuing the Art which I had so long been employ'd in, I ventur'd into a House where I saw the Doors open, and furnish'd my self as I thought verily without being perceiv'd, with two Peices of flower'd Silks, such as they call Brocaded Silk, very rich; it was not a Mercers Shop, nor a Warehouse of a Mercer, but look'd like a private Dwelling-House, and was it seems Inhabited by a Man that sold Goods for the Weavers to the Mercers, like a Broker or Factor.

That I may make short of this black Part of this Story, I was attack'd by two Wenches that came open Mouth'd at me just as I was going out at the Door, and one them pull'd me back into the Room, while the other shut the Door upon me; I would have given them good Words, but there was no room for it; two firery Dragons cou'd not have been more furious than they were; they tore my Cloths, bully'd and roar'd as if they would have murther'd me; the Mistress of the House came next, and then the Master, and all outrageous, for a while especially.

I gave the Master very good Words, told him the Door was open, and things were a Temptation to me, that I was poor, and distress'd, and Poverty was what many could not resist, and beg'd him with

Tears to have pity on me; the Mistress of the House was mov'd with Compassion, and enclin'd to have let me go, and had almost perswaded her Husband to it also, but the sawcy Wenches were run even before they were sent, and had fetch'd a Constable, and then the Master said, he could not go back, I must go before a Justice, and answer'd his Wife that he might come into Trouble himself if he should let me go.

The sight of the Constable indeed struck me with terror, and I thought I should have sunk into the Ground; I fell into faintings, and indeed the People themselves thought I would have died, when[401] the Woman argued again for me, and entreated her Husband, seeing they had lost nothing to let me go: I offer'd him to pay for the two Peices whatever the value was, tho' I had not got them, and argued that as he had his Goods, and had really lost nothing, it would be cruel to pursue me to Death, and have my Blood for the bare Attempt of taking them. I put the Constable in mind that I had broke no Doors, nor carried any thing away; and when I came to the Justice, and pleaded there that I had neither broken any thing to get in, nor carried any thing out, the Justice was enclin'd to have releas'd me; but the first sawcy Jade that stop'd me, affirming that I was going out with the Goods, but that she stop'd me and pull'd me back as I was upon the Threshold; the Justice upon that point committed me, and I was carried to *Newgate*; that horrid Place! my very Blood chills at the mention of its Name; the Place, where so many of my Comrades had been lock'd up, and from whence they went to the fatal Tree;[402] the Place where my Mother suffered so deeply, where I was brought into the World, and from whence I expected no Redemption, but by an infamous Death: To conclude, the Place that had so long expected me, and which with so much Art and Success I had so long avoided.

I was now fix'd indeed; 'tis impossible to describe the terror of my mind, when I was first brought in, and when I look'd round upon all the horrors of that dismal Place: I look'd on myself as lost, and that I had nothing to think of, but of going out of the World, and that with the utmost Infamy; the hellish Noise, the Roaring, Swearing and Clamour, the Stench and Nastiness, and all the dreadful croud of Afflicting things that I saw there; joyn'd together to make the Place seem an Emblem of Hell itself, and a kind of an Entrance into it.

Now I reproach'd myself with the many hints I had had, *as I have mentioned above*, from my own Reason, from the Sense of my good Circumstances, and of the many Dangers I had escap'd to leave off

---

[401] And then.

[402] The gallows. "Fatal tree" is also a common epithet both for the cross and for Eden's tree of forbidden fruit, in Christian writings. At this point in the narrative, the density of religious language increases perceptibly; note such ensuing terms as "redemption," "lost," and "expiate," as well as the imagery of hell when Moll begins to imagine her punishment and its possible results.

while I was well, and how I had withstood them all, and hardened my Thoughts against all Fear; it seem'd to me that I was hurried on by an inevitable and unseen Fate to this Day of Misery, and that now I was to Expiate all my Offences at the Gallows, that I was now to give satisfaction to Justice with my Blood, and that I was come to the last Hour of my Life, and of my Wickedness together: These things pour'd themselves in upon my Thoughts in a confus'd manner, and left me overwhelm'd with Melancholly and Despair.

Then I repented heartily of all my Life past, but that Repentance yielded me no Satisfaction, no Peace, no not in the least, because, *as I said to myself*, it was repenting after the Power of farther Sinning was taken away: I seem'd not to Mourn that I had committed such Crimes, and for the Fact, as it was an Offence against God and my Neighbour; but I mourn'd that I was to be punish'd for it; I was a Penitent as I thought, not that I had sinn'd, but that I was to suffer, and this took away all the Comfort, and even the hope of my Repentance in my own Thoughts.

I got no sleep for several Nights or Days after I came into that wretch'd Place, and glad I wou'd have been for some time to have died there, tho' I did not consider dying as it ought to be consider'd neither, indeed nothing could be fill'd with more horror to my Imagination than the very Place, nothing was more odious to me than the Company that was there: O! if I had but been sent to any Place in the World, and not to *Newgate*, I should have thought myself happy.

In the next Place, how did the harden'd Wretches that were there before me Triumph over me? what! Mrs. *Flanders* come to *Newgate* at last? what Mrs. *Mary*, Mrs. *Molly*, and after that plain *Moll Flanders*? They thought the Devil had help'd me they said, that I had reign'd so long, they expected me there many Years ago, and was I come at last? then they flouted me with my Dejections, welcom'd me to the Place, wish'd me Joy, bid me have a good Heart, not to be cast down, things might not be so bad as I fear'd, and the like; then call'd for Brandy, and drank to me; but put it all up to my Score,[403] for they told me I was but just come to the College,[404] *as they call'd it*; and sure I had Money in my Pocket, tho' they had none.

I ask'd one of this Crew how long she had been there? she said four Months; I ask'd her, how the Place look'd to her when she first came into it? just as it did now to me, *says she*, dreadful and frightful, that she thought she was in Hell, and I believe so still, *adds she, but it is*

---

[403]Tally; i.e., to be added to Moll's charges. Food and drink were available to prisoners, depending on their ability to pay.

[404]A nickname for Newgate, possibly because the underworld had long used this term to describe a school where novices learned the arts of crime, and (as Moll elsewhere says) lodgers in Newgate often learned more crime in prison than out.

natural to me now, I don't disturb myself about it: I suppose says I, you
are in no danger of what is to follow: Nay, *says she*, you are mistaken
there I assure you, for I am under Sentence, only I pleaded my Belly,
but I am no more with Child, than the Judge that try'd me, and I
expect to be call'd down next Sessions; *this* CALLING DOWN, is calling
down *to their former Judgement, when a Woman has been respited for her
Belly, but proves not to be with Child, or if she has been with Child, and
has been brought to Bed.* Well says I, and are you thus easy? ay, *says she*,
I can't help myself, what signifyes being sad? If I am hang'd there's
an End of me, *says she*, and away she turns Dancing, and Sings as she
goes, the following Peice of *Newgate* Wit,

> *If I swing by the String,*
> *I shall hear the*[405] *Bell ring.*

And then there's an End of poor *Jenny*.

I mention this, because it would be worth the Observation of any
Prisoner, who shall hereafter fall into the same Misfortune and come
to that dreadful Place of *Newgate*; how Time, Necessity, and Conversing with the Wretches that are there Familiarizes the Place to them;
how at last they become reconcil'd to that which at first was the greatest Dread upon their Spirits in the World, and are as impudently
Chearful and Merry in their Misery, as they were when out of it.

I can not say, as some do, this Devil is not so black, as he is painted;
for indeed no Colours can represent the Place to the Life; nor any
Soul conceive aright of it, but those who have been Sufferers there:
But how Hell should become by degrees so natural, and not only
tollerable, but even agreeable, is a thing Unintelligible, but by those
who have Experienc'd it, as I have.[406]

The same Night that I was sent to *Newgate*, I sent the News of it to
my old Governess, who was surpriz'd at it you may be sure, and spent
the Night almost as ill out of *Newgate*, as I did in it.

The next Morning, she came to see me, she did what she cou'd to
Comfort me, but she saw that was to no purpose; however, as she said,
to sink under the Weight, was but to encrease the Weight, she immediately applied herself to all the proper Methods to prevent the
Effects of it, which we fear'd; and first she found out the two fiery
Jades that had surpriz'd me; she tamper'd[407] with them, persuad'd[408]
them, offer'd them Money, and in a Word, try'd all imaginable ways
to prevent a Prosecution; she offer'd one of the Wenches 100 *l.* to go

---

[405]The Bell at St. *Sepulcher's* which Tolls
upon Execution Day. (Defoe's note)

[406]A Renaissance and eighteenth-century commonplace. See for example, Pope,

Essay on Man, II, 217ff.

[407]Tried to make a deal.

[408]Pleaded with.

away from her Mistress, and not to appear against me; ...
resolute, that tho' she was but a Servant-Maid, at 3 *l.* a Ye...
thereabouts, she refus'd it, and would have refus'd it, as my G...
said she believ'd, if she had offer'd her 500 *l.* Then she attack...
tother Maid, she was not so hard Hearted in appearance as the ot...
and sometimes seem'd inclin'd to be merciful; but the first Wenc...
kept her up, and chang'd her Mind, and would not so much as let my
Governess talk with her, but threatn'd to have her up for Tampering
with the Evidence.

Then she apply'd to the Master, that is to say, the Man whose Goods
had been stol'n, and particularly to his Wife, who as I told you was
enclin'd at first to have some Compassion for me; she found the
Woman the same still, but the Man alledg'd he was bound by the
Justice that committed me, to Prosecute, and that he should forfeit his
Recognizance.[409]

My Governess offer'd to find Friends that should get his Recogni-
zances off of the File,[410] as they call it, and that he should not suffer;[411]
but it was not possible to Convince him that could be done, or that he
could be safe any way in the World, but by appearing against me; so I
was to have three Witnesses of Fact, against me, the Master and his
two Maids, that is to say, I was as certain to be cast for my Life,[412] as I
was certain that I was alive, and I had nothing to do, but to think of
dying, and prepare for it: I had but a sad foundation to build upon, as I
said before, for all my Repentance appear'd to me to be only the Effect
of my fear of Death, not a sincere regret for the wicked Life that I had
liv'd, and which had brought this Misery upon me, or for the offending
my Creator, who was now suddenly to be my Judge.

I liv'd many Days here under the utmost horror of Soul; I had Death
as it were in view, and thought of nothing Night and Day, but of
Gibbets and Halters, evil Spirits and Devils; it is not to be express'd
by Words how I was harrass'd, between the dreadful Apprehensions of
Death, and the Terror of my Conscience reproaching me with my past
horrible Life.

The Ordinary[413] of *Newgate* came to me, and talk'd a little in his way,
but all his Divinity run upon Confessing my Crime, as he call'd it, (tho'
he knew not what I was in for) making a full Discovery, and the like,
without which he told me God would never forgive me; and he said
so little to the purpose, that I had no manner of Consolation from him;

---

[409]Bond (which he would forfeit if he
now withdrew the case).

[410]Destroy the record of his agreement
to testify.

[411]Be punished; i.e., lose his bond.

[412]Sentenced to be hanged. Two witnesses were normally sufficient to convict.

[413]The chaplain, whose duty it was to
prepare condemned prisoners for death.
However, he was often used (as apparently here) to extort confessions from
prisoners not yet convicted, or to get
information on accomplices.

and then to observe the poor Creature preaching Confession and Repentance to me in the Morning, and find him drunk with Brandy and Spirits by Noon; this had something in it so shocking, that I began to Nauseate the Man more, than his Work, and his Work too by degrees for the sake of[414] the Man; so that I desir'd him to trouble me no more.

I know not how it was, but by the indefatigable Application of my diligent Governess I had no Bill preferr'd against me the first Sessions, I mean to the Grand Jury, at *Guild-Hall*; so I had another Month, or five Weeks before me, and without doubt this ought to have been accepted by me, as so much time given me for Reflection upon what was past, and preparation for what was to come, or in a Word, I ought to have esteem'd it, as a space given me for Repentance, and have employ'd it as such; but it was not in me, I was sorry (*as before*) for being in *Newgate*, but had very few Signs of Repentance about me.

On the contrary, like the Waters in the Caveties, and Hollows of Mountains, which petrifies and turns into Stone whatever they are suffer'd to drop upon; so the continual Conversing with such a Crew of Hell-Hounds as I was, which had the same common Operation upon me, as upon other People, I degenerated into Stone; I turn'd first Stupid and Senseless, then Brutish and thoughtless, and at last raving Mad as any of them were; and in short, I became as naturally pleas'd and easie with the Place, as if indeed I had been Born there.[415]

It is scarce possible to imagine that our Natures should be capable of so much Degeneracy, as to make that pleasant and agreeable that in it self is the most compleat Misery. Here was a Circumstance, that I think it is scarce possible to mention a worse; I was as exquisitely[416] miserable as, speaking of common Cases, it was possible for any one to be that had Life and Health, and Money to help them as I had.

I had a weight of Guilt upon me enough to sink any Creature who had the least power of Reflection left, and had any Sense upon them of the Happiness of this Life, or the Misery of another then; I had at first remorse indeed, but no Repentance; I had now neither Remorse or Repentance: I had a Crime charg'd on me, the Punishments of which was Death by our Law; the Proof so evident, that there was no room for me so much as to plead not Guilty; I had the Name of old Offender, so that I had nothing to expect but Death in a few Weeks time, neither had I myself any thoughts of Escaping, and yet a certain strange Lethargy of Soul possess'd me, I had no Trouble, no Apprehensions, no Sorrow about me, the first Surprize was gone; I was, I

---

[414]Because of.
[415]Moll had been, of course. Some critics have suggested that Defoe merely forgot here (after affirming her place of birth only a few paragraphs earlier), but he may well have intended Moll's comment to be ironic.
[416]Intensely.

may well say, I know not how; my Senses, my Reason, nay, my Conscience were all a-sleep, my Course of Life for forty Years had been a horrid Complication of Wickedness, Whoredom, Adultery, Incest, Lying, Theft, and in a Word, every thing but Murther, and Treason had been my Practice from the Age of Eighteen, or thereabouts to Threescore; and now I was ingulph'd in the misery of Punishment, and had an infamous Death just at the Door, and yet I had no Sense of my Condition, no Thought of Heaven or Hell, at least, that went any farther than a bare flying Touch, like the Stitch or Pain that gives a Hint and goes off; I neither had a Heart to ask God's Mercy, or indeed to think of it, and in this I think I have given a brief Description of the compleatest Misery on Earth.

All my terrifying Thoughts were past, the Horrors of the Place, were become Familiar, and I felt no more uneasinesses at the Noise and Clamours of the Prison, than they did who made that Noise; in a Word, I was become a meer *Newgate-Bird*, as Wicked and as Outragious as any of them; nay, I scarce retain'd the Habit and Custom of good Breeding, and Manners, which all along till now run thro' my Conversation; so thoro' a Degeneracy had possess'd me, that I was no more the same thing that I had been, than if I had never been otherwise than what I was now.

In the middle of this harden'd Part of my Life, I had another sudden Surprize, which call'd me back a little to that thing call'd Sorrow, which indeed I began to be past the Sense of before: They told me one Night, that there was brought into the Prison late the Night before three Highway-Men, who had committed a Robbery somewhere on the Road to *Windsor*, *Hounslow-Heath*,[417] I think it was, and were pursu'd to *Uxbridge* by the Country,[418] and were taken there after a gallant Resistance, in which I know not how many of the Country People were wounded, and some kill'd.

It is not to be wonder'd that we who were Prisoners, were all desirous enough to see these brave topping Gentlemen that were talk'd up to be such, as their Fellows had not been known,[419] and especially because it was said they would in the Morning be remov'd into the Press-Yard,[420] having given Money to the Head-Master of the Prison, to be allow'd the liberty of that better Part of the Prison: So we that were Women plac'd ourselves in the way that we would be sure to see them; but nothing cou'd express the Amazement and Surprize I was in, when the very first Man that came out I knew to be my

---

[417]A famous haunt of highwaymen, on the principal road from London to the West of England. The heath is just west of Hounslow, about 10 miles from London. Uxbridge is northwest of Hounslow, near Buckinghamshire.

[418]Citizens of the district.

[419]I.e., they were said to be without peers.

[420]A court in Newgate where prisoners could, for a fee, receive preferential treatment.

Lancashire Husband, the same who liv'd so well at *Dunstable*, and the same who I afterwards saw at *Brickill*, when I was married to my last Husband, as has been related.

I was struck Dumb at the Sight, and knew neither what to say, or what to do; he did not know me, and that was all the present Relief I had, I quitted my Company, and retir'd as much as that dreadful Place suffers any Body to retire, and I cry'd vehemently for a great while; dreadful Creature, that I am, *said I*, How many poor People have I made Miserable? How many desperate Wretches have I sent to the Devil; This Gentleman's Misfortunes I plac'd all to my own Account: He had told me at *Chester*, he was ruin'd by that Match, and that his Fortunes were made Desperate on my Account; for that thinking I had been a Fortune he was run into Debt more than he was able to pay, and that he knew not what Course to take; that he would go into the Army, and carry a Musquet, or buy a Horse and take a Tour,[421] as he call'd it; and tho' I never told him that I was a Fortune, and so did not actually Deceive him myself, yet I did encourage the having it thought that I was so, and by that means I was the occasion originally of his Mischief.

The Surprize of this thing only,[422] struck deeper into my Thoughts, and gave me stronger Reflections than all that had befallen me before; I griev'd Day and Night for him, and the more, for that they told he was the Captain of the Gang, and that he had committed so many Robberies, that *Hind*, or *Whitney*, or the *Golden Farmer* were Fools to him;[423] that he would surely be hang'd if there were no more Men left in the Country he was born in; and that there would abundance of People come in against him.

I was overwhelm'd with grief for him; my own Case gave me no disturbance compar'd to this, and I loaded my self with Reproaches on his Account; I bewail'd his Misfortunes, and the ruin he was now come to, at such a Rate, that I relish'd nothing now, as I did before, and the first Reflections I made upon the horrid detestable Life I had liv'd, began to return upon me, and as these things return'd my abhorrance of the Place I was in, and of the way of living in it, return'd also; in a word, I was perfectly chang'd, and become another Body.

[421]Become a highwayman.

[422]This one thing.

[423]Insignificant compared to him. Captain James Hind, a famous highwayman during the reign of Charles I, was hanged, drawn, and quartered in 1652 at the age of thirty-four. Whitney (he was known by this single name) was also a highwayman, among his other criminal games, and also was executed, in 1694, at the age of thirty-four. The Golden Farmer, so called because he paid all debts in gold and because he kept a Gloucestershire farm as a front for his real occupation, was executed in 1689 at the age of sixty-three. His real name was William Davis, and he was also primarily famous as a highwayman. The exploits of all these men were well known to Defoe's contemporaries, and Defoe may have taken hints for *Moll Flanders* from stories told about them.

While I was under these influences of sorrow for him, came Notice to me that the next Sessions approaching, there would be a Bill preferr'd to the Grand Jury against me, and that I should be certainly try'd for my Life at the *Old-Baily*: My Temper was touch'd before,[424] the harden'd wretch'd boldness of Spirit, which I had acquir'd, abated, and Conscious in the Prison Guilt[425] began to flow in upon my Mind: In short, I began to think, and to think is one real Advance from Hell to Heaven; all that Hellish harden'd state and temper of Soul, which I have said so much of before, is but a deprivation of Thought; he that is restor'd to his Power of thinking, is restor'd to himself.

As soon as I began, I say, to Think, the first thing that occurr'd to me broke out thus; Lord! what will become of me, I shall certainly die! I shall be cast to be sure, and there is nothing beyond that but Death! I have no Friends, what shall I do? I shall be certainly cast; Lord, have Mercy upon me, what will become of me? This was a sad Thought, you will say, to be the first after so long time, that had started into my Soul of that kind, and yet even this was nothing but fright, at what was to come; there was not a Word of sincere Repentance in it all: However, I was indeed dreadfully dejected, and disconsolate to the last degree; and as I had no Friend in the World to communicate my distress'd Thoughts to, it lay so heavy upon me, that it threw me into Fits, and Swoonings several times a-Day: I sent for my old Governess, and she, *give her her due*, acted the Part of a true Friend, she left me no Stone unturn'd to prevent the Grand Jury; finding out one or two of the Jury Men, talk'd with them, and endeavour'd to possess them with favourable Dispositions, on Account that nothing was taken away, and no House broken, *&c.* but all would not do, they were over-ruled by the rest, the two Wenches swore home to the Fact, and the Jury found the Bill against me for Robbery and Housebreaking, that is for Felony and Burglary.

I sunk down when they brought me News of it, and after I came to myself again, I thought I should have died with the weight of it: My Governess acted a true Mother to me, she pittied me, she cryed with me, and for me; but she cou'd not help me; and to add to the Terror of it, twas the Discourse all over the House,[426] that I should die for it; I cou'd hear them talk it among themselves very often; and see them shake their Heads, and say they were sorry for it, and the like, as is usual in the Place; but still no Body came to tell me their Thoughts, till at last one of the Keepers came to me privately, and said with a Sigh, well Mrs. *Flanders*, you will be tried a *Friday*, (this was but a

---

[424]I.e., Moll's hardness was already somewhat softened.

[425]In-the-prison guilt; i.e., Moll had begun to feel the sort of guilt that results from punishment, but not yet any sorrow for the acts themselves.

[426]Newgate.

Wednesday,) what do you intend to? I turn'd as white as a Clout,[427] and said, God knows what I shall do, for my part I know not what to do; why, *says he*, I won't flatter[428] you, I would have you prepare for Death, for I doubt you will be Cast, and as they say, you are an old Offender; I doubt you will find but little Mercy; They say, *added he*, your Case is very plain, and that the Witnesses swear so home[429] against you, there will be no standing it.

This was a stab into the very Vitals of one under such a Burthen as I was oppress'd with before, and I cou'd not speak to him a Word good or bad, for a great while, but at last I burst out into Tears, and said to him, Lord! Mr. ——— What must I do? Do, *says he*, send for the Ordinary, send for a Minister, and talk with him, for indeed Mrs. *Flanders*, unless you have very good Friends, you are no Woman for this World.

This was plain dealing[430] indeed, but it was very harsh to me, at least I thought it so: He left me in the greatest Confusion imaginable, and all that Night I lay awake; and now I began to say my Prayers, which I had scarce done before since my last Husband's Death, or from a little while after; and truly I may well call it, saying my Prayers; for I was in such a Confusion, and had such horrour upon my Mind, that tho' I cry'd, and repeated several times the Ordinary Expression of, *Lord have Mercy upon me*;[431] I never brought my self to any Sense of my being a miserable Sinner, as indeed I was, and of Confessing my Sins to God, and begging Pardon for the sake of Jesus Christ; I was overwhelm'd with the Sense of my Condition, being try'd for my Life, and being sure to be Condemn'd, and then I was as sure to be Executed, and on this Account, I cry'd out all Night, Lord! what will become of me? Lord! what shall I do? Lord! I shall be hang'd, Lord have mercy upon me, and the like.

My poor afflicted Governess was now as much concern'd as I, and a great deal more truly Penitent; tho' she had no prospect of being brought to Tryal and Sentence, not but that she deserv'd it as much as I, and so she said herself; but she had not done any thing herself for many Years, other than receiving what I, and others stole, and encouraging us to steal it: But she cry'd and took on, like a distracted Body, wringing her Hands, and crying out that she was undone, that she believ'd there was a Curse from Heaven upon her, that she should be damn'd, that she had been the Destruction of all her Friends, that she had brought such a one, and such a one, and such one to the Gallows; and there she reckon'd up ten or eleven People, some of which I have given an Account of that came to untimely Ends, and

---

[427]A rag or cloth patch; this is a common eighteenth-century expression for paleness.

[428]Give false hopes.

[429]To the point, effectively.

[430]Openness and sincerity.

[431]Defoe frequently uses this phrase elsewhere to suggest "ordinary" or conventional sorrow for misdeeds, distinguishing it from true repentance.

that now she was the occasion of my Ruin, for she had persuaded me to go on, when I would have left off: I interrupted her there; no Mother, no, *said I*, don't speak of that, for you would have had me left off when I got the Mercer's Money again, and when I came home from *Harwich*, and I would not hearken to you, therefore you have not been to blame, it is I only have ruin'd myself, I have brought myself to this Misery, and thus we spent many Hours together.

Well there was no Remedy, the Prosecution went on, and on the *Thursday* I was carried down to the Sessions-House, where I was arraign'd, as they call'd it, and the next Day I was appointed to be Try'd. At the arraignment I pleaded not Guilty, and well I might, for I was indicted for Felony and Burglary; that is for feloniously stealing two Pieces of Brocaded Silk, value 46 *l.* the Goods of *Anthony Johnson*, and for breaking open his Doors; whereas I knew very well they could not pretend to prove I had broken up the Doors, or so much as lifted up a Latch.

On the *Friday* I was brought to my Tryal, I had exhausted my Spirits with Crying for two or three Days before, that[432] I slept better the *Thursday* Night than I expected, and had more Courage[433] for my Tryal, than indeed I thought possible for me to have.

When the Tryal began, and the Indictment was read, I would have spoke, but they told me the Witnesses must be heard first, and then I should have time to be heard. The Witnesses were the two Wenches, a Couple of hard Mouth'd Jades indeed, for tho' the thing was Truth in the main, yet they aggravated it to the utmost extremity, and swore I had the Goods wholly in my possession, that I had hid them among my Cloaths, that I was going off with them, that I had one Foot over the Threshold when they discovered themselves,[434] and then I put tother over, so that I was quite out of the House in the Street with the Goods before they took hold of me, and then they seiz'd me, and brought me back again, and they took the Goods upon me: The Fact in general was all true, but I believe, and insisted upon it, that they stop'd me before I had set my Foot clear of the Threshold of the House; but that did not argue much, for certain it was, that I had taken the Goods, and that I was bringing them away, if I had not been taken.

But I pleaded that I had stole nothing, they had lost nothing, that the Door was open, and I went in seeing the Goods lye there, and with Design to buy; if seeing no Body in the House, I had taken any of them up in my Hand, it cou'd not be concluded that I intended to steal them, for that I never carried them farther than the Door to look on them with the better Light.

The Court would not allow that by any means, and made a kind of a

[432]So that.
[433]Spirit, vigor.

[434]Made themselves known, revealed their presence.

Jest of my intending to buy the Goods, that being no Shop for the Selling of any thing, and as to carrying them to the Door to look at them, the Maids made their impudent Mocks upon that, and spent their Wit upon it very much; told the Court I had look'd at them sufficiently, and approv'd them very well, for I had pack'd them up under my Cloaths, and was a going with them.

In short, I was found Guilty of Felony, but acquited of the Burglary, which was but small Comfort to me, the first bringing me to a Sentence of Death, and the last would have done no more:[435] The next Day, I was carried down to receive the dreadful Sentence, and when they came to ask me what I had to say, why Sentence should not pass, I stood mute a while, but some Body that stood behind me, prompted me aloud to speak to the Judges, for that they cou'd represent things favourably for me: This encourag'd me to speak, and I told them I had nothing to say to stop the Sentence; but that I had much to say, to bespeak the Mercy of the Court, that I hop'd they would allow something in such a Case, for the Circumstances of it, that I had broken no Doors, had carried nothing off, that no Body had lost any thing; that the Person whose Goods they were, was pleas'd to say, he desir'd Mercy might be shown, which indeed he very honestly did, that at the worst it was the first Offence, and that I had never been before any Court of Justice before: And in a Word, I spoke with more Courage than I thought I cou'd have done, and in such a moving Tone, and tho' with Tears, yet not so many Tears as to obstruct my Speech, that I cou'd see it mov'd others to Tears that heard me.

The Judges sat Grave and Mute, gave me an easy Hearing, and time to say all that I would, but saying neither Yes, or No to it, Pronounc'd the Sentence of Death upon me; a Sentence that was to me like Death itself, which after it was read confounded me; I had no more Spirit left in me, I had no Tongue to speak, or Eyes to look up either to God or Man.

My poor Governess was utterly Disconsolate; and she that was my Comforter before, wanted Comfort now herself, and sometimes Mourning, sometimes Raging, was as much out of herself (as to all outward Appearance) as any mad Woman in *Bedlam*:[436] Nor was she only Disconsolate as to me, but she was struck with Horror at the Sense of her own wicked Life, and began to look back upon it with a Taste quite different from mine; for she was Penitent to the highest Degree for her Sins, as well as Sorrowful for the Misfortune: She sent for a Minister too, a serious pious good Man, and apply'd herself with such earnestness by his assistance to the Work of a sincere Repen-

---

[435]Another instance of Moll's grim humor; Moll seems to resort to comic irony most frequently when she is most serious.

[436]Short for Bethlehem Hospital, an institution for the insane.

tance, that I believe, and so did the Minister too, that she was a true Penitent, and which is still more, she was not only so for the Occasion, and at that Juncture, but she continu'd so, as I was inform'd, to the Day of her Death.

It is rather to be thought of, than express'd what was now my Condition; I had nothing before me but present Death; and as I had no Friends to assist me, or to stir for me, I expected nothing but to find my Name in the Dead Warrant, which was to come down for the Execution the *Friday* afterward, of five more and myself.

In the mean time my poor distress'd Governess sent me a Minister, who at her request first, and at my own afterwards came to visit me: He exhorted me seriously to repent of all my Sins, and to dally no longer with my Soul; not flattering myself with hopes of Life, which he said, he was inform'd there was no room to expect, but unfeignedly to look up to God with my whole Soul, and to cry for Pardon in the Name of Jesus Christ. He back'd his Discourses with proper Quotations of Scripture, encouraging the greatest Sinner to Repent, and turn from their Evil way, and when he had done, he kneel'd down and pray'd with me.

It was now, that for the first time I felt any real signs of Repentance; I now began to look back upon my past Life with abhorrence, and having a kind of view into the other Side of time, the things of Life, as I believe they do with every Body at such a time, began to look with a different Aspect, and quite another Shape, than they did before; the greatest and best things, the views of felicity, the joy, the griefs of Life were quite other things; and I had nothing in my Thoughts, but what was so infinitely Superior to what I had known in Life, that it appear'd to me to be the greatest stupidity in Nature to lay any weight upon any thing tho' the most valuable in this World.

The Word Eternity represented itself with all its incomprehensible Additions, and I had such extended Notions of it, that I know not how to express them: Among the rest, how vile, how gross, how absurd did every pleasant thing look? I mean, that we had counted pleasant before; especially when I reflected that these sordid Trifles were the things for which we forfeited eternal Felicity.

With those Reflections came in, of meer Course, severe Reproaches of my own Mind for my wretched Behaviour in my past Life; that I had forfeited all hope of any Happiness in the Eternity that I was just going to enter into, and on the contrary was entitul'd to all that was miserable, or had been conceiv'd of as Misery; and all this with the frightful Addition of its being also Eternal.

I am not capable of reading Lectures of Instruction to any Body, but I relate this in the very manner in which things then appear'd to me, as far as I am able; but infinitely short of the lively impressions which they made on my Soul at that time; indeed those Impressions are not to be explain'd by words, or if they are, I am not Mistress of Words enough to express them; It must be the Work of every sober Reader to make just Reflections on them, as their own Circumstances may direct; and without Question, this is what every one at sometime or other may feel something of; I mean a clearer Sight into things to come, than they had here, and a dark view of their own Concern in them.

But I go back to my own Case; the Minister press'd me to tell him, as far as I thought convenient, in what State I found myself as to the Sight I had of things beyond Life; he told me he did not come as Ordinary of the Place, whose business it is to extort Confessions from Prisoners, for private Ends, or for the farther detecting of other Offenders; that his business was to move me to such freedom of Discourse as might serve to disburthen my own Mind, and furnish him to administer Comfort to me as far as was in his Power; and assur'd me, that whatever I said to him should remain with him, and be as much a Secret as if it was known only to God and myself; and that he desir'd to know nothing of me, but as above, to qualifie him to apply proper Advice and Assistance to me, and to pray to God for me.

This honest friendly way of treating me, unlock'd all the Sluces of my Passions: He broke into my very Soul by it; and I unravell'd all the Wickedness of my Life to him: In a word, I gave him an Abridgement of this whole History; I gave him the Picture of my Conduct for 50 Years in Miniature.

I hid nothing from him, and he in return exhorted me to a sincere Repentance, explain'd to me what he meant by Repentance, and then drew out such a Scheme of infinite Mercy, proclaim'd from Heaven to Sinners of the greatest Magnitude, that he left me nothing to say that look'd like despair or doubting of being accepted, and in this Condition he left me the first Night.

He visited me again the next Morning, and went on with his Method of explaining the Terms of Divine Mercy, which according to him consisted of nothing more, or more Difficult than that of being sincerely desirous of it, and willing to accept it; only a sincere Regret for, and hatred of those things I had done, which render'd me so just an Object of divine Vengeance: I am not able to repeat the excellent Discourses of this extraordinary Man; 'tis all that I am able to do to say, that he reviv'd my Heart, and brought me into such a Condition, that I never knew any thing of in my Life before: I was cover'd with Shame and Tears for things past, and yet had at the same time a secret surprizing Joy at the Prospect of being a true Penitent, and obtaining the Comfort of a Penitent, I mean the hope of being forgiven; and so swift did Thoughts circulate, and so high did the impressions they had made upon me run, that I thought I cou'd freely have gone out that

Minute to Execution, without any uneasiness at all, casting[437] my Soul entirely into the Arms of infinite Mercy as a Penitent.

The good Gentleman was so mov'd also in my behalf, with a view of the influence, which he saw these things had on me, that he blessed God he had come to visit me, and resolv'd not to leave me till the last Moment, that is not to leave visiting me.

It was no less than 12 Days after our receiving Sentence, before any were order'd for Execution, and then upon a *Wednesday* the Dead Warrant, *as they call it*, came down, and I found my Name was among them; a terrible blow this was to my new Resolutions, indeed my Heart sunk within me, and I swoon'd away twice, one after another, but spoke not a word: The good Minister was sorely Afflicted for me, and did what he could to comfort me with the same Arguments, and the same moving Eloquence that he did before, and left me not that Evening so long as the Prison-keepers would suffer him to stay in the Prison, unless he wou'd be lock'd up with me all Night, which he was not willing to be.

I wonder'd much that I did not see him all the next Day, *it being but the Day before the time appointed for Execution*; and I was greatly discouraged, and dejected in my Mind, and indeed almost sunk for want of that Comfort, which he had so often, and with such Success yeilded me on his former Visits; I waited with great impatience, and under the greatest oppression of Spirits imaginable; till about four a-Clock he came to my Apartment, for I had obtain'd the Favour by the help of Money, nothing being to be done in that Place without it, not to be kept in the Condemn'd Hole,[438] as they call it, among the rest of the Prisoners, who were to die, but to have a little dirty Chamber to my self.

My Heart leap'd within me for Joy, when I heard his Voice at the Door even before I saw him; but let any one Judge what kind of Motion I found in my Soul, when after having made a short excuse for his not coming, he shew'd me that his time had been employ'd on my Account; that he had obtain'd a favourable Report from the Recorder[439] to the Secretary of State in my particular Case, and in short that he had brought me a Reprieve.

He us'd all the Caution that he was able in letting me know a thing, which it would have been a double Cruelty to have conceal'd; and yet it was too much for me; for as Grief had overset me before, so did Joy overset now, and I fell into a much more dangerous Swooning than I did at first, and it was not without a great Difficulty that I was recover'd at all.

---

[437]Moll's use of this term shifts here from physical to spiritual concerns, and she initiates the action, rather than regarding herself, as she had earlier, as a pawn of fate.

[438]A dungeon for those sentenced to hang.

[439]The magistrate who had jurisdiction in the case.

The good Man having made a very Christian Exhortation to me, not to let the Joy of my Reprieve, put the Remembrance of my past Sorrow out of my Mind; and having told me that he must leave me, to go and enter the Reprieve in the Books, and show it to the Sheriffs, stood up just before his going away, and in a very earnest Manner pray'd to God for me, that my Repentance might be made Unfeign'd and Sincere; and that my coming back as it were into Life again, might not be a returning to the Follies of Life, which I had made such solemn Resolutions to forsake, and to repent of them; I joyn'd heartily in the Petition, and must needs say, I had deeper Impressions upon my Mind all that Night, of the Mercy of God in sparing my Life; and a greater Detestation of my past Sins, from a Sense of the goodness which I had tasted in this Case, than I had in all my Sorrow before.

This may be thought inconsistent in it self, and wide from the Business of this Book; Particularly, I reflect that many of those who may be pleas'd and diverted with the Relation of the wild and wicked part of my Story, may not relish this, which is really the best part of my Life, the most Advantageous to myself, and the most instructive to others; such however will I hope allow me the liberty to make my Story compleat: It would be a severe Satyr[440] on such, to say they do not relish the Repentance as much as they do the Crime; and that they had rather the History were a compleat Tragedy, as it was very likely to have been.

But I go on with my Relation, the next Morning there was a sad Scene indeed in the Prison; the first thing I was saluted with in the Morning, was the Tolling of the great Bell at St. *Sepulchres*, as they call it, which usher'd in the Day: As soon as it began to Toll, a dismal groaning and crying was heard from the Condemn'd Hole, where there lay six poor Souls, who were to be Executed that Day, some for one Crime, some for another, and two of them for Murther.

This was follow'd by a confus'd Clamour in the House; among the several sorts of Prisoners, expressing their awkward Sorrows for the poor Creatures that were to die, but in a manner extreamly differing one from another; some cried for them; some huzza'd, and wish'd them a good Journey; some damn'd and curst those that had brought them to it, that is meaning the Evidence, or Prosecutors; many pittying them; and some few, but very few praying for them.

There was hardly room for so much Composure of Mind, as was requir'd for me to bless the merciful Providence that had as it were snatch'd me out of the Jaws of this Destruction: I remained as it were

---

[440]Satire — a common eighteenth-century spelling. Moll means it would be a derogatory thing to say about readers. Throughout the century, the word "satire" was used widely and often loosely to describe various denunciatory statements and attitudes, as well as to describe literary works ranging from personal lampoons to despairing attacks upon human nature.

Dumb and Silent, overcome with the Sense of it, and not able to express what I had in my Heart; for the Passions on such Occasions as these, are certainly so agitated as not to be able presently to regulate their own Motions.

All the while the poor condemn'd Creatures were preparing to their Death, and the Ordinary *as they call him*, was busy with them, disposing them to submit to their Sentence: I say all this while I was seiz'd with a fit of trembling, as much as I cou'd have been, if I had been in the same Condition, as to be sure the Day before I expected to be: I was so violently agitated by this Surprising Fit, that I shook as if it had been in the cold Fit of an Ague; so that I could not speak or look, but like one Distracted: As soon as they were all put into the Carts and gone, which however I had not Courage enough to see, *I say*, as soon as they were gone, I fell into a fit of crying involuntarily, and without Design, but as a meer Distemper, and yet so violent, and it held me so long, that I knew not what Course to take, nor could I stop, or put a Checque to it, no not with all the Strength and Courage I had.

This fit of crying held me near two Hours and as I believe held me till they were all out of the World, and then a most humble Penitent serious kind of Joy succeeded; a real transport it was, or Passion of Joy, and Thankfulness, but still unable to give vent to it by Words, and in this I continued most part of the Day.

In the Evening the Good Minister visited me again, and then fell to his usual good Discourses, he Congratulated my having a space yet allow'd me for Repentance, whereas the state of those six poor Creatures was determin'd,[441] and they were now pass'd the offers of Salvation; he earnestly press'd me to retain the same Sentiments of the things of Life, that I had when I had a view of Eternity; and at the End of all, told me I should not conclude that all was over, that a Reprieve was not a Pardon, that he could not yet answer for the Effects of it; however, I had this Mercy, that I had more time given me, and that it was my business to improve that time.

This Discourse, tho' very seasonable, left a kind of sadness on my Heart, as if I might expect the Affair would have a tragical Issue still, which however he had no certainty of, and I did not indeed at that time question him about it, he having said that he would do his utmost to bring it to a good End, and that he hoped he might, but he would not have me secure;[442] and the Consequence prov'd that he had Reason for what he said.

It was about a Fortnight after this, that I had some just Apprehensions that I should be included in the next dead Warrant at the

---

[441]I.e., they were dead, and their eternal habitation was already decided.

[442]I.e., he didn't want Moll to be over-confident.

ensuing Sessions; and it was not without great difficulty, and at last an humble Petition for Transportation, that I avoided it, so ill was I beholding to Fame, and so prevailing was the fatal Report of being an old Offender, tho' in that they did not do me strict Justice, for I was not in the Sense of the Law an old Offender, whatever I was in the Eye of the Judge; for I had never been before them in a judicial way before, so the Judges could not Charge me with being an old Offender, but the Recorder was pleas'd to represent my Case as he thought fit.

I had now a certainty of Life indeed, but with the hard Conditions of being order'd for Transportation, which indeed was a hard Condition in it self, but not when comparatively considered; and therefore I shall make no Comments upon the Sentence, nor upon the Choice I was put to; we shall all choose any thing rather than Death, especially when 'tis attended with an uncomfortable prospect beyond it, which was my Case.

The good Minister whose interest, tho' *a Stranger to me*, had obtain'd me the Reprieve, mourn'd sincerely for this part; he was in hopes, *he said*, that I should have ended my Days under the Influence of good Instruction, that I might not have forgot my former Distresses, and that I should not have been turned loose again among such a wretched a Crew as they generally are, who are thus sent Abroad where, *as he said*, I must have more than ordinary secret Assistance from the Grace of God, if I did not turn as wicked again as ever.

I have not for a good while mentioned my Governess, who had during most, if not all of this part been dangerously Sick, and being in as near a view of Death, by her Disease, as I was by my Sentence, was a very great Penitent; I say, I have not mention'd her, nor indeed did I see her in all this time, but being now recovering, and just able to come Abroad, she came to see me.

I told her my Condition, and what a different flux and reflux of Fears, and Hopes I had been agitated with; I told her, what I had escap'd, and upon what Terms, and she was present, when the Minister express'd his fears of my relapsing into wickedness upon my falling into the wretch'd Companies, that are generally Transported: Indeed I had a melancholly Reflection upon it in my own Mind, for I knew what a dreadful Gang was always sent away together, and I said to my Governess, that the good Minister's fears were not without Cause: Well, well, *says she*, but I hope you will not be tempted with such a horrid Example as that, and as soon as the Minister was gone, she told me, she would not have me discourag'd, for perhaps ways and means might be found out to dispose of me in a particular way, by my self, of which she would talk farther to me afterward.

I look'd earnestly at her, and I thought she look'd more chearful than she usually had done, and I entertain'd immediately a Thousand Notions of being deliver'd, but could not for my Life imagin the Methods, or think of one that was in the least seizible; but I was too much concerned in it, to let her go from me without explaining herself, which tho' she was very loth to do, yet my importunity prevail'd, and while I was still pressing, she answer'd me in few Words, thus, Why, *you have Money, have you not?* did you ever know one in your Life that was Transported, and had a Hundred Pound in his Pocket, I'll warrant you Child, *says she.*

I understood her presently, but told her I would leave all that to her, but I saw no room to hope for any thing, but a strict Execution of the order, and as it was a severity that was esteem'd a Mercy, there was no doubt but it would be strictly observ'd; she said no more, but this, *we will try what can be done,* and so we parted for that Night.

I lay in the Prison near fifteen Weeks after this order for Transportation was sign'd; what the Reason of it was, I know not, but at the end of this time I was put on Board of a Ship in the *Thames,* and with me a Gang of Thirteen, as harden'd vile Creatures as ever *Newgate* produc'd in my time; and it would really well take up a History longer than mine to describe the degrees of impudence, and audacious Villany that those Thirteen were arriv'd to; and the manner of their behaviour in the Voyage; of which I have a very diverting Account by me, which the Captain of the Ship, who carried them over gave me the Minutes of, and which he caus'd his Mate to write down at large.

It may perhaps be thought Trifling to enter here into a Relation of all the little incidents which attended me in this interval of my Circumstances; I mean between the final order for my Transportation, and the time of my going on board the Ship, and I am too near the End of my Story, to allow room for it, but something relating to me, *and my Lancashire Husband,* I must not omit.

He had, *as I have observ'd already* been carried from the Master's side[443] of the ordinary Prison, into the Press-Yard, with three of his Comrades, for they found another to add to them after some time; here for what Reason I knew not, they were kept in Custody without being brought to Tryal almost three Months, it seems they found means to Bribe or buy off some of those who were expected to come in against them, and they wanted Evidence some time to Convict them: After some puzzle on this Account, at first they made a shift to get proof enough against two of them, to carry them off; but the other two, of which my *Lancashire* Husband was one, lay still in Suspence: They had I think one positive Evidence against each of them; but the Law strictly obliging them to have two Witnesses, they cou'd make nothing of it; yet it seems they were resolv'd not to part

---

[443]One of the prison's main sections.

with the Men neither, not doubting but a farther Evidence would at last come in; and in order to this, I think Publication was made, that such Prisoners being taken, any one that had been robb'd by them might come to the Prison and see them.

I took this opportunity to satisfy my Curiosity, pretending that I had been robb'd in the *Dunstable* Coach, and that I would go to see the two Highway-Men; but when I came into the Press-Yard, I so disguis'd myself, and muffled my Face up so, that he cou'd see little of me, and consequently knew nothing of who I was, and when I came back, I said publickly that I knew them very well.

Immediately it was Rumour'd all over the Prison, that *Moll Flanders* would turn Evidence against one of the Highway Men, and that I was to come off by it from the Sentence of Transportation.

They heard of it, and immediately my Husband desir'd to see this Mrs. *Flanders* that knew him so well, and was to be an Evidence against him, and accordingly, I had leave given to go to him. I dress'd myself up as well as the best Cloths that I suffer'd myself ever to appear in there, would allow me, and went to the Press-yard, but had for some time a Hood over my Face; he said little to me at first, but ask'd me if I knew him; I told him, yes, very well; but as I conceal'd my Face, so I Counterfeited my Voice, that he had not the least guess at who I was: He ask'd me where I had seen him, I told him between *Dunstable* and *Brickhill*, but turning to the Keeper that stood by, I ask'd if I might not be admitted to talk with him alone, he said, yes, yes, as much as I pleas'd, and so very civilly withdrew.

As soon as he was gone, and I had shut the Door, I threw off my Hood, and bursting out into Tears, *my Dear*, says I, *do you not know me?* He turn'd pale and stood Speechless, like one Thunder struck, and not able to conquer the Surprize, said no more but this, *let me sit down*; and sitting down by a Table, he laid his Elbow upon the Table, and leaning his Head on his Hand, fix'd his Eyes on the Ground as one stupid:[444] I cry'd so vehemently on the other Hand, that it was a good while ee'r I could speak any more; but after I had given some vent to my Passion by Tears, I repeated the same Words: MY DEAR, *do you not know me?* at which he answer'd YES, and said no more a good while.

After some time continuing in the Surprize, *as above*, he cast up his Eyes towards me and said, *How could you be so cruel?* I did not readily understand what he meant; and I answer'd, How can you call me Cruel? What have I been Cruel to you in? *To come to me*, says he, *in such a Place as this, is it not to insult me? I have not robb'd you?* at least not on the Highway?

[444]Stupefied, stunned with surprise.

I perceiv'd by this, that he knew nothing of the miserable Circumstances I was in, and thought that having got some Intelligence of his being there, I had come to upbraid him with his leaving me; but I had too much to say to him to be affronted, and told him in few Words, that I was far from coming to Insult him, but at best I came to Condole mutually, that he would be easily satisfy'd, that I had no such View, when I should tell him that *my Condition was worse than his, and that many ways*: He look'd a little concern'd at the general Expression of my Condition being worse than his; but with a kind of a smile, look'd a little wildly, and said, How can that be? when you see me Feter'd, and in *Newgate*, and two of my Companions Executed already; can you say your Condition is worse than Mine?

Come my Dear, *says I*, we have a long peice of Work to do, if I should be to relate, or you to hear my unfortunate History; but if you are dispos'd to hear it, you will soon conclude with me that my Condition is worse than yours: How is that possible, *says he again*, when I expect to be cast for my Life the very next Sessions? Yes *says I*, 'tis very possible when I shall tell you that I have been cast for my Life three Sessions ago, and am under Sentence of Death, is not my Case worse than yours?

Then indeed he stood silent again, like one struck Dumb, and after a little while he starts up, unhappy Couple! *says he*, How can this be possible? I took him by the Hand, come MY DEAR, *said I*, sit down, and let us compare our Sorrows: I am a Prisoner in this very House, and in a much worse Circumstance than you, and you will be satisfy'd I do not come to Insult you, when I tell you the particulars; and with this we sat down together, and I told him so much of my Story as I thought was convenient, bringing it at last to my being reduc'd to great Poverty, and representing myself as fallen into some Company that led me to relieve my Distresses by a way that I had been utterly unacquainted with and that they making an attempt at a Tradesman's House I was seiz'd upon, for having been but just at the Door, the Maid-Servant pulling me in; that I neither had broke any Lock, or taken any thing away, and that notwithstanding, that I was brought in Guilty, and Sentenc'd to Die; but that the Judges having been made sensible of the Hardship of my Circumstances, had obtain'd leave to remit the Sentence upon my consenting to be transported.

I told him I far'd the worse for being taken in the Prison for one *Moll Flanders*, who was a famous successful Thief, that all of them had heard of, but none of them had ever seen, but that *as he knew well* was none of my Name; but I plac'd all to the account of my ill Fortune, and that under this Name I was dealt with as an old Offender, tho' this was the first thing they had ever known of me. I gave him a long particular of things that had befallen me, since I saw him; but I told him I had seen him since he might think I had, and then gave him an

Account how I had seen him at *Brickhill*; how furiously he was pursued, and how by giving an Account that I knew him, and that he was a very honest Gentleman, one Mr. ———, the *Hue and Cry* was stopp'd, and the High Constable went back again.

He listen'd most attentively to all my Story, and smil'd at most of the particulars, being all of them petty Matters, and infinitely below what he had been at the Head of;[445] but when I came to the Story of little *Brickill*, he was surpriz'd, *and was it you my Dear*, said he, *that gave the Check to the Mob that was at our Heels there*, at *Brickill*: Yes *said I*, it was I indeed, and then I told him the particulars which I had observ'd of him there. *Why then*, said he, *it was you that sav'd my Life at that time*, and I am glad I owe my Life to you, for I will pay the Debt to you now, and I'll deliver you from the present Condition you are in, or I will die in the attempt.

I told him by no means; it was a Risque too great, not worth his running the hazard of, and for a Life not worth his saving; 'twas no matter for that he said, it was a Life worth all the World to him; a Life that had given him a new Life; for *says he*, I was never in real Danger of being taken, but that time; till the last Minute when I was taken: Indeed *he told* me his Danger then lay in his believing he had not been pursued that way; for they had gone off from *Hockly*[446] quite another way, and had come over the enclos'd Country into *Brickill*, not by the Road and were sure they had not been seen by any Body.

Here he gave a long History of his Life, which indeed would make a very strange History, and be infinitely diverting. He told me he took to the Road about twelve Year before he marry'd me;[447] that the Woman which call'd him Brother, was not really his Sister, or any Kin to him; but one that belong'd to their Gang, and who keeping Correspondence with them, liv'd always in Town, having good store of Acquaintance, that she gave them a perfect Intelligence of Persons going out of Town, and that they had made several good Booties by her Correspondence; that she thought she had fix'd a Fortune for him, when she brought me to him, but happen'd to be Disappointed, which he really could not blame her for: That, if it had been his good Luck, that I had had the Estate, which she was inform'd I had, he had resolv'd to leave off the Road, and live a retired sober Life, but never to appear in publick till some general Pardon had been pass'd, or till he could, for Money, have got his Name into some particular Pardon, that so he might have been perfectly easy, but that as it had proved

---

[445]I.e., Moll's crimes and adventures (or rather her falsified account of them) were less impressive and spectacular than his.

[446]I.e., Hockliffe, just west of the Great Northern Road (Watling Street). The

gang had gone cross-country, cutting through private land.

[447]This addition to the story helps take Moll off the hook, for she can no longer be considered responsible for his life of crime.

otherwise he was oblig'd to put off his Equipage, and take up the old Trade again.

He gave me a long Account of some of his Adventures, and particularly one, when he robb'd the *West Chester* Coaches, near *Lichfield*, when he got a very great Booty; and after that; how he robb'd five Grasiers,[448] in the *West*, going to *Burford* Fair in *Wiltshire* to buy Sheep; he told me he got so much Money on those two Occasions, that if he had known where to have found me, he would certainly have embrac'd my Proposal of going with me to *Virginia*; or to have settled in a Plantation, on some other Parts of the *English* Colonies in *America*.

He told me he wrote two or three Letters to me, directed according to my Order, but heard nothing from me: This I indeed knew to be true, but the Letters coming to my Hand in the time of my latter Husband, I could do nothing in it, and therefore chose to give no answer, that so he might rather believe they had miscarried.

Being thus Disappointed, *he said*, he carried on the old Trade ever since, tho' when he had gotten so much Money, *he said*, he did not run such desperate Risques as he did before; then he gave me some Account of several hard and desperate Encounters which he had with Gentlemen on the Road, who parted too hardly with their Money; and shew'd me some Wounds he had receiv'd, and he had one or two very terrible Wounds indeed, as particularly one by a Pistol Bullet which broke his Arm; and another with a Sword, which ran him quite thro' the Body, but that missing his Vitals he was cur'd again; one of his Comrades having kept with him so faithfully, and so Friendly, as that he assisted him in riding near 80 Miles before his Arm was Set, and then got a Surgeon in a considerable City, remote from that Place where it was done, pretending they were Gentlemen Traveling towards *Carlisle*, and that they had been attack'd on the Road by Highway-Men, and that one of them had shot him into the Arm, and broke the Bone.

This *he said*, his Friend manag'd so well, that they were not suspected at all, but lay still till he was perfectly cur'd: He gave me so many distinct Accounts of his Adventures, that it is with great reluctance, that I decline the relating them; but I consider that this is my own Story, not his.

I then enquir'd into the Circumstances of his present Case at that time, and what it was he expected when he came to be try'd; he told me that they had no Evidence against him, or but very little; for that of three Roberries, which they were all Charg'd with, it was his good Fortune, that he was but in one of them, and that there was but one Witness to be had for that Fact, which was not sufficient; but that it

---

[448] Men who grazed or fed cattle for market: cattlemen. Burford Fair is actually in Oxfordshire.

was expected some others would come in against him; that he thought indeed, when he first see me, that I had been one that came of that Errand; but that if no Body came in against him, he hop'd he should be clear'd; that he had had some intimation, that if he would submit to Transport himself, he might be admitted to it without a Tryal, but that he could not think of it with any Temper,[449] and thought he could much easier submit to be Hang'd.

I blam'd him for that, and told him I blam'd him on two Accounts; first because, if he was Transported, there might be an Hundred ways for him that was a Gentleman, and a bold enterprizing Man to find his way back again, and perhaps some Ways and Means to come back before he went.[450] He smil'd at that Part, and said he should like the last the best of the two, for he had a kind of Horror upon his Mind at his being sent over to the Plantations as *Romans* sent condemn'd Slaves to Work in the Mines; that he thought the Passage into another State,[451] let it be what it would, much more tolerable at the Gallows, and that this was the general Notion of all the Gentlemen, who were driven by the Exigence of their Fortunes to take the Road; that at the Place of Execution there was at least an End of all the Miseries of the present State, and as for what was to follow, a Man was, in his Opinion, as likely to Repent sincerely in the last Fortnight of his Life under the Pressures and Agonies of a Jayl, and the condemn'd Hole, as he would ever be in the Woods and Wildernesses of *America*; that Servitude and hard Labour were things Gentlemen could never stoop to, that it was but the way to force them to be their own Executioners afterwards, which was much worse, and that therefore he could not have any Patience when he did but think of being Transported.

I used the utmost of my endeavour to perswade him, and joyn'd that known Womans Rhetorick to it, I mean that of Tears: I told him the Infamy of a publick Execution was certainly a greater pressure upon the Spirits of a Gentleman, than any of the Mortifications that he could meet with Abroad could be; that he had at least in the other a Chance for his Life, whereas here he had none at all; that it was the easiest thing in the World for him to manage the Captain of the Ship, who were, generally speaking, Men of good Humour, and some Gallantry; and a small matter of Conduct,[452] especially if there was any Money to be had, would make way for him to buy himself off, when he came to *Virginia*.

He look'd wishfully[453] at me, and I thought I guess'd at what he meant, *that is to say*, that he had no Money, but I was mistaken,

---

[449]Equanimity, composure, calmness. Temper is another of those words which Moll frequently uses in different senses.

[450]I.e., deviously avoid going at all.

[451]On Defoe's manipulation of this term,

see Starr, pp. 159n.

[452]Conduct money, payment for conveyance.

[453]Longingly.

his meaning was another way; *you hinted just now,* my Dear said he, that there might be a way of coming back before I went, by which I understood you, that it might *be possible to buy it off here; I had rather give 200 l. to prevent going, than 100 l. to be set at Liberty when I came there.* That is my Dear, said I, *because you do not know the Place so well as I do:* that may be, said he, *and yet I believe as well as you know it, you would do the same unless it is because,* as you told me, *you have a Mother there.*

I told him, as to my Mother, it was next to impossible but that she must be dead many Years before; and as for any other Relations that I might have there, I knew them not now: That since the Misfortunes I had been under, had reduc'd me to the Condition I had been in for some Years, I had not kept up any Correspondence with them, and that he would easily believe I should find but a cold Reception from them, if I should be put to make my first visit in the Condition of a Transported Felon; that therefore if I went thither, I resolv'd not to see them; But that I had many Views in going there, if it should be my Fate, which took off all the uneasy Part of it; and if he found himself oblig'd to go also, I should easily Instruct him how to manage himself, so as never to go a Servant at all, especially since I found he was not destitute of Money, which was the only Friend in such a Condition.

He smil'd, and said, he did not tell me he had Money; I took him up short, and told him I hop'd he did not understand by my speaking, that I should expect any supply from him if he had Money; that on the other Hand, tho' I had not a great deal, yet I did not want, and while I had any I would rather add to him, than weaken him in that Article, seeing what ever he had, I knew in the Case of Transportation he would have Occasion of it all.

He express'd himself in a most tender manner upon that Head: he told me what Money he had was not a great deal, but that he would never hide any of it from me if I wanted it; and that he assur'd me he did not speak with any such Apprehensions; that he was only intent upon what I had hinted to him before he went; that here he knew what to do with himself, but there he should be the most ignorant helpless Wretch alive.

I told him he frighted and terrify'd himself with that which had no Terror in it; that if he had Money, as I was glad to hear he had, he might not only avoid the Servitude, suppos'd to be the Consequence of Transportation; but begin the World upon a new Foundation, and that such a one as he cou'd not fail of Success in, with but the common Application usual in such Cases; that he could not but call to Mind, that it was what I had recommended to him many Years before, and had propos'd it for our mutual Subsistence, and restoring our Fortunes in the World; and I would tell him now, that to convince

him both of the certainty of it, and of my being fully acquainted
with the Method, and also fully satisfy'd in the probability of Success,
he should first see me deliver myself from the Necessity of going
over at all, and then that I would go with him freely, and of my own
Choice, and perhaps carry enough with me to satisfy him that I did
not offer it, for want of being able to live without Assistance from
him; but that I thought our mutual Misfortunes had been such,
as were sufficient to Reconcile us both to quitting this part of the
World, and living where no Body could upbraid us with what was
past, or we be in any dread of a Prison; and without the Agonies of
a condemn'd Hole to drive us to it, this where we should look back
on all our past Disasters with infinite Satisfaction, when we should
consider that our Enemies should entirely forget us, and that we
should live as new People in a new World, no Body having any thing
to say to us, or we to them.

I press'd this Home to him with so many Arguments, and answer'd
all his own passionate Objections so effectually, that he embrac'd
me, and told me, I treated him with such Sincerity, and Affection
as overcame him; that he would take my Advice, and would strive
to submit to his Fate, in hope of having the comfort of my Assistance,
and of so faithful a Counsellor, and such a Companion in his Misery;
but still he put me in mind of what I had mention'd before; Namely,
that there might be some way to get off, before he went, and that it
might be possible to avoid going at all, which he said would be
much better. I told him he should see, and be fully satisfy'd that I
would do my utmost in that Part too, and if it did not succeed, yet
that I would make good the rest.

We parted after this long Conference, with such Testimonies of
Kindness and Affection as I thought were Equal, if not Superior to
that at our parting at *Dunstable*; and now I saw more plainly than
before, the Reason why he declin'd coming at that time any farther
with me toward *London* than *Dunstable*; and why when we parted
there, he told me it was not convenient for him to come part of the
way to *London* to bring me going, as he would otherwise have done:
I have observ'd that the Account of his Life, would have made a
much more pleasing History, than this of mine; and indeed nothing
in it, was more strange than this Part, *(viz.)* that he had carried on
that desperate Trade full five and Twenty Year, and had never been
taken; the Success he had met with, had been so very uncommon,
and such, that sometimes he had liv'd handsomely and retir'd, in one
Place for a Year or two at a time, keeping himself and a Man-Servant
to wait on him, and has often sat in the Coffee-Houses, and heard
the very People who he had robb'd give Accounts of their being
robb'd, and of the Places and Circumstances, so that he cou'd easily
remember that it was the same.

In this manner, it seems, he liv'd near *Leverpool* at the time he unluckily married me for a Fortune: Had I been the Fortune he expected, I verily believe, as he said, that he would have taken up[454] and liv'd honestly all his Days.

He had with the rest of his Misfortunes the good luck not to be actually upon the spot, when the Robbery was done, which he was committed for; and so none of the Persons robb'd cou'd swear to him, or had any thing to Charge upon him; but it seems as he was taken, with the Gang, one hardmouth'd Countryman swore home to him; and they were like to have others come in according to the Publication they had made, so that they expected more Evidence against him, and for that Reason he was kept in hold.[455]

However, the offer which was made to him of admitting him to Transportation was made, as I understood, upon the intercession of some great Person who press'd him hard to accept of it before a Tryal; and indeed as he knew there were several that might come in against him, I thought his Friend was in the Right, and I lay at[456] him Night and Day to delay it no longer.

At last, with much difficulty he gave his consent, and as he was not therefore admitted to Transportation in Court, and on his Petition as I was, so he found himself under a difficulty to avoid embarking himself as I had said he might have done; his great Friend, who was his Intercessor for the Favour of that Grant, having given Security for him that he should Transport himself, and not return within the Term.[457]

This hardship broke all my Measures, for the steps I took afterwards for my own deliverance, were hereby render'd wholly ineffectual, unless I would abandon him, and leave him to go to *America* by himself; than which he protested he would much rather venture,[458] altho' he were certain to go directly to the Gallows.

I must now return to my own Case, the time of my being Transported according to my Sentence was near at Hand; my Governess who continu'd my fast Friend, had try'd to obtain a Pardon, but it could not be done unless with an Expense too heavy for my Purse, considering that to be left naked and empty,[459] unless I had resolv'd to return to my old Trade again, had been worse than my Transportation, because there I knew I could live, here I could not. The good

---

[454]Reformed.

[455]In custody, imprisoned.

[456]Assailed.

[457]Because he had volunteered for transportation, he was rather ordered to go abroad than confined on a specific ship. This made escape from his punishment difficult, for a friend had given bond for fulfillment of the agreement. (Term = while the present court was still in session; the English legal year is divided into four terms.)

[458]Take his chances at a trial.

[459]I.e., getting the pardon would have depleted all Moll's savings. (naked = destitute)

Minister stood very hard on another Account to prevent my being Transported also; but he was answer'd, that indeed my Life had been given me at his first Solicitations, and therefore he ought to ask no more; he was sensibly griev'd at my going, because, *as he said*, he fear'd I should lose the good impressions, which a prospect of Death had at first made on me, and which were since encreas'd by his Instructions, and the pious Gentleman was exceedingly concern'd about me on that Account.

On the other Hand, I really was not so sollicitous about it, as I was before, but I industriously conceal'd my Reasons for it from the Minister, and to the last he did not know, but that I went with the utmost reluctance and affliction.

It was in the Month of *February* that I was with thirteen other Convicts, *as they call'd us*, delivered to a Merchant that Traded to *Virginia*, on board a Ship, riding, as they call'd it, in *Deptford* Reach:[460] The Officer of the Prison deliver'd us on board, and the Master of the Vessel gave a Discharge for us.

We were for that Night clapt under Hatches,[461] and kept so close, that I thought I should have been suffocated for want of Air, and the next Morning the Ship weigh'd,[462] and fell[463] down the River to a Place they call *Bugby's Hole*,[464] which was done, as they told us, by the agreement of the Merchant, that all opportunity of Escape should be taken from us: However when the Ship came thither, and cast Anchor, we were allow'd more Liberty, and particularly were permitted to come upon the Deck, but not upon the Quarter-Deck, that being kept particularly for the Captain, and for Passengers.

When by the Noise of the Men over my Head, and the Motion of the Ship, I perceiv'd that they were under Sail, I was at first greatly surpriz'd, fearing we should go away directly, and that our Friends would not be admitted to see us any more; but I was easy soon after when I found they had come to an Anchor again, and soon after that we had Notice given by some of the Men where we were, that the next Morning we should have the Liberty to come upon Deck, and to have our Friends come and see us if we had any.

All that Night I lay upon the hard Boards of the Deck, as the other Prisoners did, but we had afterwards the Liberty of little Cabins for such of us as had any Bedding to lay in them; and room to stow any Box or Trunk for Cloths, and Linnen, if we had it, (which might well be put in) for some of them had neither Shirt or Shift, or a Rag of Linnen or Woollen, but what was on their Backs, or a Farthing of Money to help themselves; and yet I did not find but they far'd well

---

[460]Just east of London, on the Thames.
[461]Confined below deck.
[462]Lifted anchor.

[463]Dropped downstream.
[464]Bugsby Reach, a cove below Greenwich.

enough in the Ship, especially the Women, who got Money of the Seamen for washing their Cloths sufficient to purchase any common things that they wanted.

When the next Morning we had the liberty to come upon the Deck, I ask'd one of the Officers of the Ship, whether I might not have the liberty to send a Letter on Shore to let my Friends know where the Ship lay, and to get some necessary things sent to me. This was it seems the Boatswain, a very civil courteous sort of Man, who told me I should have that, or any other liberty that I desir'd, that we could allow me with Safety; I told him I desir'd no other, and he answer'd that the Ships Boat would go up to *London* the next Tide, and he would order my Letter to be carried.

Accordingly when the Boat went off, the Boatswain came to me, and told me the Boat was going off, and that he went in it himself, and ask'd me if my Letter was ready, he would take care of it; I had prepared myself you may be sure, Pen, Ink and Paper beforehand, and I had gotten a Letter ready directed to my Governess, and enclos'd another for my fellow Prisoner, which however I did not let her know was my Husband, not to the last; in that to my Governess, I let her know where the Ship lay, and press'd her earnestly to send me what things I knew she had got ready for me for my Voyage.

When I gave the Boatswain the Letter, I gave him a Shilling with it, which I told him was for the Charge of a Messenger or Porter, which I entreated him to send with the Letter, as soon as he came on Shore, that if possible I might have an Answer brought back by the same Hand, that I might know what was become of my things, for Sir, *says I*, if the Ship should go away before I have them on Board I am undone.

I took care when I gave him the Shilling, to let him see that I had a little better Furniture about me, than the ordinary Prisoners, for he saw that I had a Purse, and in it a pretty deal of Money, and I found that the very sight of it, immediately furnish'd me with very different Treatment from what I should otherwise have met with in the Ship; for tho' he was very Courteous indeed before, in a kind of natural Compassion to me, as a Woman in distress; yet he was more than ordinarily so, afterwards, and procur'd me to be better treated in the Ship than, *I say*, I might otherwise have been as shall appear in its Place.

He very honestly had my Letter deliver'd to my Governess own Hands, and brought me back an Answer from her in writing; and when he gave me the Answer, gave me the Shilling again, *there*, says he, there's your Shilling again too, for I deliver'd the Letter my self; I could not tell what to say, I was so surpris'd at the thing; but after some Pause, *I said*, Sir you are too kind, it had been but Reasonable that you had paid yourself Coach hire then.

No, no, *says he*, I am over paid: What, is the Gentlewoman your Sister?

No, Sir, *said I*, she is no Relation to me, but she is a dear Friend, and all the Friends I have in the World: well, *says he*, there are few such Friends in the World: why she cryes after you like a Child; Ay, *says I again*, she would give a Hundred Pound, I believe, to deliver me from this dreadful Condition I am in.

Would she so? *says he*, for half the Money I believe, I cou'd put you in a way how to deliver yourself, but this he spoke softly that no Body cou'd hear.

Alas! Sir, *said I*, but then that must be such a Deliverance as if I should be taken again, would cost me my Life; Nay, *said he*, if you were once out of the Ship you must look to yourself afterwards, that I can say nothing to; so we drop'd the Discourse for that time.

In the mean time my Governess faithful to the last Moment, convey'd my Letter to the Prison to my Husband, and got an Answer to it, and the next Day came down herself to the Ship, bringing me in the first Place a *Sea-Bed* as they call it, and all its Furniture,[465] such as was convenient, but not to let the People think it was extraordinary; she brought with her a *Sea-Chest*, that is a Chest, such as are made for Seamen, with all the Conveniencies in it, and fill'd with every thing almost that I could want; and in one of the corners of the Chest, where there was a private Drawer was my Bank of Money, *that is to say*, so much of it as I had resolv'd to carry with me; for I order'd a part of my Stock to be left behind me, to be sent afterwards in such Goods as I should want when I came to settle; for Money in that Country is not of much use where all things are bought for Tobacco, much more is it a great loss to carry it from Hence.[466]

But my Case was particular; it was by no Means proper to me to go thither without Money or Goods, and for a poor Convict that was to be sold as soon as I came on Shore, to carry with me a Cargo of Goods would be to have Notice taken of it, and perhaps to have them seiz'd by the Publick; so I took part of my Stock with me thus, and left the other part with my Governess.

My Governess brought me a great many other things, but it was not proper for me to look too well provided in the Ship, at least till I knew what kind of a Captain we should have. When she came into the Ship, I thought she would have died indeed; her Heart sunk at the sight of me, and at the thoughts of parting with me in that Condition, and she cry'd so intolerably, I cou'd not for a long time have any talk with her.

I took that time to read my fellow Prisoners Letter, which however greatly perplex'd me; he told me he was determin'd to go, but found

---

[465]Coverlets and linen.
[466]I.e., money will buy less in America than in England.

it would be impossible for him to be Discharg'd time enough for going in the same Ship, and which was more than all, he began to question whether they would give him leave to go in what Ship he pleas'd, tho' he did voluntarily Transport himself; but that they would see him put on Board such a Ship as they should direct, and that he would be charg'd upon the Captain as other convict Prisoners were; so that he began to be in dispair of seeing me till he came to *Virginia*, which made him almost desperate; seeing that on the other Hand, if I should not be there, if any Accident of the Sea, or of Mortality should take me away, he should be the most undone Creature there in the World.

This was very perplexing, and I knew not what Course to take; I told my Governess the Story of the Boatswain, and she was mighty eager with me to treat with him; but I had no mind to it, till I heard whether my Husband, or fellow Prisoner, *so she call'd him*, cou'd be at liberty to go with me or no; at last I was forc'd to let her into the whole matter, except only, that of his being my Husband; I told her I had made a positive Bargain or Agreement with him to go, if he could get the liberty of going in the same Ship, and that I found he had Money.

Then I read a long Lecture to her of what I propos'd to do when we came there, how we could Plant, Settle; and in short, grow Rich without any more Adventures, and as a great Secret, I told her that we were to Marry as soon as he came on Board.

She soon agreed chearfully to my going, when she heard this, and she made it her business from that time to get him out of the Prison in time, so that he might go in the same Ship with me, which at last was brought to pass tho' with great difficulty, and not without all the Forms of a Transported Prisoner *Convict*, which he really was not yet, for he had not been try'd, and which was a great Mortification to him. As our Fate was now determin'd, and we were both on Board, actually bound to *Virginia*, in the despicable Quality of Transported Convicts destin'd to be sold for Slaves, I for five Year, and he under Bonds and Security not to return to *England* any more, as long as he liv'd; he was very much dejected and cast down; the Mortification of being brought on Board, as he was like a Prisoner, piqu'd him very much, since it was first told him he should Transport himself, and so that he might go as a Gentleman at liberty; it is true he was not order'd to be sold when he came there, as we were, and for that Reason he was oblig'd to pay for his Passage to the Captain, which we were not; as to the rest, he was as much at a loss as a Child what to do with himself, or with what he had, but by Directions.[467]

Our first business was to compare our Stock: He was very honest

---

[467]The third edition here inserts the two paragraphs in Appendix A.

to me, and told me his Stock was pretty good when he came into the Prison, but the living there as he did in a Figure like a Gentleman, *and which was ten times as much*, the making of Friends, and soliciting his Case, had been very Expensive; and in a Word, all his Stock that he had left was an Hundred and Eight Pounds, which he had about him all in Gold.

I gave him an Account of my Stock as faithfully, that is to say of what I had taken to carry with me, for I was resolv'd what ever should happen, to keep what I had left with my Governess, in Reserve; that in Case I should die, what I had with me was enough to give him, and that which was left in my Governess Hands would be her own, which she had well deserv'd of me indeed.

My Stock which I had with me was two Hundred forty six Pounds, some odd Shillings; so that we had three Hundred and fifty four Pound between us, but a worse gotten[468] Estate was scarce ever put together to begin the World with.

Our greatest Misfortune as to our Stock, was that it was all in Money, which every one knows is an unprofitable Cargoe to be carryed to the Plantations; I believe his was really all he had left in the World, as he told me it was; but I who had between seven and eight Hundred Pounds in Bank when this Disaster befel me, and who had one of the faithfulest Friends in the World to manage it for me, considering she was a Woman of no manner of Religious Principles, had still Three Hundred Pounds left in her Hand, which I reserv'd, as above, besides some very valuable things, as particularly two gold Watches, some small Peices of Plate, and some Rings; all stolen Goods; the Plate, Rings and Watches were put up in my Chest with the Money, and with this Fortune, and in the Sixty first Year of my Age, I launch'd out into a new World, as I may call it in the Condition (as to what appear'd) only of a poor nak'd Convict, order'd to be Transported in respite from the Gallows, my Cloaths were poor and mean, but not ragged or dirty, and none knew in the whole Ship that I had any thing of value about me.

However, as I had a great many very good Cloaths, and Linnen in abundance, which I had order'd to be pack'd up in two great Boxes, I had them Shipp'd on Board, not as my Goods, but as consign'd to my real Name in *Virginia*; and had the Bills of Loading sign'd by a Captain in my Pocket; and in these Boxes was my Plate and Watches, and every thing of value except my Money, which I kept by itself in a private Drawer in my Chest, which cou'd not be found, or open'd if found, without splitting the Chest to peices.[469]

The Ship began now to fill, several Passengers came on Board, who

---

[468]More immorally or illegally accrued.

[469]The first edition here inserts the two paragraphs in Appendix A.

were embark'd on no Criminal account, and these had Accommodations assign'd them in the great Cabbin, and other Parts of the Ship, whereas we *as Convicts* were thrust down below, I know not where; but when my Husband came on Board, I spoke to the Boatswain, who had so early given me Hints of his Friendship in carrying my Letter; I told him he had befriended me in many things, and I had not made any suitable Return to him, and with that I put a Guinea into his Hands; I told him that my Husband was now come on Board, that tho' we were both under the present Misfortunes, yet we had been Persons of a differing Character from the wretched Crew that we came with, and desir'd to know of him, whether the Captain might not be mov'd, to admit us to some Conveniences in the Ship, for which we would make him what Satisfaction he pleas'd, and that we would gratifie him for his Pains in procuring this for us. He took the Guinea as I cou'd see with great Satisfaction, and assur'd me of his Assistance.

Then he told us, he did not doubt but that the Captain who was one of the best humour'd Gentlemen in the World, would be easily brought to Accommodate us, as well as we cou'd desire, and to make me easie, told me he would go up the next Tide on purpose to speak to the Captain about it. The next Morning, happening to sleep a little longer than ordinary, when I got up, and began to look Abroad, I saw the Boatswain among the Men in his ordinary Business; I was a little melancholly at seeing him there, and going forwards to speak to him, he saw me, and came towards me, but not giving him time to speak first, I said smiling, *I doubt, Sir, you have forgot us*, for I see you are very busy; he return'd[470] presently, come a long with me, and you shall see, so he took me into the great Cabbin, and there sat a good sort of a Gentlemanly Man for a Seaman[471] writing, and with a great many Papers before him.

Here, says the Boatswain to him that was a writing, is the Gentlewoman that the Captain spoke to you of, and turning to me, he said, I have been so far from forgetting your Business, that I have been up at the Captain's House, and have represented faithfully to the Captain what you said, relating to your being furnished with better Conveniences for your self, and your Husband; and the Captain has sent this Gentleman, who is Mate of the Ship down with me, on purpose to show you every thing, and to Accommodate you fully to your Content, and bid me assure you that you shall not be treated like what you were at first expected[472] to be, but with the same respect as other Passengers are treated.

The Mate then spoke to me, and not giving me time to thank the Boatswain for his kindness, confirm'd what the Boatswain had said,

---

[470] Answered.
[471] I.e., for a seaman, he looked gentlemanly.

[472] I.e., what the terms of their passage had suggested they would be — either hardened criminals or destitute.

and added that it was the Captain's delight to show himself Kind, and Charitable, especially, to those that were under any Misfortunes, and with that he shew'd me several Cabbins built up, some in the Great Cabbin, and some partition'd off, out of the Steerage, but opening into the great Cabbin on purpose for the Accommodation of Passengers, and gave me leave to chuse where I would; however I chose a Cabbin, which open'd into the Steerage, in which was very good Conveniences to set our Chest, and Boxes, and a Table to eat on.

The Mate then told me, that the Boatswain had given so good a Character of me, and of my Husband, as to our civil Behaviour, that he had orders to tell me, we should eat with him, if we thought fit, during the whole Voyage on the common Terms of Passengers; that we might lay in some fresh Provisions, if we pleas'd; or if not, he should lay in his usual Store, and we should have Share with him: This was very reviving News to me, after so many Hardships, and Afflictions as I had gone thro' of late; I thank'd him, and told him, the Captain should make his own Terms with us, and ask'd him leave to go and tell my Husband of it who was not very well, and was not yet out of his Cabbin: Accordingly I went, and my Husband whose Spirits were still so much sunk with the Indignity (as he understood it) offered him, that he was scarce yet himself, was so reviv'd with the Account I gave him of the Reception we were like to have in the Ship, that he was quite another Man, and new vigour and Courage appear'd in his very Countenance; so true is it, that the greatest of Spirits, when overwhelm'd by their Afflictions, are subject to the greatest Dejections, and are the most apt to Despair and give themselves up.

After some little Pause to recover himself, my Husband come up with me, and gave the Mate thanks for the kindness, which he had express'd to us, and sent suitable acknowledgement by him to the Captain, offering to pay him by Advance, what ever he demanded for our Passage, and for the Conveniences he had help'd us to; the Mate told him, that the Captain would be on Board in the Afternoon, and that he would leave all that till he came; accordingly in the Afternoon the Captain came, and we found him the same courteous obliging Man, that the Boatswain had represented him to be; and he was so well pleas'd with my Husband's Conversation, that in short, he would not let us keep the Cabbin we had chosen, but gave us one that, as I said before, open'd into the great Cabbin.

Nor were his Conditions exorbitant, or the Man craving and eager to make a Prey of us, but for fifteen Guineas we had our whole Passage and Provisions, and Cabbin, eat at the Captain's Table, and were very handsomely Entertain'd.

The Captain lay himself in the other part of the Great Cabbin, having let his round House,[473] *as they call it*, to a rich Planter, who went

---

[473] A cabin or apartment on the after-part of the quarterdeck.

over, with his Wife, and three Children, who eat by themselves; he had some other ordinary Passengers, who Quarter'd in the Steerage, and as for our old Fraternity, they were kept under the Hatches while the Ship lay there, and came very little on the Deck.

I could not refrain acquainting my Governess with what had happen'd, it was but just that she, who was so really concern'd for me, should have part in my good Fortune; besides I wanted her Assistance to supply me with several Necessaries, which before I was shy of letting any Body see me have, that it might not be publick; but now I had a Cabbin and room to set things in, I order'd abundance of good things for our Comfort in the Voyage, as Brandy, Sugar, Lemons, &c. to make Punch, and Treat our Benefactor, the Captain; and abundance of things for eating and drinking in the Voyage; also a larger Bed, and Bedding proportion'd to it; so that in a Word, we resolv'd to want for nothing in the Voyage.

All this while I had provided nothing for our Assistance, when we should come to the Place, and begin to call ourselves Planters; and I was far from being ignorant of what was needful on that Occasion; particularly all sorts of Tools for the Planters-Work, and for building; and all kinds of Furniture for our Dwelling, which if to be bought in the Country, must necessarily cost double the Price.

So I discours'd that Point with my Governess, and she went and waited upon the Captain, and told him, that she hop'd ways might be found out, for her two unfortunate Cousins, *as she call'd us*, to obtain our Freedom when we came into the Country, and so enter'd into a Discourse with him about the Means and Terms also, of which I shall say more in its Place; and after thus sounding the Captain, she let him know, tho' we were unhappy in the Circumstance that occasion'd our going, yet that we were not unfurnish'd to set ourselves to Work in the Country; and were resolv'd to settle, and live there as Planters, if we might be put in a way how to do it: The Captain readily offer'd his Assistance, told her the Method of entering upon such Business, and how easy, nay, how certain it was for industrious People to recover their Fortunes in such a manner: Madam, *says he*, 'tis no Reproach to any Man in that Country to have been sent over in worse Circumstances than I perceive your Cousins are in, provided they do but apply with diligence and good Judgment to the Business of that Place when they come there.

She then enquir'd of him what things it was Necessary we should carry over with us, and he like a very honest as well as knowing Man, told her thus: Madam, your Cousins in the first Place must procure some Body to buy them as Servants, in Conformity to the Conditions of their Transportation, and then in the Name of that Person, they may go about what they will; they may either Purchase some Plantations already begun, or they may purchase Land of the Government of the Country, and begin where they please, and both will be done reasonably; she bespoke his Favour in the first Article, which he promis'd to her to take upon himself; and indeed faithfully perform'd it, and as to the rest, he promis'd to recomend us to such as should give us the best Advice, and not to impose upon us, which was as much as could be desir'd.

She then ask'd him, if it would not be Necessary to furnish us with a Stock of Tools and Materials for the Business of Planting, and he said, yes, by all means, and then she begg'd his Assistance in it; she told him she would furnish us with every thing that was Convenient whatever it cost her; he accordingly gave her a long particular of things Necessary for a Planter, which by his Account came to about fourscore, or an Hundred Pounds; and in short, she went about as dexterously to buy them, as if she had been an old *Virginia* Merchant; only that she bought by my Direction above twice as much of every thing as he had given her a List of.

These she put on Board in her own Name, took his Bills of Loading for them, and Endorst those Bills of Loading to my Husband, Ensuring the Cargo afterwards in her own Name, by our order; so that we were provided for all Events, and for all Disasters.

I should have told you that my Husband gave her all his whole Stock of 108 *l.* which as I have said, he had about him in Gold, to lay out thus, and I gave her a good Sum besides; so that I did not break into the Stock, which I had left in her Hands at all, but after we had sorted out our whole Cargo, we had yet near 200 *l.* in Money, which was more than enough for our purpose.

In this Condition very chearful, and indeed joyful at being so happily Accommodated as we were; we set Sail from *Bugby's-Hole* to *Gravesend*,[474] where the Ship lay about ten Days more, and where the Captain came on Board for good and all. Here the Captain offer'd us a civility, which indeed we had no Reason to expect. Namely, to let us go on Shore, and refresh ourselves, upon giving our Words in a solemn manner, that we would not go from him, and that we would return peaceably on Board again: This was such an Evidence of his Confidence in us, that it overcome my Husband, who in a meer Principle of Gratitude, told him as he could not be in any Capacity to make a suitable return for such a Favour, so he could not think of accepting of it; nor could he be easy that the Captain should run such a Risque: After some mutual Civilities, I gave my Husband a Purse, in which was 80 Guineas, and he puts it into the Captain's hand: There Captain, *says he*, there's part of a Pledge for our Fidelity, if we deal dishonestly with you on any Account, 'tis your own, and on this we went on Shore.

Indeed the Captain had assurance enough of our Resolutions to go,

---

[474]On the Thames in Kent, about 22 miles east-southeast of London.

for that having made such Provision to Settle there, it did not seem Rational that we would chuse to remain here at the Expence and Peril of Life, for such it must have been, if we had been taken again. In a Word, we went all on Shore with the Captain, and Supp'd together in *Gravesend*; where we were very Merry, staid all Night, lay at the House where we Supp'd, and came all very honestly on Board again with him in the Morning. Here we bought ten dozen Bottles of good Beer, some Wine, some Fowls, and such things as we thought might be acceptable on Board.

My Governess was with us all this while, and went with us Round into the Downs,[475] as did also the Captain's Wife with whom she went back; I was never so sorrowful at parting with my own Mother as I was at parting with her, and I never saw her more: We had a fair Easterly Wind sprung up the third Day after we came to the *Downs*, and we sail'd from thence the 10th of *April*; nor did we touch any more at any Place, till being driven on the Coast of *Ireland* by a very hard Gale of Wind, the Ship came to an Anchor in a little *Bay*, near the Mouth of a River, whose Name I remember not, but they said the River came down from *Limerick*, and that it was the largest River in *Ireland*.

Here being detain'd by bad Weather for some time, the Captain who continu'd the same kind good humour'd Man as at first, took us two on Shore with him again: He did it now in kindness to my Husband indeed, who bore the Sea very ill, and was very Sick, especially when it blew so hard: Here we bought in again, store of fresh Provisions, especially Beef, Pork, Mutton and Fowls, and the Captain stay'd to Pickle up five or fix Barrels of Beef to lengthen out the Ships Store. We were here not above five Days, when the Weather turning mild, and a fair Wind, we set Sail again and in two and Forty Days came safe to the Coast of *Virginia*.

When we drew near to the Shore, the Captain call'd me to him, and told me that he found by my Discourse, I had some Relations in the Place, and that I had been there before, and so he suppos'd I understood the Custom, in their disposing the convict Prisoners when they arriv'd; I told him I did not, and that as to what Relations I had in the Place, he might be sure I would make my self known to none of them while I was in the Circumstances of a Prisoner, and that as to the rest, we left ourselves entirely to him to Assist us, as he was pleas'd to promise us he wou'd do. He told me I must get some Body in the Place to come and buy us[476] as Servants, and who must answer for us to

---

[475]The roadstead in the North Sea, off Kent.

[476]This paragraph contradicts an earlier passage (p. 242) which indicated that the husband was not ordered to be sold. See

p. 351 for a possible explanation of why this inconsistency occurs. The third edition notices the inconsistency and alters the text accordingly: see Passage 8, Appendix B.

the Governor of the Country, if he demanded us; I told him we should do as he should direct; so he brought a Planter to treat with him, as it were for the Purchase of these two Servants, my Husband and me, and there we were formally sold to him, and went a Shore with him: The Captain went with us, and carried us to a certain House, whether it was to be call'd a Tavern or not, I know not, but we had a Bowl of Punch there made of Rum, &c. and were very Merry. After some time the Planter gave us a Certificate of Discharge, and an Acknowledgement of having serv'd him faithfully, and we were free from him the next Morning, to go whither we would.

For this Peice of Service the Captain demanded of us 6000 weight of Tobacco, which he said he was Accountable for to his Freighter, and which we immediately bought for him, and made him a present of 20 Guineas, besides, with which he was abundantly satisfy'd.

It is not proper to Enter here into the particulars of what Part of the Colony of *Virginia* we Settled in, for divers Reasons; it may suffice to mention that we went into the great River of *Potomack*, the Ship being bound thither; and there we intended to have Settled at first, tho' afterwards we altered our Minds.

The first thing I did of Moment after having gotten all our Goods on Shore, and plac'd them in a Storehouse, or Warehouse, which with a Lodging we hir'd at the small Place or Village, where we Landed; I say the first thing was to enquire after my Mother, and after my Brother, (that fatal Person who I married as a Husband, as I have related at large;[477]) a little enquiry furnish'd me with Information that Mrs. ———, that is my Mother was Dead; that my Brother (or Husband) was alive, which I confess I was not very glad to hear; but which was worse, I found he was remov'd from the Plantation where he liv'd formerly, and where I liv'd with him, and liv'd with one of his Sons in a Plantation just by the Place where we Landed, and where we had hir'd a Warehouse.

I was a little surpriz'd at first, but as I ventured, to satisfy my self, that he could not know me, I was not only perfectly easy, but had a great mind to see him, if it was possible to do so without his seeing me; in order to that I found out by enquiry the Plantation where he liv'd, and with a Woman of that Place, who I got to help me, like what we call a *Chairwoman*,[478] I rambl'd about towards the Place, as if I had only a mind to see the Country, and look about me; at last I came so near that I saw the Dwelling-house: *I ask'd the Woman* whose Planta-tion that was, *she said*, it belong'd to such a Man, and looking out a little to our right Hands, there says she, is the Gentleman that owns the Plantation, and his Father with him: What are their Christian

[477]Fully.
[478]I.e., charwoman, a woman hired by
the day to do odd jobs of household work.

Names? said I, I know not *said she*, what the old Gentlemans Name is, but his Sons Name is *Humphry*, and I believe, *says she*, the Fathers is so too; you may guess, if you can, what a confus'd mixture of Joy and Fright possest my Thoughts upon this Occasion, for I immediately knew that this was no Body else, but my own Son, by that Father she shewed me, who was my own Brother: I had no Mask, but I ruffled my Hoods so about my Face, that I depended upon it, that after above 20 Years absence, and withal not expecting any thing of me in that part of the World, he would not be able to know any thing of me; but I need not have us'd all that Caution, for the old Gentleman was grown dim Sighted, by some Distemper, which had fallen upon his Eyes, and could but just see well enough to walk about, and not run against a Tree, or into a Ditch.[479] The Woman that was with me, had told me that, by a meer Accident, knowing nothing of what importance it was to me: As they drew near to us, *I said*, does he know you Mrs. *Owen?* so they call'd the Woman, yes, *said she*, if he hears me speak, he will know me; but he can't see well enough to know me, or any Body else; and so she told me the Story of his Sight, as I have related: This made me secure, and so I threw open my Hoods again, and let them pass by me: It was a wretched thing for a Mother thus to see her own Son, a handsome comely young Gentleman in flourishing Circumstances, and durst not make herself known to him; and durst not take any notice of him; let any Mother of Children that reads this, consider it, and but think with what anguish of Mind I restrain'd myself; what yearnings of Soul I had in me to embrace him, and weep over him; and how I thought all my Entrails turn'd within me, that my very Bowels mov'd,[480] and I knew not what to do; as I now know not how to express those Agonies: When he went from me I stood gazing and trembling, and looking after him as long as I could see him; then sitting down on the Grass, just at a Place I had mark'd, I made as if I lay down to rest me, but turn'd from her, and lying on my Face wept, and kiss'd the Ground that he had set his Foot on.

I cou'd not conceal my Disorder so much from the Woman, but that she perceiv'd it, and thought I was not well, which I was oblig'd to pretend was true; upon which she press'd me to rise, the Ground being damp and dangerous, which I did accordingly, and walk'd away.

As I was going back again, and still Talking of this Gentleman, and his Son, a new Occasion of melancholy offer'd itself *thus*: The Woman

[479]The old man's blindness here may allusively link Moll's history with the Biblical stories of Isaac and Jacob: Isaac's blindness had permitted his son Jacob to trick him into an undeserved birthright blessing, and Jacob was divinely punished for this trickery by being himself tricked into an undesired marriage. Defoe seems to invert the cause-effect relationship. See Genesis 27–29.

[480]The bowels were considered the seat of the tender and sympathetic emotions; Moll means that she was deeply moved, to the depths of her being.

began, as if she would tell me a Story to divert me; there goes, *says she*, a very odd Tale among the Neighbours where this Gentleman former- ly liv'd: What was that, *said I*? why, says she, that old Gentleman going to *England*, when he was a young Man, fell in Love with a young Lady there, one of the finest Women that ever was seen, and Married her, and brought her over hither to his Mother, who was then living. He liv'd here several Years with her, *continu'd she*, and had several chil- dren by her, of which the young Gentleman that was with him now, was one, but after some time, the old Gentlewoman his Mother talk- ing to her, of something relating to herself, when she was in *England*, and of her Circumstances in *England*, which were bad enough; the Daughter-in-Law, began to be very much surpriz'd, and uneasy, and in short, examining further into things it appear'd past all Contradiction, that she the old Gentlewoman was her own Mother, and that con- sequently, that Son was his Wives own Brother, which struck the whole Family with Horror, and put them into such Confusion, that it had almost ruin'd them all; the young Woman would not live with him; the Son, her Brother and Husband, for a time went Distracted, and at last, the young Woman went away for *England*, and has never been heard of since.

It is easy to believe that I was strangely affected with this Story; but 'tis impossible to describe the Nature of my Disturbance: I seem'd astonish'd at the Story, and ask'd her a Thousand Questions about the particulars, which I found she was thoroughly acquainted with; at last I began to enquire into the Circumstances of the Family, how the old Gentlewoman, *I mean, my Mother* died, and how she left what she had; for my Mother had promis'd me very solemnly, that when she died, she would do something for me, and leave it so, as that, if I was Living, I should one way or other come at it, without its being in the Power of her Son, *my Brother and Husband* to prevent it: She told me she did not know exactly how it was order'd; but she had been told, that *my Mother* had left a Sum of Money, and had tyed her Plantation for the Payment of it, to be made good to the Daughter, if ever she could be heard of, either in *England*, or else where; and that the Trust was left with this Son, who was the Person that we saw with his Father.

This was News too good for me to make light of,[481] and you may be sure fill'd my Heart with a Thousand Thoughts, what Course I should take, how, and when, and in what manner I should make myself known, or whether I should ever make myself known, or no.

Here was a Perplexity that I had not indeed skill to manage myself in, neither knew I what Course to take: It lay heavy upon my mind Night, and Day, I could neither Sleep or Converse so that my Hus- band perceiv'd it, and wonder'd what ail'd me, strove to divert me, but

---

[481]Take lightly, consider trivial.

it was all to no purpose; he press'd me to tell him what it was troubled me, but I put it off, till at last importuning me continually, I was forc'd to form a Story, which yet had a plain Truth to lay it upon[482] too; I told him I was troubled because I found we must shift our Quarters, and alter our Scheme of Settling, for that I found I should be known, if I stay'd in that part of the Country, for that my Mother being dead, several of my Relations were come into that Part where we then was, and that I must either discover myself to them, which in our present Circumstances was not proper on many Accounts, or remove, and which to do I knew not, and that this it was that made me so Melancholly, and so Thoughtful.

He joyn'd with me in this, that it was by no means proper for me to make myself known to any Body in the Circumstances, in which we then were; and therefore he told me he would be willing to remove to any other part of the Country, or even to any other Country[483] if I thought fit; but now I had another Difficulty, which was, that if I remov'd to any other Colony, I put myself out of the way of ever making a due Search after those Effects, which my Mother had left: Again, I could never so much as think of breaking the Secret of my former Marriage to my new Husband; It was not a Story, as I thought, that would bear telling, nor could I tell what might be the Consequences of it; and it was impossible to search into the bottom of the thing without making it publick all over the Country, as well who I was, as what I now was also.

In this perplexity I continu'd a great while, and this made my Spouse very uneasy; for he found me perplex'd, and yet thought I was not open with him, and did not let him into every part of my Grievance; and he would often say, he wondred what he had done, that I would not Trust him with what ever it was, especially if it was Grievous, and Afflicting; the Truth is, he ought to have been trusted with every thing; for no Man in the World could deserve better of a Wife; but this was a thing I knew not how to open to him, and yet having no Body to disclose any part of it to, the Burthen was too heavy for my mind; for let them say what they please of our Sex not being able to keep a Secret; my Life is a plain Conviction to me of the contrary; but be it our Sex, or the Man's Sex, a Secret of Moment should always have a Confident, a bosom Friend, to whom we may Communicate the Joy of it, or the Grief of it, be it which it will, or it will be a double weight upon the Spirits, and perhaps become even insupportable in itself; and this I appeal to all human Testimony for the Truth of.

And this is the Cause why many times Men as well as Women, and Men of the greatest, and best Qualities other ways, yet have found

---

[482]I.e., the lie had a foundation of truth under it.

[483]I.e., colony.

themselves weak in this part, and have not been able to bear the weight of a secret Joy, or of a secret sorrow; but have been oblig'd to disclose it, even for the meer giving vent to themselves, and to unbend the Mind opprest, with the Load and Weights, which attended it; nor was this any Token of Folly, or Thoughtlessness at all, but a natural Consequence of the thing; and such People, had they struggl'd longer with the Oppression, would certainly have told it in their Sleep, and disclos'd the Secret, let it have been of what fatal Nature soever, without regard to the Person to whom it might be expos'd: This Necessity of Nature, is a thing which Works sometimes with such vehemence, in the Minds of those who are guilty of any atrocious Villany, such as secret Murther in particular, that they have been oblig'd to Discover it, tho' the Consequence would necessarily be their own Destruction: Now tho' it may be true that the divine Justice ought to have the Glory of all those Discoveries and Confessions, yet 'tis as certain that Providence which ordinarily Works by the Hands of Nature, makes use here of the same natural Causes to produce those extraordinary Effects.

I could give several remarkable Instances of this in my long Conversation with Crime, and with Criminals; I knew one Fellow, that while I was a Prisoner in *Newgate*, was one of those they called then *Night-Flyers*, I know not what other Word they may have understood it by since; but he was one, who by Connivance[484] was admitted to go Abroad[485] every Evening, when he play'd his Pranks, and furnish'd those honest People they call Thief-Catchers[486] with business to find out next Day, and restore *for a Reward*, what they had stolen the Evening before: This Fellow was as sure to tell in his sleep all that he had done, and every Step he had taken, what he had stole, and where, as sure as if he had engag'd to tell it waking, and that there was no Harm or Danger in it; and therefore he was oblig'd after he had been out to lock himself up, or be lock'd up by some of the Keepers that had him in Fee,[487] that no Body should hear him; but on the other Hand, if he had told all the particulars, and given a full account of his Rambles and Success to any Comrade, any Brother Thief, or to his Employers, *as I may justly call them*, then all was well with him, and he slept as quietly as other People.

As the publishing this Account of my Life, is for the sake of the just Moral of every part of it, and for Instruction, Caution, Warning and

---

[484]Bribing officials.

[485]Outside the prison. This practice was thought to be fairly common in Defoe's time.

[486]I.e., thief-takers, men who made their living as informers, skulking around the underworld picking up information wherever they could find it. They were encouraged by large rewards; a conviction for highway robbery, for example, might net the informer as much as 40 £ under a seventeenth-century law. Moll is being ironic in calling them "honest."

[487]In their pay or service. Moll implies that corrupt prison officials organized such "night-flying."

Improvement to every Reader, so this will not pass I hope for an unnecessary Digression concerning some People being oblig'd to disclose the greatest Secrets either of their own, or other Peoples Affairs.

Under the certain Oppression of this weight upon my Mind, I labour'd in the Case I have been Naming; and the only relief I found for it, was to let my Husband into so much of it, as I thought would convince him of the Necessity there was, for us to think of Settling, in some other Part of the World, and the next Consideration before us, was, which part of the *English* settlements we should go to; my Husband was a perfect Stranger to the Country, and had not yet so much as a Geographical knowledge of the Situation of the several Places; and I, that till I wrote this, did not know what the word Geographical signify'd, had only a general Knowledge from long Conversation with People that came from, or went to several Places; but this I knew, that *Maryland, Pensilvania,* East and West *Jersy, New York,* and *New England,* lay all North of *Virginia,* and that they were consequently all colder Climates, to which, for that very Reason, I had an Aversion; for that as I naturally lov'd warm Weather, so now I grew into Years, I had a stronger Inclination to shun a cold Climate; I therefore consider'd of going to *Carolina,* which is the only Southern Colony of the *English,* on the Continent of *America,* and hither I propos'd to go; and the rather, because I might with great ease come from thence at any time, when it might be proper to enquire after my Mothers effects, and to make myself known enough to demand them.

With this Resolution, I propos'd to my Husband our going away from where we was, and carrying all our Effects with us to *Carolina,* where we resolv'd to Settle, for my Husband readily agreed to the first Part (*viz.*) that it was not at all proper to stay where we was, since I had assur'd him we should be known there, and the rest I effectually conceal'd from him.

But now I found a new Difficulty upon me: The main Affair grew heavy upon my Mind still, and I could not think of going out of the Country, without *some how or other* making enquiry into the grand Affair of what my Mother had done for me; nor cou'd I with any patience bear the thought of going away, and not make myself known to my old Husband, (*Brother*) or to my Child, his Son, only I would fain have had this done without my new Husband having any knowledge of it, or they having any knowledge of him, or that I had such a thing as a Husband.

I cast about innumerable ways in my Thoughts how this might be done: I would gladly have sent my Husband away to *Carolina,* with all our Goods, and have come after myself; but this was impracticable, he would never stir without me, being himself perfectly unacquainted with the Country, and with the Methods of settling there, or any where else: Then I thought we would both go first with part of our Goods, and that when we were Settled I should come back to *Virginia*, and fetch the remainder; but even then I knew he would never part with me, and be left there to go on alone; the Case was plain, he was bred a Gentleman, and by Consequence was not only unacquainted,[488] but indolent, and when we did Settle, would much rather go out into the Woods with his Gun, which they call there Hunting, and which is the ordinary Work of the *Indians*, and which they do as Servants; I say he would much rather do that, than attend the natural Business of his Plantation.

These were therefore difficulties unsurmountable, and such as I knew not what to do in, I had such strong impressions on my Mind about discovering myself to my *Brother*, formerly my *Husband*, that I could not withstand them; and the rather, because it run constantly in my Thoughts, that if I did not do it, while he liv'd, I might in vain endeavour to convince my Son afterward, that I was really the same Person, and that I was his Mother, and so might both lose the assistance and comfort of the Relation, and the benefit of whatever it was my Mother had left me; and yet on the other Hand, I cou'd never think it proper to discover myself to them in the Circumstances I was in; as well relating to the having a Husband with me, as to my being brought over by a legal Transportation, as a Criminal; on both which Accounts it was absolutely necessary to me to remove from the Place where I was, and come again to him, as from another Place, and in another Figure.

Upon those Considerations, I went on with telling my Husband, the absolute necessity there was of our not Settling in *Potowmack* River, at least that we should be presently made publick there, whereas if we went to any other Place in the World, we should come in, with as much Reputation, as any Family that came to Plant: That as it was always agreeable to the Inhabitants to have Families come among them to Plant, who brought Substance with them, either to purchase Plantations, or begin New ones, so we should be sure of a kind agreeable Reception, and that without any possibility of a Discovery of our Circumstances.

I told him in general too, that as I had several Relations in the Place where we was, and that I durst not now let myself be known to them, because they would soon come into a knowledge of the Occasion and Reason of my coming over, which would be to expose myself to the last degree; so[489] I had Reason to believe that my Mother who died here had left me something, and perhaps considerable, which it might be very well worth my while to enquire after; but that this too could not be done without exposing us publickly, unless we went from hence; and then where ever we Settled, I might come as it were to

---

[488]Inexperienced.   [489]Also (?)

visit and to see my Brother and Nephews, make myself known to them, claim and enquire after what was my Due, be receiv'd with Respect, and at the same time have justice done me with chearfulness and good will; whereas if I did it now, I could expect nothing but with trouble, such as exacting it by force, receiving it with Curses and Reluctance, and with all kinds of Affronts; which he would not perhaps bear to see; that in Case of being oblig'd to legal Proofs of being really her Daughter, I might be at loss, be oblig'd to have recourse to *England*, and it may be to fail at last, and so lose it, whatever it might be: With these Arguments, and having thus acquainted my Husband with the whole Secret so far as was needful to him, we resolv'd to go and seek a Settlement in some other Colony, and at first Thoughts, *Carolina* was the Place we pitch'd upon.

In order to this we began to make enquiry for Vessels going to *Carolina*, and in a very little while got information, that on the other side the *Bay, as they call it*, namely, in *Maryland* there was a Ship, which came from *Carolina*, loaden with Rice, and other Goods, and was going back again thither, and from thence to *Jamaica*, with Provisions: On this News we hir'd a Sloop to take in our Goods, and taking as it were a final farewel of *Potowmack* River, we went with all our Cargo over to *Maryland*.

This was a long and unpleasant Voyage, and my Spouse said it was worse to him than all the Voyage from *England*, because the Weather was but indifferent, the Water rough, and the Vessel small and inconvenient; in the next Place we were full a hundred Miles up *Potowmack* River, in a part which they call *Westmorland* County, and as that River is by far the greatest in *Virginia*, and I have heard say, it is the greatest River in the World that falls into another River, and not directly into the Sea; so we had base Weather in it, and were frequently in great Danger; for tho' they call it but a River, 'tis frequently so broad, that when we were in the middle, we could not see Land on either Side for many Leagues together: Then we had the great River, or Bay of *Chesapeake* to cross, which is where the River *Potowmack* falls into it, near thirty Miles broad, and we entered more great vast Waters, whose Names I know not, so that our Voyage was full two hundred Mile, in a poor sorry Sloop with all our Treasure, and if any Accident had happened to us, we might at last have been very miserable; supposing we had Lost our Goods and saved our Lives only, and had then been left naked and destitute, and in a wild strange Place, not having one Friend or Acquaintance in all that part of the World? The very thoughts of it gives me some horror, even since the Danger is past.

Well, we came to the Place in five Days sailing, I think they call it *Philip's Point*,[490] and behold when we came thither, the Ship bound to

[490] A peninsula between the mouths of the Katturine and Nanticoke Rivers, in Dorchester County, Maryland.

Carolina, was loaded and gone away but three Days before. This was a Disappointment, but however, I that was to be discourag'd with nothing, told my Husband that since we could not get Passage to *Carolina,* and that the Country we was in, was very fertile and good; we would if he lik'd of it, see if we could find out any thing for our Turn where we was, and that if he lik'd things we would Settle here.

We immediately went on Shore, but found no Conveniences just at that Place, either for our being[491] on Shore, or preserving our Goods on Shore, but was directed by a very honest Quaker, who we found there to go to a Place, about sixty Miles East; that is to say, nearer the Mouth of the *Bay,* where he said he liv'd, and where we should be Accommodated, either to Plant, or to wait for any other Place to Plant in, that might be more Convenient, and he invited us with so much kindness and simple Honesty that we agreed to go, and the Quaker himself went with us.

Here we bought us two Servants, (*viz.*) an *English* Woman-Servant just come on Shore from a Ship of *Leverpool,* and a *Negro* Man-Servant; things absolutely necessary for all People that pretended to Settle in that Country: This honest Quaker was very helpful to us, and when we came to the Place that he propos'd to us, found us out a convenient Storehouse, for our Goods, and Lodging for ourselves, and our Servants; and about two Months, or thereabout afterwards, by his Direction we took up a large peice of Land from the Governor of that Country, in order to form our Plantation, and so we laid the thoughts of going to *Carolina* wholly aside, having been very well receiv'd here, and Accommodated with a convenient Lodging, till we could prepare things, and have Land enough cur'd, and Timber and Materials provid'd for building us a House, all which we manag'd by the Direction of the Quaker; so that in one Years time, we had near fifty Acres of Land clear'd, part of it enclos'd, and some of it Planted with Tobacco, tho' not much; besides, we had Garden ground, and Corn sufficient to help supply our Servants with Roots, and Herbs, and Bread.

And now I perswaded my Husband to let me go over the *Bay* again, and enquire after my Friends; he was the willinger to consent to it now, because he had business upon his Hands sufficient to employ him, besides his Gun to divert him, which they call Hunting there, and which he greatly delighted in; and indeed we us'd to look at one another , sometimes with a great deal of Pleasure, reflecting how much better that was, not than *Newgate* only, but than the most prosperous

---

[491]Lodging, residing. Such settlements usually afforded practically no conveniences; for an interesting account of such places, see Henry J. Berkeley, "Extinct River Towns of the Chesapeake Bay Region," *Maryland Historical Magazine,* XIX (1924), 125–34.

of our Circumstances in the wicked Trade that we had been both carrying on.

Our Affair was in a very good posture, we purchased of the Proprietors of the Colony, as much Land for 35 Pound, paid in ready Money, as would make a sufficient Plantation to employ between fifty and sixty Servants, and which being well improv'd, would be sufficient to us as long as we could either of us live; and as for Children I was past the prospect of any thing of that kind.

But our good Fortune did not End here, I went, *as I have said*, over the *Bay*, to the Place, where my Brother, once a Husband, liv'd; but I did not go to the same Village, where I was before, but went up another great River, on the East side of the River *Potowmack*, call'd *Rapahannock* River, and by this means came on the back of his Plantation, which was large, and by the help of a Navigable Creek, or little River, that run into the *Rapahannock*, I came very near it.

I was now fully resolv'd to go up *Point-blank* to my Brother (Husband) and to tell him who I was; but not knowing what Temper I might find him in, or how much out of Temper rather, I might make him by such a rash visit, I resolv'd to write a Letter to him, first to let him know, who I was, and that I was come not to give him any trouble upon the old Relation, which I hop'd was entirely forgot; but that I apply'd to him as a Sister to a Brother, desiring his Assistance in the Case of that Provision, which our Mother at her decease had left for my Support, and which I did not doubt but he would do me Justice in, especially considering that I was come thus far to look after it.

I said some very tender kind things in the Letter about his Son, which I told him he knew to be my own Child, and that as I was guilty of nothing in Marrying him any more than he was in Marrying me, neither of us having then known our being at all related to one another; so I hop'd he would allow me the most Passionate desire of once seeing my one, and only Child, and of showing something of the Infirmities of a Mother in preserving a violent Affection for him, who had never been able to retain any thought of me one way or other.

I did believe that having receiv'd this Letter, he would immediately give it to his Son to Read; I having understood his Eyes being so dim, that he cou'd not see to read it; but it fell out[492] better than so, for as his Sight was dim, so he had allow'd his Son to open all Letters that came to his Hand for him, and the old Gentleman being from Home, or out of the way when my Messenger came, my Letter came directly to my Sons Hand, and he open'd and read it.

He call'd the Messenger in, after some little stay, and ask'd him

[492] Happened.

where the Person was who gave him the Letter? the Messenger told him the Place, which was about seven Miles off, so he bid him stay, and ordering a Horse to be got ready, and two Servants, away he came to me with the Messenger: Let any one judge the Consternation I was in, when my Messenger came back, and told me the old Gentleman was not at Home, but his Son was come along with him, and was just coming up to me: I was perfectly confounded, for I knew not whether it was Peace or War, nor cou'd I tell how to behave: However, I had but a very few Moments to think, for my Son was at the Heels of the Messenger, and coming up into my Lodgings, ask'd the Fellow at the door, something; I suppose it was, *for I did not hear it, so as to understand it*, which was the Gentlewoman that sent him, for the Messenger said, *there she is Sir*, at which he comes directly up to me, kisses me, took me in his Arms, and embrac'd me with so much Passion, that he could not speak, but I could feel his Breast heave and throb like a Child that Cries, but Sobs, and cannot cry it out.

I can neither express or describe the Joy, that touch'd my very Soul, when I found, *for it was easy to discover that Part*, that he came not as a Stranger, but as a Son to a Mother, and indeed as a Son, who had never before known what a Mother of his own was; in short, we cryed over one another a considerable while, when at last he broke out first, MY DEAR MOTHER, says he, *are you still alive! I never expected to have seen your Face*; as for me, I cou'd say nothing a great while.

After we had both recover'd ourselves a little, and were able to talk, he told me how things stood, as to what I had written to his Father, he told me he had not shewed my Letter to his Father, or told him any thing about it; that what his Grandmother left me, was in his Hands, and that he would do me Justice to my full Satisfaction; that as to his Father, he was old and infirm both in Body and Mind, that he was very Fretful, and Passionate, almost Blind, and capable of nothing; and he question'd whether he would know how to act in an Affair, which was of so nice a Nature as this, and that therefore he had come himself, as well to satisfy himself in seeing me, which he could not restrain himself from, as also to put it into my Power to make a Judgement after I had seen how things were, whether I would discover myself to his Father, or no.

This was really so prudently, and wisely manag'd, that I found my Son was a Man of Sense, and needed no Direction from me; I told him, I did not wonder that his Father was as he had describ'd him, for that his Head was a little touch'd before I went away; and principally his Disturbance was, because I could not be perswaded to conceal our Relation, and to live with him as my Husband, after I knew that he was my Brother: That as he knew better than I, what his Fathers present Condition was, I should readily joyn with him in such Measures as he would direct: That I was indifferent, as to seeing his

Father, since I had seen him first, and he cou'd not have told me better News, than to tell me that what his Grandmother had left me, was entrusted in his Hands, who I doubted not, now he knew who I was, would *as he said*, do me Justice: I enquir'd then how long my Mother had been dead, and where she died, and told so many particulars of the Family, that I left him no room to doubt the Truth of my being really and truly his Mother.

My Son then enquir'd where I was, and how I had dispos'd myself; I told him I was on the *Maryland* side of the *Bay*, at the Plantation of a particular Friend, who came from *England* in the same Ship with me, that as for that side of the *Bay* where he was, I had no Habitation; he told me I should go Home with him, and live with him, if I pleas'd, as long as I liv'd: That as to his Father he knew no Body, and would never so much as guess at me; I consider'd of that a little, and told him, that tho' it was really no concern to me[493] to live at a distance from him; yet I could not say it would be the comfortablest thing in the World to me to live in the House with him; and to have that unhappy Object always before me, which had been such a blow to my Peace before; that tho' I should be glad to have his Company (my Son) or to be as near him as possible while I stay'd, yet I could not think of being in the House where I should be also under constant Restraint, for fear of betraying myself in my Discourse, nor should I be able to refrain some Expressions in my Conversing with him as my Son, that might discover the whole Affair, which would by no means be Convenient.

He acknowledged that I was right in all this, but then DEAR MOTHER, says he, *you shall be as near me as you can*; so he took me with him on Horseback to a Plantation, next to his own, and where I was as well entertain'd as I cou'd have been in his own; having left me there he went away home, telling me we would talk of the main Business the next Day, and having first called me his Aunt, and given a Charge to the People, who it seems were his Tenants, to treat me with all possible Respect; about two Hours after he was gone, he sent me a Maid-Servant, and a *Negro* Boy to wait on me, and Provisions ready dress'd for my Supper; and thus I was as if I had been in a new World, and began secretly now to wish that I had not brought my *Lancashire* Husband from *England* at all.

However, that wish was not hearty neither, for I lov'd my *Lancashire* Husband entirely, as indeed I had ever done from the beginning; and he merited from me as much as it was possible for a Man to do, but that by the way.

The next Morning my Son came to visit me again almost as soon as

---

[493] I.e., Moll tells him that she does not necessarily desire to live far away from her ex-husband, but she doesn't want to be too close either.

I was up; after a little Discourse, he first of all pull'd out a Deer skin Bag, and gave it me, with five and fifty *Spanish* Pistoles[494] in it, and told me that was to supply my Expences from *England*, for tho' it was not his Business to enquire, yet he ought to think I did not bring a great deal of Money out with me; it not being usual to bring much Money into that Country: Then he pull'd out his Grandmother's Will, and read it over to me, whereby it appear'd, that she had left a small Plantation, *as he call'd it*, on *York* River, that is, where my Mother liv'd, to me, with the Stock of Servants and Cattle upon it, and given it in Trust to this Son of mine for my Use, when ever he should hear of my being alive, and to my Heirs, if I had any Children, and in default of Heirs, to whomsoever I should by Will dispose of it; but gave the Income of it, till I should be heard of, or found, to my said Son; and if I should not be living, then it was to him, and his Heirs.

This Plantation, tho' remote from him, he said he did not let out, but manag'd it by a head Clerk, or Steward, as he did another that was his Fathers, that lay hard by it, and went over himself three or four times a Year to look after it; I ask'd him what he thought the Plantation might be worth, *he said*, if I would let it out, he would give me about sixty Pounds a Year for it; but if I would live on it, then it would be worth much more, and he believ'd would bring me in about 150 *l.* a Year; but seeing I was likely either to Settle on the other side of the *Bay*, or might perhaps have a mind to go back to *England* again, if I would let him be my Steward he would manage it for me, as he had done for himself, and that he believ'd he should be able to send me as much Tobacco to *England* from it, as would yeild me about 100 *l.* a Year, sometimes more.

This was all strange News to me, and things I had not been us'd to; and really my Heart began to look up more seriously, than I think it ever did before, and to look with great Thankfulness to the Hand of Providence, which had done such wonders for me, who had been myself the greatest wonder of Wickedness, perhaps that had been suffered to live in the World; and I must again observe, that not on this Occasion only, but even on all other Occasions of Thankfulness, my past wicked and abominable Life never look'd so Monstrous to me, and I never so compleatly abhorr'd it, and reproach'd myself with it, as when I had a Sense upon me of Providence doing good to me, while I had been making those vile Returns on my part.[495]

But I leave the Reader to improve these Thoughts, as no doubt they will see Cause, and I go on to the Fact; my Sons tender Carriage, and kind Offers fetch'd Tears from me, almost all the while he talk'd with me; indeed I could scarce Discourse with him, but in the inter-

[494]Gold coins, worth slightly less than a pound each.
[495]I.e., Moll feels most conscience-

stricken when she recognizes her lack of desert of the prosperity she has received.

vals of my Passion; however, at length I began, and expressing myself with wonder at my being so happy to have the Trust of what I had left, put into the Hands of my own Child; I told him, that as to the Inheritance of it, I had no Child but him in the World,[496] and was now past having any, if I should Marry, and therefore would desire him to get a Writing Drawn, which I was ready to execute, by which I would after me give it wholly to him, and to his Heirs; and in the mean time smiling, I ask'd him, what made him continue a Batchelor so long; his answer was kind, and ready, that *Virginia* did not yield any great plenty of Wives, and that since I talk'd of going back to *England*, I should send him a Wife from *London*.

This was the Substance of our first days Conversation, the pleasantest Day that ever past over my Head in my Life, and which gave me the truest Satisfaction: He came every Day after this, and spent great part of his time with me, and carried me about to several of his Friends Houses, where I was entertain'd with great Respect; also I Dined several times at his own House, when he took care always to see his half dead Father so out of the way, that I never saw him, or he me: I made him one Present, and it was all I had of value, and that was one the gold Watches, of which I mention'd above that I had two in my Chest, and this I happen'd to have with me, and I gave it him at his third Visit: I told him, I had nothing of any value to bestow but that, and I desir'd he would now and then kiss it for my sake; *I did not indeed tell him* that I had stole it from a Gentlewomans side, at a Meeting-House in *London*, that's by the way.

He stood a little while hesitating, as if doubtful whether to take it or no; but I press'd it on him, and made him accept it, and it was not much less worth than his Leather-pouch full of *Spanish* Gold; no, tho' it were to be reckon'd, as if at *London*, whereas it was worth twice as much there, where I gave it him;[497] at length he took it, kiss'd it, and told me the Watch should be a Debt upon him, that he would be paying, as long as I liv'd.

A Few Days after he brought the Writings of Gift, and the Scrivener with them, and I sign'd them very freely, and deliver'd them to him with a hundr'd Kisses; for sure nothing ever pass'd between a Mother, and a tender dutiful Child, with more Affection: The next Day he brings me an Obligation under his Hand and Seal, whereby he engag'd himself to Manage, and Improve the Plantation for my account, and with his utmost Skill, and to remit the Produce to my order whereever I should be, and withal, to be oblig'd himself to make up the Produce a hundred Pound a Year to me: When he had done so, he told me, that as I came to demand it before the Crop was off, I

[496]Moll, or Defoe, conveniently forgets at least five children who were alive when she last saw them.

[497]I.e., it would have been worth almost 55 pistoles even in London, but in America it is worth twice that.

had a right to the Produce of the current Year, and so he paid me an hundred Pound in *Spanish* Peices of Eight, and desir'd me to give him a Receipt for it as in full for that Year, ending at *Christmas* following; this being about the latter End of *August*.

I stay'd here above five Weeks, and indeed had much a do to get away then. Nay, he would have come over the *Bay* with me, but I would by no means allow him to it; however, he would send me over in a Sloop of his own, which was built like a Yatch,[498] and serv'd him as well for Pleasure as Business: This I accepted of, and so after the utmost Expressions both of Duty, and Affection, he let me come away, and I arriv'd safe in two Days at my Friends the Quakers.

I Brought over with me for the use of our Plantation, three Horses with Harness, and Saddles; some Hogs, two Cows, and a thousand other things, the Gift of the kindest and tenderest Child that ever Woman had: I related to my Husband all the particulars of this Voyage, except that I called my Son (my Cousin;) and first I told him, that I had lost my Watch, which he seem'd to take as a Misfortune; but then I told him how kind my Cousin had been, that my Mother had left me such a Plantation, and that he had preserv'd it for me, in hopes some time or other he should hear from me; then I told that I had left it to his Management, that he would render me a faithful Account of its Produce; and then I pull'd him out the hundred Pound in Silver, as the first Years produce, and then pulling out the Deer skin Purse, with the Pistoles, and here my Dear, *says I,* is the gold Watch. My Husband, *so is Heavens goodness sure to work the same Effects, in all sensible Minds, where Mercies touch the Heart;* lifted up both his Hands, and with an extasy of Joy, *What is God a doing* says he, *for such an ungrateful Dog as I am!* Then I let him know, what I had brought over in the Sloop, besides all this; I mean the Horses, Hogs, and Cows, and other Stores for our Plantation; all which added to his surprize, and fill'd his Heart with thankfulness, and from this time forward I believe he was as sincere a Penitent, and as thoroughly a reform'd Man, as ever God's goodness brought back from a Profligate, a Highway-Man, and a Robber. I could fill a larger History than this, with the Evidences of this Truth, and but that I doubt that part of the Story will not be equally diverting as the wicked Part I have had thoughts of making a Volume of it by itself.

As for myself, as this is to be my own Story, not my Husbands, I return to that Part which relates to myself; we went on with our Plantation, and manag'd it with the help and diversion of such Friends as we got there, by our obliging Behaviour, and especially the honest Quaker, who prov'd a faithful generous and steady Friend to us; and we had very good Success; for having a flourishing Stock to begin

---

[498]Yacht.

with, as *I have said*; and this being now encreas'd, by the Addition of a Hundred and fifty Pound *Sterling* in Money, we enlarg'd our Number of Servants, built us a very good House, and cur'd every Year a great deal of Land. The second Year I wrote to my old Governess, giving her part with us of the Joy of our Success, and order'd her how to lay out the Money I had left with her, which was 250 *l.* as above, and to send it to us in Goods, which she perform'd, with her usual Kindness and Fidelity, and all this arriv'd safe to us.

Here we had a supply of all sorts of Cloaths, as well for my Husband, as for myself; and I took especial care to buy for him all those things that I knew he delighted to have; as two good long Wigs, two silver hilted Swords, three or four fine Fowling peices, a fine Saddle with Holsters and Pistoles[499] very handsome with a Scarlet Cloak; and in a Word, every thing I could think of to oblige him; and to make him appear, as he really was, a very fine Gentleman: I order'd a good Quantity of such Houshold-stuff, as we yet wanted, with Linnen of all sorts for us both, as for my self, I wanted very little of Cloths, or Linnen, being very well furnished before: The rest of my Cargo consisted in Iron-Work, of all sorts, Harness for Horses, Tools, Cloaths for Servants, and Woollen-Cloth, stuffs, Serges, Stockings, Shoes, Hats and the like such as Servants wear, and whole peices also to make up for Servants, all by direction of the Quaker; and all this Cargo arriv'd safe, and in good Condition, with three Women Servants, lusty Wenches, which my old Governess had pick'd up for me, suitable enough to the Place, and to the Work we had for them to do; one of which happen'd to come double, having been got with Child by one of the Seamen in the Ship, as she own'd afterwards, before the Ship got so far as *Gravesend*; so she brought us a stout Boy, about 7 Months after her Landing.

My Husband you may suppose was a little surpriz'd at the arriving of all this Cargo from *England*, and talking with me after he saw the Account of the particular; my Dear *says he*, what is the meaning of all this? I fear you will run us too deep in Debt: When shall we be able to make Return for it all? I smil'd, and told him that it was all paid for, and then I told him, that not knowing what might befal us in the Voyage, and considering what our Circumstances might expose us to; I had not taken my whole Stock with me, that I had reserv'd so much in my Friends Hands, which now we were come over safe, and was Settled in a way to live, I had sent for as he might see.

He was amaz'd, and stood a while telling upon his Fingers, but said nothing, at last he began thus, Hold lets see, *says he, telling upon his Fingers still*; and first on his Thumb, there's 246 *l.* in Money at first, then two gold Watches, Diamond Rings, and Plate, *says he*, upon the

[499] Pistols.

fore Finger, then upon the next Finger, here's a Plantation on *York* River, a 100 *l.* a Year,[500] then 150 in Money; then a Sloop load of Horses, Cows, Hogs and Stores, and so on to the Thumb again; and now, *says he*, a Cargo cost 250 *l.* in *England*, and worth here twice the Money; well, *says I*, What do you make of all that? make of it, *says he*, why who says I was deceiv'd, when I married a Wife in *Lancashire?* I think I have married a Fortune, and a very good Fortune too, *says he.*

In a Word, we were now in very considerable Circumstances, and every Year encreasing; for our new Plantation grew upon our Hands insensibly;[501] and in eight Year which we lived upon it, we brought it to such a pitch, that the Produce was, at least, 300 *l.* Sterling a Year; I mean, worth so much in *England.*

After I had been a Year at Home again, I went over the Bay to see my Son, and to receive another Year's Income of my Plantation; and I was surpriz'd to hear, just at my Landing there, that my old Husband was dead, and had not been bury'd above a Fortnight. This, I confess, was not disagreeable News, because now I could appear as I was in a marry'd Condition; so I told my Son before I came from him, that I believed I should marry a Gentleman who had a Plantation near mine; and tho' I was legally free to marry, as to any Obligation that was on me before, yet that I was shye of it, least the Blot should some time or other be reviv'd, and it might make a Husband uneasy; my Son the same kind dutiful and obliging Creature as ever, treated me now at his own House, paid me my hundred Pound, and sent me Home again loaded with Presents.

Some time after this, I let my Son know I was marry'd, and invited him over to see us; and my Husband wrote a very obliging Letter to him also, inviting him to come and see him; and he came accordingly some Months after, and happen'd to be there just when my Cargo from *England* came in, which I let him believe belong'd all to my Husband's Estate, not to me.

It must be observ'd, that when the old Wretch, my Brother (Husband) was dead, I then freely gave my Husband an Account of all that Affair, and of this Cousin, as I had call'd him before, being my own Son by that mistaken unhappy Match: He was perfectly easy in the Account, and told me he should have been as easy if the old Man, as we call'd him, had been alive; for, *said he*, it was no Fault of yours; nor of his; it was a Mistake impossible to be prevented; he only reproach'd him with desiring me to conceal it, and to live with him as a Wife, after I knew that he was my Brother; that, he said, was a vile part: Thus all these little Difficulties were made easy, and we liv'd together with the greatest Kindness and Comfort imaginable; we are now grown Old: I am come back to *England,*

---

[500]I.e., a plantation worth £100 a year.   [501]Imperceptibly.

being almost seventy Years of Age, my Husband sixty eight, having perform'd much more than the limited Terms of my Transportation: And now notwithstanding all the Fatigues, and all the Miseries we have both gone thro', we are both of us in good Heart and Health; my Husband remain'd there sometime after me to settle our Affairs, and at first I had intended to go back to him, but at his desire I alter'd that Resolution, and he is come over to *England* also, where we resolve to spend the Remainder of our Years in sincere Penitence, for the wicked Lives we have lived.

Written in the Year 1683.

F I N I S.

CRITICISM AND COMMENTARY

In the essays and excerpts that follow, bracketed figures indicate the end of a page in the selection as it appears in the original source. Whenever necessary, footnotes have been renumbered and page references to the novel have been changed to conform to the pagination of this edition, but there has been no attempt to make quotations from other editions of the novel conform to the wording of this edition.

FROM the Preface to the Novelist's Library Edition of Defoe (1810)*

JOHN BALLANTYNE

The air of writing with all the plausibility of truth must, in almost every case, have its own peculiar value; as we admire the paintings of some Flemish artists, where, though the subjects drawn are mean and disagreeable, and such as in nature we would not wish to study or look close upon, yet the skill with which they are represented by the painter gives an interest to the imitation upon canvas which the original entirely wants. But, on the other hand, when the power of exact and circumstantial delineation is applied to objects which we are anxiously desirous to see in their proper shape and colours, we have a double source of pleasure, both in the art of the painter, and in the interest which we take in the subject represented. Thus the style of probability with which De Foe invested his narratives was perhaps ill bestowed, or rather wasted, upon some of the works [381] which he thought proper to produce, and cannot recommend to us the subject of *Colonel Jack* and *Moll Flanders;* but, on the other hand, the same talent throws an air of truth about the delightful history of *Robinson Crusoe*, which we never could have believed it possible to have united with so extraordinary a situation as is assigned to the hero.... [382]

FROM Estimate of De Foe's Secondary Novels (1829)†

CHARLES LAMB

While all ages and descriptions of people hang delighted over the "Adventures of Robinson Crusoe," and shall continue to do so, we trust, while the world lasts, how few comparatively will bear to be told that there exist other fictitious narratives by the same writer,—four of them at least of no inferior interest, except what results from a less

*Source: Sir Walter Scott, *The Lives of the Novelists*, Everyman's Library Edition (New York: E. P. Dutton & Co., 1928), pp. 381–82. Reprinted by permission of E. P. Dutton & Co. and J. M. Dent & Sons Ltd. This essay was formerly ascribed to Sir Walter Scott.

†Source: W. J. Widdleton, *Eliana* (1865), pp. 115–17. Originally printed in Walter Wilson, *Memoirs of the Life and Times of Daniel Defoe* (1830), Vol. III, pp. 126–28.

felicitous choice of situation! "Roxana," "Singleton," "Moll Flanders," "Colonel Jack," are all genuine offspring of the same father. They bear the veritable impress of De Foe. An unpractised midwife that would not swear to the nose, lip, forehead, and eye of every one of them! They are, in their way, as full of incident, and some of them every bit as romantic; only they want the uninhabited island, and the charm that has bewitched the world, of the striking solitary situation.

. . . . .

The narrative manner of De Foe has a naturalness [115] about it beyond that of any other novel or romance writer. His fictions have all the air of true stories. It is impossible to believe, while you are reading them, that a real person is not narrating to you everywhere nothing but what really happened to himself. To this the extreme *homliness* of their style mainly contributes. We use the word in its best and heartiest sense, — that which comes *home* to the reader. The narrators everywhere are chosen from low life, or have had their origin in it: therefore they tell their own tales (Mr. Coleridge has anticipated us in this remark), as persons in their degree are observed to do, with infinite repetition, and an overacted exactness, lest the hearer should not have minded, or have forgotten, some things that had been told before. Hence the emphatic sentences marked in the good old (but deserted) Italic type; and hence, too, the frequent interposition of the reminding old colloquial parenthesis, "I say," "Mind," and the like, when the story-teller repeats what, to a practised reader, might appear to have been sufficiently insisted upon before: which made an ingenious critic observe, that his works, in this kind, were excellent reading for the kitchen. And, in truth, the heroes and heroines of De Foe can never again hope to be popular with a much higher class of readers than that of the servant-maid or the sailor. Crusoe keeps its rank only by tough prescription. Singleton, the pirate; Colonel Jack, the thief; Moll Flanders, both thief and harlot; Roxana, harlot and something worse, — would be startling ingredients in the bill-of-fare of modern literary delicacies. But, then, what pirates, what thieves, and what harlots, is *the thief*, *the harlot*, and *the pirate* of De Foe! [116] We would not hesitate to say, that in no other book of fiction, where the lives of such characters are described, is guilt and deliquency made less seductive, or the suffering made more closely to follow the commission, or the penitence more earnest or more bleeding, or the intervening flashes of religious visitation upon the rude and uninstructed soul more meltingly and fearfully painted. They, in this, come near to the tenderness of Bunyan; while the livelier pictures and incidents in them, as in Hogarth or in Fielding, tend to diminish that fastidiousness to the concerns and pursuits of common life which an unrestrained passion for the ideal and the sentimental is in danger of producing. [117]

From Daniel Defoe (1856)*

ANONYMOUS

Why did not Defoe, with such an unexampled capability as a writer of fiction, occupy himself earnestly in his art? Why did he not expend thought, toil, and long years in elaborating two such works as "Robinson Crusoe," or the commencement of "Colonel Jack," instead of scribbling page after page, without consideration enough to avoid dullness, stories replete with obscenities he must have disapproved, and nonsense that he must have grinned at with contempt even while the pen was in his hand? Foster, in his graphic and fascinating sketch of Defoe and his times, bids us remember, when judging of "Moll Flanders" and "Roxanna," the tone of society at the time of their appearance. Without a doubt, measured by the standard of the vicious literature of the Restoration and the two succeeding ages, they do not especially sin against purity of morals. But in this we cannot find a valid apology for Defoe, who, in composing them, put his hands to works that all serious men of his own religious views must have regarded with warm disapproval. Defoe was not by profession amongst the frivolous or godless of his generation; he was loud in his condemnation of the stage, of gambling, and of debauchery; he not only knew that voluptuous excess was criminal, but he raised his voice to shame it out of society,—and yet he exercised his talents in depicting scenes of sensual enjoyment, which no virtuous nature can dwell on without pain, no vicious one without pleasure. What was his motive? Money. [524]

From Daniel Defoe (1871)†

ANONYMOUS

In all [Defoe's] fictions,... he identifies himself with his characters; and even his villains—women as well as men—bear a family likeness to their literary father. It seems hard to say this of such characters as Moll Flanders, Roxana, and Colonel Jack; but while committing[318] hateful sins and crimes, and relating what they have done, they moralize upon their evil deeds with the seriousness and sobriety of a sedate old gentleman whose one object in life is the benefit of his fellow-creatures. Yet the descent from the light and purity of the great romance to the oppressive and noxious atmosphere

*Source: *Littel's Living Age*, L, 640 (August, 1856), 524. Originally printed in *Dublin University Magazine*, 1856.
†Source: *Cornhill Magazine*, 23 (1871), 318–20.

of the minor novels is great indeed. *Robinson Crusoe* stands out from its companions like a noble mountain amidst a range of stunted hillocks; it is a book so manly in tone, so feminine in sweetness, so Christian in feeling, that it deserves a place on the same shelf with the *Faery Queene* and the *Pilgrim's Progress*. But on what shelf, and with what companions, shall we place *Roxana* and *Moll Flanders*, *Colonel Jack*, and *Captain Singleton*? Not certainly with books in which splendid powers are perverted to evil, and vice is tricked out to wear the semblance of virtue; but among books that display, with the fidelity of a photograph, human nature at its worst, vice in all its grossness, and the low aims of low people in all their vulgarity. Love, in the highest meaning of the word, was unknown to Defoe, and is not, therefore, portrayed in his novels. He wrote only of what he knew, and of this he knew nothing. His women are without grace, without purity, without dignity, they are even without passion; and when led astray, are not influenced by their affections, but by a love of greed. Their aims are mercenary, their manners loose, their language commonplace; they are wholly destitute of sentiment and of the charm of poetry. But they act and speak like living beings, instead of moving like puppets. The truth of the likenesses reconciles us to their coarseness. They interest us, because of the one touch of nature, and as specimens of our common humanity.

Defoe professes to write always with a moral, and even with a religious purpose. He was an honest and severe Presbyterian.... He had from his youth belonged to a strait sect, and had shown himself willing to suffer persecution for his creed. When his minor fictions were published Defoe was more than sixty years of age, and had just produced one of the wholesomest and most beautiful tales we possess in the language. Is it possible that these far inferior books were written years before, when he was immured in Newgate, and when, doubtless, he acquired much of the special knowledge they exhibit, and that the extraordinary popularity of *Robinson Crusoe*, which gained its high position at a bound, induced him to give them also to the world? It would be a satisfaction to think that such novels as *Moll Flanders* and *Roxana* were not among the last works of an old man. His aim, it may be admitted, was to portray the ugliness of vice and the divine beauty of virtue, and certainly he displays vice after a very undraped fashion. If people don't dislike it, he says it is their own fault; and their fault, too, if they do not gain [319] instruction from the inevitable moral which follows the representation. But the first object of fiction is amusement; and this, in the novels we are speaking of, can only be gathered from the vicious or criminal adventures of the characters described. Books such as these are not taken up for the sake of instruction. It is impossible, therefore, to accept Defoe's asseverations that his sole object in writing his fictions was didactic, and we agree with Mr. Wilson and Mr. Lee, that they cannot be recommended for indiscriminate perusal.[320]

FROM A History of English Prose Fiction (1882)*

BAYARD TUCKERMAN

If the author of "Robinson Crusoe" could realize so thoroughly the difficulties and expedients of a man living on a desert island, he could deal yet more easily with the adventures and shifts of thieves and abandoned women which formed the subject of his other tales. In these minor works, now little known, Defoe displayed equal talents, but did not attain equal results. The enduring interest which must ever attach to the central idea of "Robinson Crusoe"—the complete isolation of the man—gave that work a very exceptional claim to the attention of posterity. But it had other merits, which are not apparent in the same perfection in Defoe's lesser novels. Its design was single and concentrated, its chief character [187] natural and strongly marked, its plot coherent and complete. Moll Flanders and Colonel Jack are indeed well-drawn and real persons, and the design of the works which bear their names is clear, but in both cases the plot is merely a series of independent adventures, and the characters themselves could not, from their nature, long attract the attention of readers. "Colonel Jack," "Captain Singleton," "Moll Flanders," and "Roxana," have been surpassed, and are neglected, "Robinson Crusoe" is, of its kind, perfect, and therefore enduring.

. . . . . .

Defoe was throughout his life a reformer; a large proportion of the many pamphlets and occasional writings which fell from his pen have for their object the reformation or exposure of some abuse. Yet a large number of his fictitious characters are thieves and harlots. The criminal classes occupied the public mind in the first half of the eighteenth century to a remarkable degree, and Defoe was not mistaken in thinking that novels concerning those classes would interest and sell. He knew that the public taste was low, and his business was to cater to public taste. He said, in "More Reformation":

> Let this describe the nation's character,
> One man reads Milton, forty Rochester;
> The cause is plain, the temper of the time,
> One wrote the lewd, the other the sublime.[188]

To satisfy the forty who read Rochester, Defoe described the lives and occupations of pirates, pickpockets, highwaymen, and women of

*Source: *A History of English Prose Fiction* (New York: G. P. Putnam's Sons, 1882), pp. 187–90.

abandoned character. The title-pages of some of these novels cannot with decency be quoted, and the novels themselves are filled with criminal and licentious scenes. But the reforming inclination of Defoe himself, and that which we find in the general literature of the time, induced him to turn these scenes to a moral account. Moll Flanders is a low, cunning, thoroughly bad woman, and her life is placed quite bare before the reader. Yet Defoe asserts that the book is designed to teach a good lesson.[1] . . . Defoe, thoroughly a man of his time, thought that he could put the coarsest and most vicious matter before his reader, and reasonably expect him to profit by the moral, without being hurt by contact with the vice. "All possible care," he says, "has been taken to give no lewd ideas, no immodest turns in the dressing up of this story. . . . To this purpose some the vicious part of her life, which could not be modestly told, is quite left out, and several other parts very much shortened. What is left, 'tis hoped will not offend the chastest reader, or the modestest hearer." To any one acquainted with "Moll Flanders" this seems a strange statement. It exhibits the standard[189] of the age. Mrs. Behn said almost the same thing about her novels and plays. To make up for the low, vicious life unrolled before us, it is not enough that Moll at last "grew rich, lived honest, and died penitent."[190]

FROM The Development of the English Novel (1899)*

WILBUR L. CROSS

'Robinson Crusoe' was the most immediately popular fiction that had yet been written. At once it became a part of the world's literature, and it remains such to this day. Defoe took advantage of its vogue to write many other adventures on land and sea. Captain Singleton's tour across Africa is as good reading as Stanley; and to the uninitiated, it seems quite as true to fact. In 'Moll Flanders' is gathered together a mass of material concerning the dregs of London — thieves and courtesans — that remains unequalled even among the modern naturalists. . . . [29]

Defoe†

VIRGINIA WOOLF

The fear which attacks the recorder of centenaries lest he should find himself measuring a diminishing spectre and forced to foretell its

[1]See the preface to "Moll Flanders."

*Source: *The Development of the English Novel* (New York and London: The Macmillan Company, 1899), p. 29.

†Source: Virginia Woolf, *The Common Reader* (New York: Harcourt, Brace & World,

approaching dissolution is not only absent in the case of *Robinson Crusoe* but the mere thought of it is ridiculous. It may be true that *Robinson Crusoe* is two hundred years of age upon the twenty-fifth of April 1919, but far from raising the familiar speculations as to whether people now read it and will continue to read it, the effect of the bi-centenary is to make us marvel that *Robinson Crusoe*, the perennial and immortal, should have been in existence so short a time as that. The book resembles one of the anonymous productions of the race rather than the effort of a single mind; and as for celebrating its centenary we should as soon think of celebrating the centenaries of Stonehenge itself. Something of this we may attribute to the fact that we have all had *Robinson Crusoe* read aloud to us as children, and were thus much in the same state of mind towards Defoe and his story that the Greeks were in towards Homer. It never occurred to us that there was such a person as Defoe, and to have been told that *Robinson Crusoe* was the work of a man with a pen in his hand would either have disturbed us unpleasantly or meant nothing at all. The impressions of childhood are those that last longest and cut deepest. It still seems that the name of Daniel Defoe has no right to appear upon[121] the title-page of *Robinson Crusoe*, and if we celebrate the bi-centenary of the book we are making a slightly unnecessary allusion to the fact that, like Stonehenge, it is still in existence.

The great fame of the book has done its author some injustice; for while it has given him a kind of anonymous glory it has obscured the fact that he was a writer of other works which, it is safe to assert, were not read aloud to us as children. Thus when the Editor of the *Christian World* in the year 1870 appealed to "the boys and girls of England" to erect a monument upon the grave of Defoe, which a stroke of lightning had mutilated, the marble was inscribed to the memory of the author of *Robinson Crusoe*. No mention was made of *Moll Flanders*. Considering the topics which are dealt with in that book, and in *Roxana, Captain Singleton, Colonel Jack* and the rest, we need not be surprised, though we may be indignant, at the omission. We may agree with Mr. Wright, the biographer of Defoe, that these "are not works for the drawing-room table". But unless we consent to make that useful piece of furniture the final arbiter of taste, we must deplore the fact that their superficial coarseness, or the universal celebrity of *Robinson Crusoe*, has led them to be far less widely famed than they deserve. On any monument worthy of the name of monument the names of *Moll Flanders* and *Roxana*, at least, should be carved as deeply as the name of Defoe. They stand among the few English novels which we can call indisputably great. The occasion of the bi-centenary of their more famous companion may well[122] lead us to

Inc., 1925), pp. 121–31. Copyright, 1925, by Harcourt, Brace & World, Inc., renewed, 1953, by Leonard Woolf. Reprinted by permission of Leonard Woolf, The Hogarth Press Limited, and Harcourt, Brace & World, Inc. This essay was written in 1919.

consider in what their greatness, which has so much in common with his, may be found to consist.

Defoe was an elderly man when he turned novelist, many years the predecessor of Richardson and Fielding, and one of the first indeed to shape the novel and launch it on its way. But it is unnecessary to labour the fact of his precedence, except that he came to his novel-writing with certain conceptions about the art which he derived partly from being himself one of the first to practise it. The novel had to justify its existence by telling a true story and preaching a sound moral. "This supplying a story by invention is certainly a most scandalous crime", he wrote. "It is a sort of lying that makes a great hole in the heart, in which by degrees a habit of lying enters in." Either in the preface or in the text of each of his works, therefore, he takes pains to insist that he has not used his invention at all but has depended upon facts, and that his purpose has been the highly moral desire to convert the vicious or to warn the innocent. Happily these were principles that tallied very well with his natural disposition and endowments. Facts had been drilled into him by sixty years of varying fortunes before he turned his experience to account in fiction. "I have some time ago summed up the Scenes of my life in this distich," he wrote:

> No man has tasted differing fortunes more,
> And thirteen times I have been rich and poor.

He had spent eighteen months in Newgate and talked with thieves, pirates, highwaymen, and coiners before[123] he wrote the history of Moll Flanders. But to have facts thrust upon you by dint of living and accident is one thing; to swallow them voraciously and retain the imprint of them indelibly, is another. It is not merely that Defoe knew the stress of poverty and had talked with the victims of it, but that the unsheltered life, exposed to circumstances and forced to shift for itself, appealed to him imaginatively as the right matter for his art. In the first pages of each of his great novels he reduces his hero or heroine to such a state of unfriended misery that their existence must be a continued struggle, and their survival at all the result of luck and their own exertions. Moll Flanders was born in Newgate of a criminal mother; Captain Singleton was stolen as a child and sold to the gipsies; Colonel Jack, though "born a gentleman, was put 'prentice to a pickpocket"; Roxana starts under better auspices, but, having married at fifteen, she sees her husband go bankrupt and is left with five children in "a condition the most deplorable that words can express".

Thus each of these boys and girls has the world to begin and the battle to fight for himself. The situation thus created was entirely to Defoe's liking. From her very birth or with half a year's respite at most, Moll Flanders, the most notable of them, is goaded by "that worst of

devils, poverty", forced to earn her living as soon as she can sew,
driven from place to place, making no demands upon her creator for
the subtle domestic atmosphere which he was unable to supply, but
drawing upon him for all he knew of[124] strange people and
customs. From the outset the burden of proving her right to exist is
laid upon her. She has to depend entirely upon her own wits and
judgement, and to deal with each emergency as it arises by a rule-of-
thumb morality which she has forged in her own head. The briskness
of the story is due partly to the fact that having transgressed the
accepted laws at a very early age she has henceforth the freedom of the
outcast. The one impossible event is that she should settle down in
comfort and security. But from the first the peculiar genius of the
author asserts itself, and avoids the obvious danger of the novel of
adventure. He makes us understand that Moll Flanders was a woman
on her own account and not only material for a succession of adventures. In proof of this she begins, as Roxana also begins, by falling
passionately, if unfortunately, in love. That she must rouse herself and
marry some one else and look very closely to her settlements and
prospects is no slight upon her passion, but to be laid to the charge
of her birth; and, like all Defoe's women, she is a person of robust
understanding. Since she makes no scruple of telling lies when they
serve her purpose, there is something undeniable about her truth
when she speaks it. She has no time to waste upon the refinements of
personal affection; one tear is dropped, one moment of despair
allowed, and then "on with the story". She has a spirit that loves to
breast the storm. She delights in the exercise of her own powers.
When she discovers that the man she has married in Virginia is her
own brother she is violently disgusted;[125] she insists upon leaving
him; but as soon as she sets foot in Bristol, "I took the diversion of
going to Bath, for as I was still far from being old so my humour, which
was always gay, continued so to an extreme". Heartless she is not, nor
can any one charge her with levity; but life delights her, and a heroine
who lives has us all in tow. Moreover, her ambition has that slight
strain of imagination in it which puts it in the category of the noble
passions. Shrewd and practical of necessity, she is yet haunted by a
desire for romance and for the quality which to her perception makes
a man a gentleman. "It was really a true gallant spirit he was of, and it
was the more grievous to me. 'Tis something of relief even to be
undone by a man of honour rather than by a scoundrel", she writes
when she had misled a highwayman as to the extent of her fortune. It
is in keeping with this temper that she should be proud of her final
partner because he refuses to work when they reach the plantations
but prefers hunting, and that she should take pleasure in buying him
wigs and silver-hilted swords "to make him appear, as he really was, a
very fine gentleman". Her very love of hot weather is in keeping, and

the passion with which she kissed the ground that her son had trod on, and her noble tolerance of every kind of fault so long as it is not "complete baseness of spirit, imperious, cruel, and relentless when uppermost, abject and low-spirited when down". For the rest of the world she has nothing but good-will.

Since the list of the qualities and graces of this seasoned old sinner is by no means exhausted we can[126] well understand how it was that Borrow's apple-woman on London Bridge called her "blessed Mary" and valued her book above all the apples on her stall; and that Borrow, taking the book deep into the booth, read till his eyes ached. But we dwell upon such signs of character only by way of proof that the creator of Moll Flanders was not, as he has been accused of being, a mere journalist and literal recorder of facts with no conception of the nature of psychology. It is true that his characters take shape and substance of their own accord, as if in despite of the author and not altogether to his liking. He never lingers or stresses any point of subtlety or pathos, but presses on imperturbably as if they came there without his knowledge. A touch of imagination, such as that when the Prince sits by his son's cradle and Roxana observes how "he loved to look at it when it was asleep", seems to mean much more to us than to him. After the curiously modern dissertation upon the need of communicating matters of importance to a second person lest, like the thief in Newgate, we should talk of it in our sleep, he apologises for his digression. He seems to have taken his characters so deeply into his mind that he lived them without exactly knowing how; and, like all unconscious artists, he leaves more gold in his work than his own generation was able to bring to the surface.

The interpretation that we put on his characters might therefore well have puzzled him. We find for ourselves meanings which he was careful to disguise even from his own eye. Thus it comes about that we[127] admire Moll Flanders far more than we blame her. Nor can we believe that Defoe had made up his mind as to the precise degree of her guilt, or was unaware that in considering the lives of the abandoned he raised many deep questions and hinted, if he did not state, answers quite at variance with his professions of belief. From the evidence supplied by his essay upon the "Education of Women" we know that he had thought deeply and much in advance of his age upon the capacities of women, which he rated very high, and the injustice done to them, which he rated very harsh.

> I have often thought of it as one of the most barbarous customs in the world, considering us as a civilised and a Christian country, that we deny the advantages of learning to women. We reproach the sex every day with folly and impertinence; which I am confident, had they the advantages of education equal to us, they would be guilty of less than ourselves.

The advocates of women's rights would hardly care, perhaps, to claim Moll Flanders and Roxana among their patron saints; and yet it is clear that Defoe not only intended them to speak some very modern doctrines upon the subject, but placed them in circumstances where their peculiar hardships are displayed in such a way as to elicit our sympathy. Courage, said Moll Flanders, was what women needed, and the power to "stand their ground"; and at once gave practical demonstration of the benefits that would result. Roxana, a lady of the same profession, argues more subtly against the slavery of marriage. She[128] "had started a new thing in the world" the merchant told her; "it was a way of arguing contrary to the general practise". But Defoe is the last writer to be guilty of bald preaching. Roxana keeps our attention because she is blessedly unconscious that she is in any good sense an example to her sex and is thus at liberty to own that part of her argument is "of an elevated strain which was really not in my thoughts at first, at all". The knowledge of her own frailties and the honest questioning of her own motives, which that knowledge begets, have the happy result of keeping her fresh and human when the martyrs and pioneers of so many problem novels have shrunken and shrivelled to the pegs and props of their respective creeds.

But the claim of Defoe upon our admiration does not rest upon the fact that he can be shown to have anticipated some of the views of Meredith, or to have written scenes which (the odd suggestion occurs) might have been turned into plays by Ibsen. Whatever his ideas upon the position of women, they are an incidental result of his chief virtue, which is that he deals with the important and lasting side of things and not with the passing and trivial. He is often dull. He can imitate the matter-of-fact precision of a scientific traveller until we wonder that his pen could trace or his brain conceive what has not even the excuse of truth to soften its dryness. He leaves out the whole of vegetable nature, and a large part of human nature. All this we may admit, though we have to admit defects as grave in many writers[129] whom we call great. But that does not impair the peculiar merit of what remains. Having at the outset limited his scope and confined his ambitions he achieves a truth of insight which is far rarer and more enduring than the truth of fact which he professed to make his aim. Moll Flanders and her friends recommended themselves to him not because they were, as we should say, "picturesque"; nor, as he affirmed, because they were examples of evil living by which the public might profit. It was their natural veracity, bred in them by a life of hardship, that excited his interest. For them there were no excuses; no kindly shelter obscured their motives. Poverty was their taskmaster. Defoe did not pronounce more than a judgement of the lips upon their failings. But their courage and resource and tenacity delighted him. He found their society full of good talk, and pleasant stories, and faith in each other, and morality of a home-made kind. Their fortunes had that infinite variety which he praised and relished and beheld with wonder in his own life. These men and women, above all, were free to talk openly of the passions and desires which have moved men and women since the beginning of time, and thus even now they keep their vitality undiminished. There is a dignity in everything that is looked at openly. Even the sordid subject of money, which plays so large a part in their histories, becomes not sordid but tragic when it stands not for ease and consequence but for honour, honesty, and life itself. You may object that Defoe is [130] humdrum, but never that he is engrossed with petty things.

He belongs, indeed, to the school of the great plain writers, whose work is founded upon a knowledge of what is most persistent, though not most seductive, in human nature. The view of London from Hungerford Bridge, grey, serious, massive, and full of the subdued stir of traffic and business, prosaic if it were not for the masts of the ships and the towers and domes of the city, brings him to mind. The tattered girls with violets in their hands at the street corners, and the old weather-beaten women patiently displaying their matches and bootlaces beneath the shelter of arches, seem like characters from his books. He is of the school of Crabbe and of Gissing, and not merely a fellow-pupil in the same stern place of learning, but its founder and master. [131]

On *Moll Flanders**

DOROTHY VAN GHENT

The editorial preface to a popular modern reprint of *Moll Flanders* speaks of the book as "one of the most remarkable examples of true realism in the whole range of fiction." The statement suggests that "true realism" is specifically that kind of realism which *Moll Flanders* exhibits; by implication, other kinds — if there are other kinds — would not be "true." There can be no gainsaying the realism of *Moll Flanders*: Defoe's book describes minutely the local scene, London; it refers circumstantially to contemporary customs (although not to those of the mid-seventeenth century in which Moll supposedly had her career, but to those of the early eighteenth century when Defoe was writing); it employs "documents" (Moll's "memorandums," quoted letters, hospital bills, etc.) in order to increase the illusion of verifiable fact; and, in general, it aims at "objective," "reportorial," "photographic" representation, as if from the standpoint of an artless observer. In

*Source: Dorothy Van Ghent, *The English Novel: Form and Function* (New York: Holt, Rinehart and Winston, Inc. 1953), pp. 33–43. Copyright 1953 by Dorothy Van Ghent. Reprinted by permission of Holt, Rinehart and Winston, Inc.

other words, the whole book is oriented toward what we call "facts" — specifically toward those "facts" which are events and objects that have spatial-temporal determination. But it is unfortunate that factual orientation in the novel should have come to determine the definition of realism in the novel; for "realism" inevitably implies a doctrine of the "real"; and it implies, when it is used to describe the factually oriented novel, that spatial-temporal facts are the only "real," and therefore that the factually oriented novel is closer to "reality" — a more trustworthy representation of reality — than any other kind of novel. What is suggested by the statement quoted at the beginning of this essay is not an evaluation of *Moll Flanders* as literature, but a certain popular philosophical conviction of the exclusive "reality" of material facts, a conviction that the so-defined "realistic" novel seems to flatter and support; and what is blurred over by the statement is the *hypothetical* structure of even the most "documentary" or "circumstantial" kind of fiction, a hypothetical structure that it shares generically with all fiction.[33]

The hypothesis on which *Moll Flanders* is based might be phrased in this way: given a human creature "conditioned" to react only to material facts, then the world where that person lived might cogently assume the shape that Moll's world assumes — a shape astonishingly without spiritual dimension. In a parallel fashion one might phrase the hypothesis on which *The Pilgrim's Progress* is based: given a person for whom relationship with God was the only "reality," then, in his world, material facts would show as misleading appearances, and the shape taken by his adventures would be altogether spiritually dimensioned. If the world of the particular novel is to create itself fully for us, we must waive for the moment our own *a priori* convictions as to whether material fact or relationship with God is the prime reality; we must approach the fictional hypothesis with as much respect for its conditions and as much attention to its logic as we would give to a scientific or mathematical hypothesis. Defoe's "realism" must be looked upon as a consistent use of certain devices for the creation of a special kind of world, just as Bunyan's allegorical method is a consistent use of certain devices (some of them "realistic" in the same sense as Defoe's) for the creation of a special kind of world. Eventually, the trained and sensitized reader finds that novels called "realistic" are as symbolic as Bunyan's allegory.

The questions we must ask of *Moll Flanders* are those we ask of any other novel: what are its elements? how are they made to cohere in a unity? how are its special technical devices (in this case, those of "realism") appropriate to the making of this particular world? We notice, for instance, that Moll's world contains many *things* — tangible things such as watches and wigs and yardage goods and necklaces and dresses and barrels and bales and bottles and trunks. We may make some judgment as to the kind of world presented in a novel simply on the basis of the frequency with which an author uses certain substantives and images, to the exclusion of others. In *Moll*, there is relatively great frequency in the use of words naming that kind of object which constitutes material wealth. This singularity of *Moll Flanders* becomes striking when we try to remember how many dresses Christiana had for her long journey, and whether Mr. Worldly Wiseman wore a wig or carried a watch.

But let us make a further distinction: these tangible, material objects with which Moll is so deeply concerned are not at all vivid in texture. When Molls tells us that she put on a "good pearl necklace," we do not know whether the pearls were large or small or graded or uniform in size,[34] or whether the necklace hung low on her bosom or was wound around her throat three times, nor do we know if the pearls were real or artificial; the word "good" here indicates simply that the pearls looked costly to a sophisticated eye, and were of a kind that a woman of substantial social position might wear; the "good pearl necklace" is mentioned not in a way that will make a sense image for us, but only in a way that will suggest the market value of the necklace and (through the market value) its value as an indicator of social prestige. Similarly, when she tells us that she gave her son a fine gold watch, we have no sense image of the watch; we do not know its size or design or delicacy or heft; we know only that it is a watch which would bring a good price. Therefore, in saying that the world of *Moll Flanders* is made up to a large extent of *things*, we do not mean that it is a world rich in physical, sensuous textures — in images for the eye or for the tactile sense or for the tongue or the ear or for the sense of temperature or the sense of pressure. It is extraordinarily barren of such images. And yet sense images are certainly "real" even in a world exclusively composed of "facts"; they are the constant means by which we are made aware of facts (the scientific observer himself is dependent upon their evidence). Clearly, then, an intense selectivity has limited the facts of Moll Flanders' world to a certain few kinds of facts, and has ignored great masses of other facts that we think of as making up the plenum of factual reality. Such selectivity warns us that this realistic novel is not actually an "objective," "reportorial," "photographic" representation of reality; its selectivity is that of the work of art, whose purpose is not that of an "objective" report.

What is important in Moll's world of things is the counting, measuring, pricing, weighing, and evaluating of the things in terms of the wealth they represent and the social status they imply for the possessor. What is unimportant (and we learn as much by what is unimportant as by what is important) is sensuous life, the concrete experience of things as they have individual texture. The unimportance of sensuous life in Moll's world is fairly astonishing inasmuch as Moll herself is a lusty, full-bodied, lively-sensed creature. Our instrument or medium of knowledge about Moll's world is Moll. The medium is a sensual medium (what woman, weak in sensuality, would remark, as Moll does: "I never was in bed with my husband, but I wished myself in the arms of his brother ... in short, I committed adultery and incest with him every day in my desires ..." or would have given us the scenes in the inns at Gloucester [35] and Bath?); but communicated through this medium is an assemblage of objects entirely desensualized, inaccessible to sense, abstract — abstract because represented only by name and by market value on the commercial and social markets. We may speak of this contradiction as an irony, and we shall wish to use the word "irony" here as indicating one characteristic *mode of relationship between elements in a novelistic structure.* Irony can imply many kinds of discrepancy, contrast, contradiction; paradox is a form of irony; there is irony in a statement that appears to say one thing and actually signifies another; and there is irony in a life situation or in a story situation that contrasts with or contradicts what might be expected from certain of the circumstances. We are always aware of Moll's sensuality, even though it often lies subterraneously or at a subverbal level in the novel; a great many of her adventures are sexual; but the life of the flesh is faded completely by the glare of the life of the pocketbook; and the incipience of sensuality, its always latent presence, contrasts ironically with the meagerness and abstractness of a sensibility which frantically converts all sense experience into cash value.

   We shall continue to speak of ironies in *Moll Flanders*, and as we shall be speaking of them as aspects of the book's internal structure, let us formulate what we mean by the structural function of irony. We shall do so most easily by analogy. A round arch is made up of a number of wedge-shaped blocks, and each of these blocks is pulled earthward in obedience to gravity, but each also exerts a sideways push against its neighbor because of its wedge shape and the weight of other blocks around and over it. If there were only the one pull, freely earthward, the blocks would fall and there would be no arch; but because of the counterforce, acting in the sideways direction, the structure of the arch is defined and preserved. The contrasting significances of an ironic statement or of an ironic situation may be compared with the counteracting stresses that hold the arch up and hold it together — that give it its structure. In *Moll Flanders*, a complex system of ironies or counterstresses holds the book together as a coherent and significant work of art. We may speak of the ironies, then, as "structural." In the example that we have cited, Moll's latent sensuality acts as a counterstress to her devotion to financial abstractions, and the cross-pulls of these two tendencies define Moll and her world meaningfully for us.

To illustrate further, let us follow some of her characteristic mental processes. Here is one chief inflection of her psychology—the reader will [36] find it repeated again and again as he listens to her tale. It appears in her account of her first marriage, her marriage to the younger brother of her seducer. Five years she has been married to him, she has had two children by him, she has known a long and important period (important because she is still very young) of domesticity and marital tenderness and motherhood. How does she tell us of these matters?

> It concerns the story in hand very little to enter into the further particulars . . . only to observe that I had two children by him, and that at the end of the five years he died. He had been really a very good husband to me, and we lived very agreeably together; but as he had not received much from them [the parents], and had in the little time he lived acquired no great matters, so my circumstances were not great, nor was I much mended by the match. Indeed, I had preserved the elder brother's bonds to me to pay me £500, which he offered me for my consent to marry his brother; and this, with what I had saved of the money he formerly gave me, and about as much more by my husband, left me a widow with about £1200 in my pocket.

We know in some degree from this context, and with added conviction from other similar contexts, what Moll means by a "very good husband" and by saying that they lived "very agreeably": the man had enough money to keep Moll from want, he spent money freely enough to maintain her in comfort and in that kind of social respectability which the spending of money guarantees—therefore he was "good" and their life was "agreeable." Any other characterization of this husband or of their marital life we should not be able to guess at; for Moll, simply by her exclusion of any other kind of perception from her story, stringently limits our own imagination of character; and we must judge that Moll has no other perception of character. The phrases "received much," "acquired no great matters," "my circumstances were not great," and "mended by the match," all focus together on one kind of referent: money. And when we find similar phrases in other contexts, we shall expect that "much" and "matters" and "circumstances" and "great" and "mended" (though these words might have immensely different meanings in other books) will have the same common referent again. As Moll uses them, they are very abstract words, colorless little words, words as limited in meaning as a mathematical sign. By their frequency they compose a picture of Moll's mentality and sensibility, so exclusively focused, so narrow [37] and intense, that if (conceivably) we were offered the same description of symptoms in a clinical case history, we should say that it was a picture of a madwoman. But Moll's is not a case history; it is a hypothesis of personality development in an acquisitive world; and in this world Moll is by no means a clinical subject — she is "well adjusted."

What five years of her young womanhood, marriage, domesticity, and motherhood mean to Moll are certain finances, certain bonds amounting to so much, a certain quantity of cash in her pocket. Of her children by this husband, she says,

> My two children were, indeed, taken happily off my hands by my husband's father and mother, and that was all they got by Mrs. Betty.

The statement informs us, with powerful obliquity, that the way to be happy through children is to have them taken off one's hands; it informs us also that children may be useful in settling family debts. With the greatest placidity and aplomb on Moll's part, the children are neatly converted into a shrewd price by which she gets out of a bad bargain with clean skirts. Schematically, what has been happening here is the conversion of all subjective, emotional, and moral experience — implicit in the fact of Moll's five years of marriage and motherhood — into pocket and bank money, into the materially measurable. It is a shocking formula, shocking in its simplicity and abruptness and entireness. It confronts us again with the irony, or system of ironies, that is structural to the book. A great mass of responses that might be expected from the circumstances (marriage, death, birth) is not what is presented; what is presented of that pyramid of human experience, as its only symbol and significance, is a cash sign. And yet another irony is involved: that is the paradox of Moll's superb "sanity," witnessed by her perfect "adjustment" to her world, and her violent abnormality as a representative of the species called human. A person is sane who is socially adapted in his time and his place, in tune with his culture, furnished with the mental and moral means to meet contingencies (to "mend" his circumstances, in Moll's phrase, when they need mending), accepting the values that his society accepts, and collaborating in their preservation. By these tokens, Moll is eminently sane. She is a collector of quantities of things and of cash, for in the world in which she lives, the having of things and of cash is necessary for survival; it is an expression of the will to live. She has one thing [38] to sell, in order to obtain them, and that is her sex. When this commodity fails her, she simply takes the things and the cash — steals them. In either case, she shows her sanity, her "adjustment" to her world, her ability to meet all contingencies. In this sense she is "normal," exhibiting in her activities and attitudes the social norm of her world; in terms of the full emotional variety of what we think of as the "human," she is monstrously abnormal. Her abnormality is her exclusive abstractiveness as a counter of cash; her subjective life is sunken nearly to a zero.

What will Moll do when she is under severe emotional stress; that is, when there is nothing in her situation that she can abstract into numbers, measurements, cash value, and when whatever is left for her perception to work on is the internal or subjective life of feeling and emotion? At the crisis of her career, she is taken for thieving, put into Newgate prison; and Newgate is hell. We have only Moll's own words for this experience, and how are Moll's words — dictated by a perceptive apparatus adapted exclusively for enumerating and calculating — to describe hell for us? Hell, Milton's Satan said, is a place within the self; that is, it is a subjective place, a place defined by horror and suffering and deep distress of spirit. In all her other circumstances, Moll has never failed to describe and define with the utmost precision such experience as she is capable of. But the hell of Newgate is "impossible to describe." The impossible description of this dead end of human suffering she fills up with negatives, words denying any possibility of description, for she has only negatives and blank counters for the subjective.

> ... indeed, nothing could be filled with more horror ... nothing was more odious to me than the company that was there ... indeed no colours can represent that place to the life.

To get over these impossibilities, the hell of Newgate is expressed by generalized reference to noises and smells (Newgate is most painful because it is not "respectable"; there are loud noises and bad smells here as there are in the slums), and by abstract stereotypes of fiendishness.

> ... the hellish noise, the roaring, swearing, and clamour, the stench and nastiness, and all the dreadful afflicting things that I saw there ... ; I thought of nothing night or day, but of gibbets and [39] halters, evil spirits and devils; it is not to be expressed how I was harassed ...

With the intervention of the minister, Moll says she is "perfectly changed," she becomes "another body." But since her perceptions are limited to their familiar categories of number and quantity, suitable for inventorying gold watches and bonds and purse change, but scarcely suitable for the description of grief or guilt or purity, the heaven of her repentance is as ineffable as the hell of Newgate. "The word eternity," she says,

> represented itself with all its incomprehensible additions, and I had such extended notions of it that I know not how to express them. Among the rest, how absurd did every pleasant thing look! — I mean, that we had counted before — when I reflected that these sordid trifles were the things for which we forfeited eternal felicity.

But immediately, after these weightless matters, these incomprehensible additions and extended notions, Moll and her husband are back at the reckoning, the formulary conversion of death and birth, heaven and hell, into cash.

> Our first business was to compare our stock. He was very honest to me,
> and told me his stock was pretty good ... I gave him an account of my
> stock as faithfully ... My stock which I had with me was £246 some odd
> shillings; so that we had £354 between us ...

With her heart lifted up in gratitude to Providence, Moll plans an
irreproachable life, for an irreproachable life is now truly possible:
Christian virtue and "stock" have become metaphysically identified,
an eternal equation in the mysterious plan of things. From now on,
God punches the buttons of this cash-register world, and it is virtue
that lies in the till. Most grotesque of ironies: the "sordid trifles,"
the "pleasant things" that now look so "absurd" to Moll, the things
for which she now refuses to forfeit her "eternal felicity," come to her
henceforth in greater quantities than ever before, precisely as the
sign of grace and redemption, the temporal guarantee of her eternal
felicity.

In speaking of the structure of *Moll Flanders* in terms of a hierarchy
of ironies — a system of stresses and counterstresses (to return to our
figure of the arch) that "hold the book together" in significant unity —
we are [40] faced with the need, sooner or later, of making some
tentative distinction between what the author might have intended
ironically and what actually functions ironically in the book. This
question, of the author's deliberate intention, arises particularly in
connection with irony; for we think of an author as knowing what he
is doing better than another person might know what he is doing,
and if he is being elaborately ironic, then — one would assume — he
must "intend" at least some of the irony. Irony is "double-talk."
But if the author is "sincere" and intends no double-talk, would it
not be more consistent usage, on our part, to say that the book is
"sincere" in the same sense that the author is sincere, that it contains
no double-talk, no ironies?

Let us illustrate this difficulty as it suggests itself in the specifically
moralizing portions of *Moll Flanders*. Moll robs a child, comes near to
murdering the infant, and moralizes the adventure thus:

> ... as I did the poor child no harm, I only thought I had given the parents
> a just reproof for their negligence, in leaving the poor lamb to come
> home by itself, and it would teach them to take more care another time ...

She rolls a drunk, after a night spent whoring, comes home to count
and weigh her loot, and accompanies her highly satisfactory calcula-
tions with moving reflections on the sins which fathers visit upon their
children by drunkenness and wenching; she is even inspired to quote
Solomon on the foul disease. These reflections are followed by a
complacent account of how the adventure, into which she had led
the gentleman, had brought him to reform his ways, restored him to
the bosom of a loving wife, and secured the happiness of an innocent

family. It is to these moralizing thoughts of Moll's that Defoe is
undoubtedly referring the reader, in his Author's Preface, when he
advises us to make "virtuous and religious uses" of the story. He even
mentions, in his Preface, the incident of the robbery of the little girl,
and the moral message he associates with this incident is precisely
that given it by Moll herself — parents who deck their children in
finery and allow them to go to dancing school alone are given a
"good memento" of what may ensue; and, generally, the moral that
he would have us find in Moll's accounts of her criminal practices
is that which Moll (now a reformed soul and "honest" woman at the
time of writing her memoirs) is herself always anxious to inculcate.
But what,[41] objectively, is the relationship of Moll's moralizing
thoughts to her adventures? Her adventures are criminal, but she
herself is not a criminal type; she is not a woman of the underworld,
but a woman of the bourgeois world; her aspirations are thoroughly
middle-class — she wants, above all, economic security and middle-
class respectability. She thinks middle-class thoughts; her morality
is middle-class morality — platitudinous, stereotypic, a morality suited
to the human species in its peculiar aspect as cash-calculator, and a
morality, therefore, most particularly suitable to the prostitute.

Criminal in action, Moll will have to moralize crime as a social
good: and so she does. Her robbery of a child will have prevented
many future crimes of this kind; her depredations upon one drunk will
have preserved the happiness of many families: all the readers of
Moll Flanders will have received her benefactions. Moll's moralizing
thoughts are the harmonies of the cash-register world in which she
lives, for the cash register, like the celestial spheres, has its harmonies
too, as the buttons are punched, the mechanism throbs, and the till
rolls out. But these harmonies are so divergent from the harmonies
of what we know, from our own observations and from the history
of ethical ideas, as the spiritually and morally sensitive life, that their
meaning in the total context of the book offers itself as ironic meaning: the morality that is preached by Moll is a burlesque of morality.

But if Defoe "intended" Moll's little moral sermons as the message
of his book (and he does, in his Author's Preface, so guarantee them
for us as his own persuasions), how can they be said to be ironic?
We are left with two possibilities. Either *Moll Flanders* is a collection
of scandal-sheet anecdotes naïvely patched together with the platitudes that form the morality of an impoverished soul (Defoe's), a
"sincere" soul but a confused and degraded one; or *Moll Flanders* is
a great novel, coherent in structure, unified and given its shape and
significance by a complex system of ironies. The most irreducible
fact about the book is that we read it — and reread it — with gusto
and marvel. We could not do this if it were the former of our alterna-
tives. That it may be the latter is justified by the analysis it yields

itself to, as an ironic structure, and most of all justified by our pleasure in it. Shall we, then, waive the question of Defoe's "intention" and "sincerity"? Speculations as to these apparently can add nothing to the book nor can they take anything from it; the book remains what it is. And we do not have appropriate instruments for analysis of [42] Defoe's intention and sincerity, in the deepest meaning of intention and sincerity. We might guess that a great book could not be written by an impoverished soul, and that imponderable traits of moral sensitivity and prophetic intuition might lie in an author and realize themselves in his book without his recognition of them: these would be guesses. Not guess, but inescapable assurance from the quality of the book, is Defoe's understanding of his creature, Moll, whatever else he might not have recognized or understood in the work that was going on under his own hand as the product of his observant eye and his faculty for clean selection and coherent arrangement. In understanding his creature without the slightest divarication from her movements and her thoughts, he gave to Moll the immense and seminal reality of an Earth Mother, progenetrix of the wasteland, sower of our harvests of technological skills, bombs, gadgets, and the platitudes and stereotypes and absurdities of a morality suitable to a wasteland world. [43]

FROM Defoe as Novelist: *Moll Flanders**

IAN WATT

Defoe's novels are landmarks in the history of fiction largely because they are the first considerable narratives which embody all the elements of formal realism. But although formal realism helps to define the uniqueness of the novel, it obviously does not by any means exhaust our critical desiderata about it; the novel may have a distinctive representational technique, but if it is to be considered a valuable literary form it must also have, like any other literary form, a structure which is a coherent expression of all its parts.... Doubts about the coherence of *Moll Flanders*,... combined with the extent of the critical disagreement about Defoe's status as a novelist, make necessary a fuller analysis of its total structure, and particularly of the relationship between three of its main components, plot, character and moral theme.

A brief recapitulation of the plot of *Moll Flanders* will make clear its episodic nature. The story falls into two main parts: the first and longer

*Source: Ian Watt, *The Rise of the Novel* (Berkeley: University of California Press, 1957), pp. 104–18, 130–34. Reprinted by permission of the University of California Press and Chatto and Windus Ltd.

one devoted to the heroine's career as a wife, and the second to her criminal activities and their consequences. The first part is composed of five main episodes, each of them ended by the death or departure of a husband; and there are two main sub-episodes, one of them concerning the abortive affair with a married man at Bath, and the other with the stratagems whereby her friend the Redriff widow secures a mate.

It is true that three of the main episodes are not wholly independent. The first marriage, closely related as it is both with Moll's first efforts to improve her condition and her seduction [104] by the Elder Brother, forms a satisfactory and indeed symbolic prelude to the novel as a whole, although it has no later connection with the plot. The third marriage, with her half-brother, leads to the discovery of the secret of her birth, and thus has links both with the beginning of Moll's life and with the final scenes in Virginia where she finds him and her son again. While the fourth marriage, to James or Jemmy, the Irish, Lanca- shire or highwayman husband (it is typical of Defoe's onomastic nonchalance that such copious alternative identifications should seem desirable), is connected to the later part of the book from Moll's trial at the Old Bailey onwards. On the other hand, although some of the plot components in the first part are related to each other, the inter- locking remains rudimentary, and during long intervals it is wholly submerged in the details of Moll's other activities.

The second, and for many readers the most interesting, part of the book is mainly devoted to Moll's career as a thief; its only connection with the rest of the plot is that it finally leads first to her arrest, then to the reunion with James in prison, to her later transportation, and eventually to her return to Virginia and her family there. Ultimately, therefore, Moll's criminal adventures end in a renewal of our contact with the two main episodes of the earlier half of the plot, and thus make possible a fairly neat conclusion to the novel as a whole.

This degree of continuity, based on the relationships between the heroine, her mother, half-brother, favourite husband and only signi- ficant child, gives *Moll Flanders* a degree of structural coherence which makes it unique among Defoe's novels. The only comparable plot is that of *Roxana*, and there the unifying mechanism, though simpler, is somewhat similar: a child grown to maturity, relic of the seamy past, haunts the present and the heroine's possibilities of prosperous retirement. In neither novel, however, does Defoe show any clear intention of winding up his plot with any sense of complete- ness or finality. In *Roxana*, after taking the mother-daughter relation- ship with a seriousness which seems to be tending to a tragic *dénoue- ment*, he ends the novel with the whole matter in the air; while *Moll Flanders* closes in some confusion with the heroine and later her hus- band coming back to England. Even when a resolution of the plot would seem to be both easy and logical, Defoe apparently prefers and certainly achieves the inconsequential and the incomplete.[105]

These inconclusive endings are typical of Defoe, and in one sense they are undeniably effective; they serve as a final reminder that the order of the narrative is determined only by the sequence of actual events in the lives of the protagonists. Defoe flouts the orderliness of literature to demonstrate his total devotion to the disorderliness of life.

This unqualified allegiance to the pseudo-biographical mode goes far to explain the type of plot Defoe used. We do not know how far he was indebted to any particular formal model in writing *Moll Flanders*, and the actual prototype of the heroine, if any, has not been established. It is, however, quite clear that the only likely analogues of Defoe's fiction are provided by some biographical form of writing, that all these forms consist of a loose stringing together of incidents in chronological sequence, and that they derive whatever unity they possess from the fact that all these incidents happen to the same person.

The closest analogy in point of subject-matter to *Moll Flanders* is provided by the rogue biographies, a native tradition which was much more exclusively devoted to realistic social documentation than were the picaresque novels. The genre had begun in completely factual compilations, such as Thomas Harman's *Caveat for Common Cursitors* (1566), and had developed into a partly fictional form influenced by picaresque tales and jest-books. The rogue biographies are certainly episodic, but they are unlike *Moll Flanders* as a whole in that the norms of daily life tend to be lost in a welter of anecdotes concerning trickery and deception which are not particularly plausible. A similar unreality, however, is usually to be found in those very episodes in *Moll Flanders* which offer the closest parallel to the staple materials of the rogue biographies[1] — episodes such as the mutual deception of the heroine and her Lancashire husband, her turning the tables on the mercer and getting damages for false arrest, or her rhyming courtship with her half-brother,[2] a poetical *tour de force* which is surely not very much at home in the life history of a lady who shows few other signs of familiarity with the Muses.

The mere fact, however, that these few incidents stand out[106] from the rest of Defoe's narrative indicates how great the difference is between most of *Moll Flanders* and the rogue biographies. These incidents, like those typical of the rogue biographies, all have a contrived air: in this they resemble the traditional conception of plot

[1]For a study of the closest seventeenth-century analogue to *Moll Flanders*, see Ernest Bernbaum, *The Mary Carleton Narratives, 1663-1673* (Cambridge, Mass., 1914), especially pp. 85–90.
[2]113–27, 189–98, 65–67.

in fiction, where the author chose his story because it was in some way so neat, so amusing or so striking that it stood out from the common run of experience and asked to be told and retold. The novel, however, has characteristically used a plot of a very different type, based on an action which belongs wholly to ordinary experience; and it is on this kind of action that *Moll Flanders* is in the main based.

It would appear, then, that Defoe's plot in *Moll Flanders* is closer to authentic biography, whether of criminals, travellers or other persons, than to the semi-fictional rogue biography. It is interesting, in this connection, to note that, two years before writing *Moll Flanders*, Defoe compiled a more or less genuine Memoir, the *Life of Mr. Duncan Campbell*, a well-known fortune-teller, and that there he stated: 'Of all the writings delivered in an historical manner to the world, none certainly were ever held in greater esteem than those which give us the lives of distinguished private men at full length; and, as I may say, to the life'.[3] Defoe's high regard for genuine biography is reflected in the way his own novels always pass themselves off as authentic autobiography. This alone would involve the type of narrative structure he used: he had only to absorb himself completely in his own make-believe that *Moll Flanders* was the life of a real person, and an episodic but life-like plot sequence was inevitable. It is unlikely that Defoe ever reflected on the other literary consequences of such a plot; if he did, he was probably quite content to sacrifice whatever formal disabilities might ensue in exchange for the absolute authenticity which they made possible, and indeed relatively easy.

The disabilities are obvious and serious. Aristotle thought that the episodic plot whose unity depends only on its being the history of one character was the worst kind of plot, because 'there are many actions of one man which cannot be made to form one action; and also because history is concerned with what actually happened, as opposed to poetry which deals with the probable or necessary'.[4] It may be that in the novel these objections are not final, but there is much to be said for the [107] view that, on the contrary, Defoe's concentration on producing pseudo-history, although a crucial step in the development of the kind of plot suited to the novel's formal realism, was so exclusive that the other ends of fiction, the ends of poetry in Aristotle's sense, were inevitably crowded out of the picture. Inevitably, because the disabilities that ensue from an episodic plot do not end there, but deny Defoe the advantages of a structure which will give coherence and larger implication to the thoughts and acts of his characters.

Moll Flanders is certainly, as E. M. Forster says, a novel of character;[5] the plot throws the whole burden of interest on the heroine, and many readers have felt that she supports it triumphantly. On the other hand,

---

[3]'The Introduction.'   [5]*Aspects of the Novel*, p. 61.
[4]*Poetics*, 8, 9.

Leslie Stephen has reproached Defoe with a lack of 'all that goes by
the name of psychological analysis in modern fiction',[6] and not altogether without justification, at least if our emphasis is on the word
analysis. There is probably no episode in *Moll Flanders* where the
motivation is unconvincing, but for somewhat damaging reasons — few
of the situations confronting Defoe's heroine call for any more complex discriminations than those of Pavlov's dog: Defoe makes us
admire the speed and resolution of Moll's reactions to profit or
danger; and if there are no detailed psychological analyses, it is because
they would be wholly superfluous.

There are two main ways in which later novelists have manifested
their powers of psychological understanding: indirectly, by revealing
the character's personality through his actions; or directly, by specific
analysis of the character's various states of mind. Both these methods,
of course, can be and usually are combined; and they are usually found
in conjunction with a narrative structure designed to embody the
character's development, and to present him with crucial moral
choices which bring his whole personality into play. There is very little
of these things in *Moll Flanders*. Defoe does not so much portray his
heroine's character as assume its reality in every action, and carry his
reader with him — if we accede to the reality of the deed, it is difficult
to challenge the reality of the doer. It is only when we attempt to fit
all her acts together, and see them as an expression of a single personality, that doubts arise; nor are [108] these doubts allayed when we discover how little we are told about some of the things we should need
to know for a full picture of her personality, and how some of the
things we are told seem contradictory.

These deficiencies are especially apparent in Defoe's treatment of
personal relationships. We are told very little, for example, about the
quality of Moll Flander's loves, and even our information about their
quantity is suspiciously meagre. When she accuses herself of having
'lain with thirteen men', we cannot but resent the fact that some six
lovers have been hidden not only from her fifth husband, but, much
more unforgiveably, from us. Even among those lovers we know, we
cannot be sure which Moll preferred. We have a strong impression
that James is her favourite, and that she leaves him for the fifth or
banking one only out of dire economic necessity; yet she tells us that
on her honeymoon with the latter she 'never lived four pleasanter
days together', and that five years of an 'uninterrupted course of ease
and content' ensued. When James later reappears, however, our
earlier impression recurs with renewed force:

> He turned pale, and stood speechless, like one thunderstruck, and, not
> able to conquer the surprise, said no more but this, 'Let me sit down';
> and sitting down by a table, he laid his elbow on the table, and leaning his

[6]'Defoe's Novels', p. 17.

head on his hand, fixed his eyes on the ground as one stupid. I cried so vehemently, on the other hand, that it was a good while ere I could speak any more; but after I had given some vent to my passion by tears, I repeated the same words, 'My dear, do you not know me?' At which he answered, Yes, and said no more a good while.[7]

Defoe's laconic narrative manner could be supremely evocative when it was focussed on personal relationships, but this happened rather rarely, probably because neither Defoe nor Moll Flanders conceived of such intangible concerns as important and continuing elements in human life. We are certainly given very little help in understanding Moll's conflicting feelings during her marriage with the banker. Like the first two husbands, he is individualised only to the extent of being given an ordinal number; and Moll's life with him is treated as a brief and wholly self-contained episode whose emotional premise [109] does not have to be reconciled with other features of her life and character. Defoe, indeed, emphasises this discontinuity by telling us that James wrote three times to Moll at this time suggesting that they go off to Virginia as she had earlier proposed,[8] but only after the fifth husband has been long dead: another novelist would have made such pleas an opportunity for clarifying his heroine's conflicting feelings towards the two men, but Defoe gives us only the bare facts, long after they have lost their potential power for psychological illumination.

If we attempt to draw any conclusion from Defoe's treatment of these particular personal relationships it must surely be that Moll Flanders was unaffectedly happy with both husbands, and that although her love of one of them was deeper, she did not allow this sentiment to interfere with the solid comforts which the other was able to provide. She is, obviously, affectionate but no sentimentalist. We get a somewhat different picture, however, when we come to consider her character, not as a wife, but as a mother. On the one hand, she can behave with complete sentimental abandon, as when she kisses the ground her long-separated son Humphry has been standing on; on the other hand, although she shows some fondness for two or three of her children, she is by normal standards somewhat callous in her treatment of most of them — the majority are mentioned only to be forgotten, and, once left in the care of relatives or foster-mothers, are neither redeemed subsequently nor even inquired after when opportunity permits. Here the conclusion about her character must surely be that, although there are extenuating circumstances, she is often a heartless mother. It is difficult to see how this can be reconciled either with her kissing the ground that Humphry has trodden, or with the fact that she herself loudly condemns unnatural mothers,[9] but never makes any such accusation against herself even in her deepest moments of penitent self-reprobation.

One explanation of this apparent contradiction would make it a matter, not of psychological understanding but of literary technique: briefly that in reading Defoe we must posit a kind of limited liability for the narrative, accepting whatever is specifically stated, but drawing no inferences from omissions, however significant they may seem. If Moll Flanders does not seem to [110] regret James during her fifth marital career, this is only because Defoe did not conceive of the attitudes of characters to each other as enduring realities on which his narrative technique should focus. If Moll Flanders is silent about the eventual fate of all her children except Humphry and the four reported dead, we must not infer that she is without proper maternal feeling, but only that Defoe did not keep his characters in mind when they were off the stage. In both cases, in fact, our interpretation should not be allowed to go beyond what is positively stated by Defoe or Moll Flanders.

There is also another explanation for the lack of full evidence from which to deduce Moll Flanders's personality through her conduct of personal relations: the fact that the criminal individualism which Moll pursues in her later days tends to minimise the importance of personal relationships. Like the other inhabitants of the criminal milieu, she has to assume false names and false identities, and much of her life is devoted to maintaining these pretences. Nearly all her personal contacts, therefore, are coloured by this role; they can never be deep or unreserved, and they are necessarily transitory in a sense, therefore Defoe is being realistic when he portrays the personal relationships of Moll Flanders as a series of essentially casual encounters, very like those of the real vagrants and criminals described by Mayhew in the next century. Here is one such report:

> In the morning I was turned out [from a union], and after I had left I picked up with a young woman who had slept in the union overnight. I said I was going on the road across country to Birmingham, and I axed her to go with me. I had never seen her before. She consented and we went along together begging our way.... I lost the young woman when I was put in prison in Manchester. She never came to see me in quod. She cared nothing for me. She only kept company with me to have someone on the road along with her; and I didn't care for her, not I.[10]

The laconic authenticity of this passage is very similar to that of Defoe, and it typifies the desultory nature of personal relations in the criminal milieu. This milieu, indeed, has effects on personal relations not unlike

[9]137–39.
[10]*Mayhew's Characters*, ed. Quennell (London, 1951), pp. 294–296.

those which economic individualism produces in *Robinson Crusoe*; Mayhew's vagrant, Moll[111] Flanders, and most of Defoe's other characters all belong on Crusoe's island; essentially solitary, they take a severely functional view of their fellows.

Neither Defoe's narrative focus, then, nor the nature of his subject, is such as to reveal Moll's personality through the part she plays in personal relationships. This does not in itself undermine the plausibility of Defoe's presentation of his heroine's psychology: some of the apparent discrepancies noted above are mainly negative — the result of lack of information: while the basic difficulty might reasonably be resolved by assuming that Moll Flanders is naturally warm-hearted but that circumstances often force her to play a lone hand. The very fact that Moll Flanders has no stable setting in personal relationships, however, presents considerable difficulties in determining whether this is so. Usually when we attempt to make up our minds about anyone's total personality we take into account as many views about the person as possible, and by comparing them with our own are able to achieve a kind of stereoscopic effect.

No such enlightenment is forthcoming on Defoe's heroine. The episodic nature of the plot means that, although there are some two hundred characters in *Moll Flanders*, no one of them knows the heroine for more than a fraction of her career; while the autobiographical mode of presentation means that their attitudes to Moll Flanders are only given to us if and how she wishes. Their evidence actually reveals a unanimity of a very suspect kind — Defoe's heroine apparently excites in those best qualified to judge her — James, the Governess, Humphry, for instance — the most unqualified and selfless devotion. On the other hand, the reader, observing that Moll Flanders herself is never wholly honest and disinterested in her dealings with them, or indeed with anyone else, may well feel inclined to interpret their apparent adoration as evidence of a paranoid delusion on Moll Flanders's part rather than as an accurate appraisal of her character on theirs. Everyone seems to exist only for her, and no one seems to resent it. One might have expected the Governess, for example, to regret Moll's reformation since it deprives her of a prize source of stolen goods; instead, she becomes 'a true penitent'[11] as soon as the heroine has no further use for her services.[112]

If none of those close to Moll Flanders seem at all aware of her true character, and if we continue to suspect that her own account of herself may be partial, our only remaining resource for an objective view of her personality is Defoe himself. Here again, however, we at once encounter difficulties. For Moll Flanders is suspiciously like her author, even in matters where we would expect striking and obvious differ-

[11]225.

ences. The facts show that she is a woman and a criminal, for example; but neither of these roles determines her personality as Defoe has drawn it.

Moll Flanders, of course, has many feminine traits; she has a keen eye for fine clothes and clean linen, and shows a wifely concern for the creature comforts of her males. Further, the early pages of the book undoubtedly present a young girl with a lifelike clarity, and later there are many touches of a rough cockney humour that is undeniably feminine in tone. But these are relatively external and minor matters, and the essence of her character and actions is, to one reader at least, essentially masculine. This is a personal impression, and would be difficult, if not impossible, to establish: but it is at least certain that Moll accepts none of the disabilities of her sex, and indeed one cannot but feel that Virginia Woolf's admiration for her was largely due to admiration of a heroine who so fully realised one of the ideals of feminism: freedom from any involuntary involvement in the feminine role.

Moll Flanders is also similar to her author in another respect: she seems fundamentally untouched by her criminal background, and, on the contrary, displays many of the attitudes of a virtuous and public-minded citizen. Here, again, there is no glaring inconsistency, but there is a marked pattern of attitudes which distinguishes Moll from other members of her class: ... she is full of virtuous indignation at the 'hardened wretches' of Newgate, and they repay in kind by hooting at her derisively; and when finally she is transported she has the satisfaction of observing, from her privileged comfort in the captain's quarters, that the 'old fraternity' are 'kept under hatches'.[12] Moll Flanders obviously places criminals into two classes: most of them are vicious reprobates who richly deserve their fate; but she and a few of her friends are essentially [113] virtuous and deserving people who have been unfortunate—she is even morally pure in her whoring since it is, as she assures us, by necessity and not 'for the sake of the vice'.[13] Like Defoe, in fact, she is a good Puritan who, despite a few necessary and regrettable compromises, has, in the main and in defiance of illustrious precedent, lived in a world of pitch and not been defiled.

It is this freedom from the probable psychological and social consequences of everything she does which is the central implausibility of her character as Defoe has drawn it. It applies, not only to her crimes, but to everything she does. If we take the incest theme, for example, we find that although her half-brother becomes incapable in body and mind mainly because Moll Flanders has left him, after revealing her terrible secret, she herself is quite unaffected by the

[12]215, 247.
[13]104, 109.

circumstance, once she has left Virginia. Nor are her son's feelings towards her influenced, apparently, by the fact that he is the offspring of
an incestuous marriage; nor even by the fact that his mother, after
deserting him for some twenty years, only returns because, having
been transported back to his vicinity, she thinks that she may now have
an estate to inherit, an estate which he would otherwise enjoy.

Moll Flanders's character, then, is not noticeably affected either by
her sex, by her criminal pursuits, or indeed by any of the objective
factors which might have been expected to set her apart from her
author; on the other hand, she shares with Defoe and most of his
heroes many of the character traits that are usually regarded as middle-
class. She is obsessed with gentility and keeping up appearances; her
pride is much involved in knowing how to get good service and
proper accommodation; and she is in her heart a rentier, for whom life
has no greater terror than when her 'main stock wastes apace'.[14] More
specifically it is apparent that, like Robinson Crusoe, she has, by some
process of osmosis, picked up the vocabulary and attitudes of a tradesman. Indeed her most positive qualities are the same as Crusoe's, a
restless, amoral and strenuous individualism. It is, no doubt, possible
to argue that these qualities might be found in a character of her sex,
station and personal vicissitudes; but it is not likely, and it is surely
more reasonable to assume that all these contradictions are the consequence of a process to [114] which first-person narration is peculiarly
prone; that Defoe's identification with Moll Flanders was so complete
that, despite a few feminine traits, he created a personality that was in
essence his own.

The hypothesis of the unconscious identification between Defoe
and his heroine seems equally valid when we come to analyse the third
aspect of the total structure of *Moll Flanders* — its larger moral significance.

The 'Author's Preface' states that 'there is not a wicked action in
any part of it, but is first or last rendered unhappy or unfortunate'.
This moral claim for *Moll Flanders* amounts only to the assertion that
it teaches a somewhat narrow kind of ethical lesson — vice must be
paid for and crime does not pay. Even this, however, is not substanti-
ated by the narrative itself. What seems to have happened is that
Defoe succumbed to the eternal danger of the crime story: to be
interesting the author has to project himself as completely as possible
into the mind of the crook, but, having once donned the colours of
crime, he plays to win. Defoe cannot bear to let Moll Flanders come
on evil days. Her fortunes vary, it is true; but she never falls so low as
to be forced to break her early resolve never to 'work housework',[15]

[14]104.
[15]5, 12–15.

and she retains her middle-class status even in prison. For the most part, whether as wife, mistress or thief, she is exceptionally successful, and when the crash comes she saves enough of her ill-gotten gains to stock a plantation and yet retain a considerable balance in England.

Moll's penitent prosperity, then, is based on her criminal career, and the sincerity of her reformation is never put to the acid test of sacrificing material for moral good. The plot, in fact, flatly contradicts Defoe's purported moral theme.

It remains conceivable, however, that some other kinds of moral significance could have been embodied in the narrative, presumably by other means than those of the implications of the plot. Defoe, for example, might have used direct editorial commentary to force the reader to see his protagonist from the proper viewpoint by drawing attention to her inveterate selfishness and the superficiality of her repentance. Such editorial intrusion, however, would have interfered with Defoe's primary purpose, that of giving the impression that *Moll Flanders* is a[115] literal and authentic autobiography, and the method was therefore unacceptable.

Whatever moral significance Defoe wished to attach to his story, therefore, had to spring directly from the moral consciousness of his heroine. This meant that she had to function both as a character and as an editorial mouthpiece and she therefore had to recount the story from the perspective of her later penitence. This also involved difficulties; partly because Moll's loves and larcenies would obviously lose most of their attraction for the reader if they were too heavily sprinkled with the ashes of repentance; and partly because such a perspective called for a very rigorous separation in time between the consciousness that had performed the evil deeds and the reformed consciousness that was responsible for their redaction.

Defoe's unawareness of these problems is suggested by the way his 'Author's Preface' evades the crucial issue of the relation of the novel to Moll's 'own memorandums', which it was allegedly 'written from'. The 'pen employed in finishing her story' mentions a 'copy which first came to hand' and which needed much bowdlerising to 'make it speak language fit to be read'; but the existence is also inferred of later, and presumably chaster, documents which showed Moll 'grown humble and penitent, as she afterwards pretends to be'. On these, however, Defoe is silent, and we therefore cannot tell which — if any — of the moral and religious reflections in the text were actually made by the heroine, nor at what period in her life.

This irresolution about the time scale is sometimes apparent even in the wording of the penitent reflections. It is evident, for instance, that one of Moll's earliest and not altogether venial sins is that of bigamy: she is not divorced from her second husband and there is no report of his death; her later amorous career, therefore, is one of cumulative bigamy interspersed with adultery. The problem, however, only enters her moral consciousness once, when she is conscience-stricken by her Bath gallant's determination not to continue their 'unhappy correspondence'. She writes: 'But I never once reflected that I was all this while a married woman, a wife to Mr. B——, the linen draper, who, though he had left me by the necessity of his circumstances, had no power to discharge me from the marriage contract which was between us, or to give me a legal liberty to marry again; so that I had been no less a whore and adultress [116] all this while. I then reproached myself with the liberties I had taken, and how I had been a snare to this gentleman....'[16]

At first sight this passage appears to be the reflection made by a penitent Moll looking back on her former heedlessness; if so, one cannot but doubt the rigour of her spiritual scrutiny, since there are no such reflections about the two later — and equally bigamous — marriages. If, however, we look at the passage again it becomes evident that the point cannot be pursued because there is a real confusion about the time at which the reflection is supposed to be made. In writing 'I then reproached myself', 'then' surely implies that Moll Flanders reproached herself at the time the event occurred; if this is so, she or her author have surely forgotten that the original time status of the paragraph, which begins 'I never once reflected', implied that the moral reflections were made long after the event when remorse had finally supervened.

Defoe, then, failed to locate his didactic commentary convincingly in any particular period of his heroine's moral development; and this may stand as an example of his general failure to resolve the formal problems to which his moral purpose and his autobiographical narrative mode committed him. One reason for this is no doubt that Defoe did not give either his art or his conscience the searching attention which his moral aims involved; on the other hand, we must remember that he was in fact faced with a problem which was then new and has since remained the central problem of the novel: how to impose a coherent moral structure on narrative without detracting from its air of literal authenticity.

Formal realism is only a mode of presentation, and it is therefore ethically neutral: all Defoe's novels are also ethically neutral because they make formal realism an end rather than a means, subordinating any coherent ulterior significance to the illusion that the text represents the authentic lucubrations of an historical person. But the individual case-book is an arid study except in the hands of a skilled interrogator who can elicit the things we want to know, which are often the very things the person concerned does not know or is unwilling to admit: the problem of the novel was to discover and reveal these deeper meanings without any breach of formal realism.

Later novelists were to see that although formal realism[117] imposed a more absolute and impersonal optical accuracy upon the manner in which literature performed its ancient task of holding the mirror up to nature, there were nevertheless ways in which a moral pattern could be conveyed, although they were perhaps more difficult and indirect than those of previous literary forms. For, in place of direct comment, or the power of tone and imagery, the pattern had to depend upon the manipulation of the mirror in time, in place, in closeness, in brilliance. 'Point of view' was to become the crucial instrument whereby the writer expressed his moral sensibility, and pattern came to be the result of the hidden skill whereby the angles at which the mirror was held were made to reflect reality as the novelist saw it. No such pattern emerges from Defoe's treatment of plot and characterisation in *Moll Flanders*; as for the moral consciousness of his heroine, it continues to elude us in the infinite regress produced by the lack of co-ordination between the different aspects of his narrative purpose.[118]

. . . . .

The preceding [is] not intended as a denial of the importance of Defoe as a novelist, but only as a demonstration of a fact that might perhaps have been taken for granted if it had not been challenged or overlooked by many recent critics: the fact that Defoe's novels lack both the consistency in matters of detail of which many lesser writers are capable, and the larger coherences found in the greatest literature. Defoe's forte was the brilliant episode. Once his imagination seized on a situation he could report it with a comprehensive fidelity which was much in advance of any previous fiction, and which, indeed, has never been surpassed. These episodes are irresistible in quotation; and the pre-eminence of *Moll Flanders* is perhaps mainly due to its strong claim to be not so much a great novel as Defoe's richest anthology.[130]

How far we should allow Defoe's gift for the perfect episode to outweigh his patent shortcomings — weaknesses of construction, inattention to detail, lack of moral or formal pattern — is a very difficult critical problem. There is something about Defoe's genius which is as confident and indestructible as the resilient selfhood of his heroine, and which all but persuades us to accept the notorious critical heresy that the single talent well employed can make up for all the others.

The talent, of course, is the supreme one in the novel: Defoe is the master illusionist, and this almost makes him the founder of the new form. Almost, but not quite: the novel could be considered established only when realistic narrative was organised into a plot which, while retaining Defoe's lifelikeness, also had an intrinsic coherence; when the novelist's eye was focussed on character and personal relationships as essential elements in the total structure, and not merely as subordinate instruments for furthering the verisimilitude of the actions described; and when all these were related to a controlling moral intention. It was Richardson who took these further steps, and it is primarily for this reason that he, rather than Defoe, is usually regarded as the founder of the English novel.

Defoe created his own personal genre, which stands wholly alone in the history of literature, as befits the creator of Robinson Crusoe: and this solitary position is directly related to the role of individualism in his works, as is suggested by the curiously close parallel between his fiction and the plays of an earlier individualist and literary innovator, Christopher Marlowe.

Both men were lowly born, poor, well educated, restless, energetic; both found it difficult to find a satisfactory place in the society of their day, and both eventually achieved contact with the mysteries of power through the seamier side of government, as informers and secret agents. Their lives are reflected in their writings. Both expressed themselves most fully through characters who are radically alienated from society, and who appear to be unconscious autobiographical projections; certainly, despite their vastly different circumstances they have a strong family resemblance—Tamburlaine to Barabas and Faustus, Robinson Crusoe to Moll Flanders and Colonel Jacque. The presence of such central characters is associated both in Marlowe and Defoe with similar structural and thematic difficulties. The plots tend to be episodic, and the basic [131] conflict is not fully embodied in terms of relationships between the characters—all tends to resolve itself into an *ego contra mundum*. The issue of the conflict is similarly ambiguous: the moral, social and religious norms which are eventually brought in to punish the hero for his defiant self-assertion are less convincingly presented than his breaches of them, so that their triumph seems at best perfunctory, and leaves us in some doubt as to how fully it is endorsed by the author.

The most positive value that emerges from the works of Defoe and Marlowe is certainly not that of the traditional moral order; as in the case of Stendhal, the supreme expression of individualism in French literature, the vision of life presented is remarkable not for its wisdom but for its energy. This duality, perhaps, poses the central problem both for the moral evaluation of individualism in general, and of the figure of Moll Flanders. Her wisdom is not impressive; it is at best of a low atavistic kind wholly directed to the problems of survival; but nothing could be more impressive than her energy, and it too has a moral premise, a kind of inarticulate and yet fortifying stoicism. Everything happens to Moll Flanders and nothing leaves scars; the very tone of her reminiscences assures us that no vicissitude can ever impair her comfortable vitality; our grossest crimes and our most contemptible moral weaknesses, apparently, will never deprive us of the love of others or even of our own self-respect; the whole book, indeed, is a series of variations on individualism's eternal challence to the orthodoxy of the present and the wisdom of the past, a sequence in which the heroine, an unabashed Parolles, asserts defiantly, 'Simply the thing I am shall make me live'.

These words epitomise the claim which both the form and the content of Defoe's novels make on posterity; and it is very appropriate that the claim should have been fully allowed only when, after the passing of nearly two centuries which had accorded them only a somewhat sub-literary fame,[17] they found a new resonance in the last few decades, decades when the novel, and its associated way of life, individualism, seem to have come full circle.

At a time when the technique of the novel had reached an unexampled complication, Defoe's formal artlessness seemed[132] more piquant than ever before. It was easy to see the cumbrousness of Richardson or the artificiality of Fielding, because the novel had gone far beyond their solutions of its formal problems. But Defoe did not compete, and it was refreshing to acclaim a writer who still spoke vividly to us although he had not, apparently, given a moment's reflection as to the technical problems involved in so doing: and, in the novel form at least, artless authenticity seemed preferable to all but the highest art. So Virginia Woolf and E. M. Forster gave us a Defoe of the 'twenties, an ally in the onslaught on the mechanical craftsmanship of Arnold Bennett and Galsworthy.

At the same time, and in the succeeding decades, the intellectual and social bases of individualism were being challenged as never before, and this also bestowed an ironical topicality on the work of an early recorder of its triumphs and degradations. The Second World War, especially, brought us closer to the prophetic nature of Defoe's picture of individualism. Camus used Defoe's allegorical claim for *Robinson Crusoe* as epigraph to his own allegory, *La Peste* (1948): 'It is as reasonable to represent one kind of imprisonment by another, as it is to represent anything that really exists by that which exists not'. At the same time André Malraux wrote that only three books, *Robinson Crusoe, Don Quixote* and *The Idiot*, retained their truth for those who had seen prisons and concentration camps.[18]

Defoe's concentration on isolated individuals, it would seem, is closer to the view of life held by many writers today than to those held in the intervening centuries. It is likely that these writers read more into Defoe than he seriously intended, and that the modern alienation

---

[17] See Charles E. Burch, 'British Criticism of Defoe as a Novelist, 1719–1860', *Englische Studien*, LXVIII (1932), 178–198.
[18] *Les Noyers de l'Altenburg* (Paris, 1948), pp. 119–121.

is much more complex and less voluntary than that of Robinson Crusoe and Moll Flanders. But whatever Defoe's consciousness of the symbolic quality of his novels may have been, it is certain that, at the end of the long tradition of the European novel, and of the society whose individualism, leisure and unexampled security allowed it to make personal relations the major theme of its literature, Defoe is a welcome and portentous figure. Welcome because he seems long ago to have called the great bluff of the novel — its suggestion that personal relations really are the be-all and end-all of life; portentous because he, and only he, among the great writers of the past, has presented the struggle for survival in the [133] bleak perspectives which recent history has brought back to a commanding position on the human stage.

The accidents of history, then, treated Defoe fortunately, although he courted them as no other writer has done, and deserves his reward. They impelled him to a step which was decisive in the history of the novel. His blind and almost purposeless concentration on the actions of his heroes and heroines, and his unconscious and unreflective mingling of their thoughts and his about the inglorious world in which they both exist, made possible the expression of many motives and themes which could not, perhaps, have come into the tradition of the novel without Defoe's shock tactics: motives such as economic egoism and social alienation; and themes such as the conflicts between old and new sets of values as they are manifested in daily life. Very few writers have created for themselves both a new subject and a new literary form to embody it. Defoe did both. In his somewhat monocular concentration on making his matter seem absolutely convincing, there was much he did not see. But what is left out is probably the price for what is so memorably and unprecedentedly put in. [134]

In Defence of *Moll Flanders**

ARNOLD KETTLE

I

Professor Ian Watt's *The Rise of the Novel* is one of the works of literary criticism of the last decade that have added substantially and rewardingly to our ability to read eighteenth-century literature better. If this paper revolves around some disagreements with Mr Watt that is to be taken as a mark of gratitude rather than an attempt to denigrate. It is because *The Rise of the Novel* has a deservedly wide currency

*Source: John Butt, ed., *Of Books and Humankind* (London: Routledge & Kegan Paul Ltd., 1964), pp. 55–67. Reprinted by permission.

that it is worth examining what seems to be fundamentally wrong in Mr Watt's approach to Defoe.[1]

It is with *Moll Flanders* that I am concerned and I agree with Mr Watt that it is the key work in any estimate of Defoe's significance as a novelist. In *The Rise of the Novel* forty-two pages are spent on *Moll* and constitute the fullest discussion of the book I know. Towards the end of the discussion the conclusions are summarized:

> Defoe's forte was the brilliant episode. Once his imagination seized on a situation he could report it with a comprehensive fidelity which was [55] much in advance of any previous fiction, and which, indeed, has never been surpassed . . .
>
> How far we should allow Defoe's gift for the perfect episode to out-weigh his patent shortcomings — weaknesses of construction, inattention to detail, lack of moral or formal pattern — is a very difficult critical problem.[2]

It is a problem, however, about which Mr Watt has left us in little doubt as to where he stands. The passage I have quoted is followed by a couple of pages of generous and perceptive appreciation of Defoe's genius, happily described as 'confident and indestructible'. But these pages cannot eclipse the thirty-five that have preceded them in which scepticism — peppered, it is true, with valuable observations and insights — has reigned. Mr Watt praises Defoe highly for verisimilitude and not for much else. The conclusion is clearly stated:

> His blind and almost purposeless concentration on the actions of his heroes and heroines, and his unconscious and unreflective mingling of their thoughts and his about the inglorious world in which they both exist, made possible the expression of many motives and themes which could not, perhaps, have come into the tradition of the novel without Defoe's shock tactics . . .[3]

Blind, purposeless, unconscious, unreflective: the adjectives are damaging and lead us — for all Mr Watt's scrupulous reservations — in the same direction as Dr Leavis's 'brush-off' footnote in *The Great Tradition*:

> Characteristic of the confusion I am contending against is the fashion (for which the responsibility seems to go back to Virginia Woolf and Mr E. M. Forster) of talking of *Moll Flanders* as a 'great novel'. Defoe was

[1] I should add, in fairness, that I am also concerned to correct what I now regard as inadequacies in my own approach to Defoe in my *Introduction to the English Novel*, vol. I (London, 1951). For a realization of these inadequacies I am indebted not only to time, with its gift of second chances, but, in particular, to Mr Watt, to Mr Alick West and to Professor Bonamy Dobrée who was the first person I heard talk of Defoe with the right kind of enthusiasm.

[2] *The Rise of the Novel* (London, 1957), p. 130. [See also this volume, p. 306.]

[3] Ibid., p. 134.

a remarkable writer, but all that need be said about him as a novelist was said by Leslie Stephen in *Hours in a Library* (First Series). He made no pretension to practising the novelist's art, and matters little as an influence. In fact, the only influence that need be noted is that represented by the use made of him in the nineteen-twenties by the practitioners of the fantastic *conte* (or pseudo-moral fable) with its empty pretence of significance.[4]

It is worth recalling that this footnote—which has, incidentally, along with a couple of others in the same work, had more influence in [56] keeping students of English literature away from the eighteenth-century novel than any other pronouncement—is attached to a sentence which distinguishes as major novelists those who 'not only change the possibilities of the art for practitioners and readers, but . . . are significant in terms of the human awareness they promote: awareness of the possibilities of life'.

It is precisely on such grounds that I would claim that *Moll Flanders* is indeed a great novel.

II

Mr Watt uses, to pinpoint his doubts about Defoe's literary status the famous passage in *Moll Flanders* in which Moll doesn't steal the watch in the meeting-house.

The next thing of moment was an attempt at a gentlewoman's gold watch. It happened in a crowd, at a meeting house, where I was in very great danger of being taken. I had full hold of her watch, but giving a great jostle as if somebody had thrust me against her, and in the juncture giving the watch a fair pull, I found it would not come, so I let it go that moment, and cried as if I had been killed, that somebody had trod upon my foot, and that there was certainly pickpockets there, for somebody or other had given a pull at my watch; for you are to observe that on these adventures we always went very well dressed, and I had very good clothes on, and a gold watch by my side, as like a lady as other folks.

I had no sooner said so but the other gentlewoman cried out, 'A Pickpocket' too, for somebody, she said, had tried to pull her watch away.

When I touched her watch I was close to her, but when I cried out I stopped as it were short, and the crowd bearing her forward a little, she made a noise too, but it was at some distance from me, so that she did not in the least suspect me; but when she cried out, 'A Pickpocket', somebody cried out, 'Ay, and here has been another; this gentlewoman has been attempted too.'

At that very instant, a little farther in the crowd, and very luckily too, they cried out, 'A Pickpocket', again, and really seized a young fellow in the very act. This, though unhappy for the wretch, was very opportunely for my case, though I had carried it handsomely enough before;

[4]*The Great Tradition* (London, 1948), p. 2.

but now it was out of doubt, and all the loose part of the crowd ran that way, and the poor boy was delivered up to the rage of the street, which is a cruelty I need not describe, and which, however, they are always glad of, rather than be sent to Newgate, where they lie often a long time and sometimes they are hanged, and the best they can look for, if they are convicted, is to be transported. [57]

Mr Watt's comments on this scene may be summarized as follows. It is very convincing: full marks for verisimilitude and prose. But (*a*) the tone is too laconic, the scene is not planned as a coherent whole; (*b*) the point of view of the narrator is not consistent; (*c*) the relationship of the passage to the rest of the book is suspect; (*d*) the passage suffers from a general fault of the book — repeated falls in tension between episodes. Let us examine these criticisms.

(*a*) Mr Watt complains that

> Defoe gets into the middle of the action, with 'I had full hold of her watch', and then suddenly changes from laconic reminiscent summary to a more detailed and immediate presentation, as though only to back up the truth of his initial statement. Nor has the scene been planned as a coherent whole: we are soon interrupted in the middle of the scene by an aside explaining something that might have been explained before, the important fact that Moll Flanders was dressed like a gentlewoman herself: this transition adds to our trust that no ghost-writer has been imposing order on Moll Flanders's somewhat rambling reminiscences, but if we had seen Moll dressed 'as like a lady as other folks' from the beginning, the action would have run more strongly, because uninterruptedly, into the next incident of the scene, the raising of the alarm.[5]

Surely the point Mr Watt objects to is an important part of Defoe's intended effect. Moll isn't a novelist, planning ahead. She lives from moment to moment; she suddenly remembers things she ought to have said before; and she remembers them haphazardly, partly because that is the way people do remember things, but also because she is such an incurable self-deceiver, yet doesn't want to deceive herself or other people. Moll wants to be honest — with herself, with us, even with the woman she steals from — but of course she can't be. And the confusion is expressed in the organization and disorganization of her prose. If Moll's consciousness is a disorganized and impromptu business, so is her life.

(*b*) Defoe goes on to stress the practical moral, which is that the gentlewoman should have 'seized the next body that was behind her', instead of crying out. In so doing, Defoe lives up to the didactic purpose professed in the 'Author's Preface', but at the same time he directs our attention to the important problem of what the point of view of the narrator is supposed to be. We presume that it is a repentant Moll, speaking

[5]Op. cit., p. 97.

towards the end of her life: it is therefore surprising that in the next paragraph she should gaily describe her 'governess's' procuring[58] activities as 'pranks'. Then a further confusion about the point of view becomes apparent: we notice that to Moll Flanders other pickpockets, and the criminal fraternity in general, are a 'they', not a 'we'. She speaks as though she were not implicated in the common lot of criminals; or is it, perhaps, Defoe who has unconsciously dropped into the 'they' he himself would naturally use for them? And earlier, when we are told that 'the other gentlewoman' cried out, we wonder why the word 'other'? Is Moll Flanders being ironical about the fact that she too was dressed like a gentlewoman, or has Defoe forgotten that, actually, she is not?[6]

This carries the same point further. Of course, there are inconsistencies here. They are the very life's blood of the book. It is true that Moll speaks as though she were not implicated in the common lot of criminals. She doesn't think of herself as a criminal. When she learns what the other criminals in Newgate think of her she is morally outraged. Occasionally, for a moment, like Joyce Cary's Sara, she catches sight of herself in some mirror and sees herself, surprised. And she *does* think of herself, in the episode under discussion, as a gentlewoman. What Mr Watt sees as Defoe's carelessness I see as his imaginative absorption in his subject, a penetration into the layers of self-deception of which a human being, even a relatively honest one, is capable. Sir Leslie Stephen's reproach, in the essay Dr Leavis admires so much, that Defoe's novels lack 'all that goes by the name of psychological analysis in modern fiction' makes sense only if one is concerned to blame Defoe for not being Proust. There is no need for formal analysis of Moll's psychological processes in the meeting-house. They are revealed in all their complex, awful, funny, human contradictoriness in the very texture of the scene. This is a triumph of art.

(c) The connection between the meeting-house scene and the narrative as a whole confirms the impression that Defoe paid little attention to the internal consistence of his story. When she is transported to Virginia Moll Flanders gives her son a gold watch as a memento of their reunion; she relates how she 'desired that he would now and then kiss it for my sake', and then adds sardonically that she did not tell him 'that I stole it from a gentlewoman's side, at a meeting house in London'. Since there is no other episode in *Moll Flanders* dealing with watches, gentlewomen and meeting-houses, we must surely infer that Defoe had a faint recollection of what he had written a hundred pages earlier . . .

These discontinuities strongly suggest that Defoe did not plan his novel as a coherent whole, but worked piecemeal, very rapidly, and without any subsequent revision.[7][59]

[6]Ibid., p. 98.
[7]Ibid, pp. 98–9.

There is a confusion of critical method here. It may well be (and, as Mr Watt says, external as well as internal evidence suggests it) that Defoe worked piecemeal and that his novels therefore lack a certain planned coherence. But this is a general critical statement about the kind of book we are dealing with, relevant no doubt, but not to be confused with our judgment of artistic success. The passage Mr Watt refers to can be read equally well as a further example of Moll's difficulty of separating the false from the true and of the curious tricks of the extended conscience. She happens to connect watch-stealing with the meeting-house episode because that gave her a shock and imprinted itself deep in her memory; she may even have found it necessary, for her peace of mind, to transform her failure — with its uncomfortable accompaniment of the taking of the boy pickpocket — into a comfortable success. Certainly time has dealt interestingly with the episode. This may not have been Defoe's intention. But certainly the main *point* in the Virginia scene from which Mr Watt quotes is to illuminate the wry twinge of half-conscience, half-triumph that Moll by now feels. She has become complacent in a way which in former days, for all her conscience-blocking, she dared not be. Whether she is referring to the same watch doesn't matter. To suggest that it does would seem to reveal an attitude towards the novel and novel-writing not quite relevant to the sort of book Defoe offers us. I will return to this point.

(*d*) The question of fall of tension between episodes is a valid point of criticism. That opening sentence, 'The next thing of moment was etc.' does indeed betray a weakness, a technical problem unsolved. There is, it is true, the sense in which Moll does indeed see her life as a kind of inventory of episodes, with nothing much of note between them. There is also the sense in which the book proceeds from one moral warning to the next on the old beggar-book level, and there is no doubt that this aspect of his book tends all the time to conflict with Defoe's major concern — to show us what Moll Flanders is like (in the way that the remnants of the old *Hamlet* revenge-drama tend to conflict with Shakespeare's major concern in his play).

In his analysis of the meeting-house scene Mr Watt omits to discuss what is surely its greatest, most moving moment; the taking of the boy pickpocket. The effect here is not at all due to verisimilitude or any of the qualities habitually, and rightly, granted to Defoe; it is almost entirely moral and psychological. The phrase 'and very luckily too' leads us into it. What is lucky for Moll is the lynching of [60] the boy for whom she can afford no more fellow-feeling than a single use of the adjective 'poor' and the dubious consolation that lynching is better than hanging or transportation.

The effect that Defoe achieves here is one that is central to the nature of *Moll Flanders* as a work of art. Moll's reactions to the episode, humanly speaking, are quite inadequate. It is easy, therefore, to underestimate Defoe's art, which can look, at first glance, to be inadequate in the same way. The paragraph is a flat one, a disclaimer, a refusal to see what has happened. But the phrase 'a cruelty I need not describe' is an indication of cowardice not on Defoe's part but Moll's. Of course she can't bear to dwell on the scene: it is too near the bone. But that last sentence of the paragraph is, objectively considered, all compassion. The phrase 'and sometimes they are hanged', the whole rhythm of the sentence, the toneless forcing out of facet after facet of horror, all these contribute to a marvellous effect. Moll is playing it all down; she can't do anything else, she who has put herself beyond the possibility of looking at such a scene objectively. But Defoe allows *us* to see all round the situation even if Moll can't. And a far more important link between this whole episode and the later reaches of the novel than the link represented by the watch which turns up in Virginia is the connection between this last sentence and the whole Newgate episode of the book. It is only then that we get the full force of the word 'luckily'.

I stress the power of this paragraph because it illustrates very well the nature of the moral organization of *Moll Flanders*, a feature of the book that Mr Watt, and almost everyone else, plays down.

III

The underlying tension which gives *Moll Flanders* its vitality as a work of art can be expressed by a contradiction which is at once simple and complicated. Moll is immoral, shallow, hypocritical, heartless, a bad woman: yet Moll is marvellous. Defoe might almost (though he wouldn't have dreamed of it) have subtitled his book 'A Pure Woman'.

Moll's splendour — her resilience and courage and generosity — is inseparable from her badness. The fair and the foul are not isolable qualities to be abstracted and totted up in a reckoning, balancing one against the other. The relationship is far more interesting. One is reminded, perhaps, of Yeats's Crazy Jane: [61]

> 'Fair and foul are near of kin
> And fair needs foul', I cried.
> 'My friends are gone, but that's a truth
> Nor grave nor bed denied,
> Learned in bodily lowliness
> And in the heart's pride'.

That is too metaphysical for Moll; she wouldn't say that fair needs foul. But the contradiction Yeats is expressing and, in expressing, resolving, is essentially the contradiction Defoe's book expresses. And the phrase 'the heart's pride' is not inappropriate to Moll.

The episode in *Moll Flanders* which tells us most about the under-lying pattern of the book is the one very near the beginning in which Moll as a little girl talks of her fear of going into service and her desire to be a gentlewoman. Mr Watt picks out this passage as one of the few examples in the book of an irony that we can be quite sure is fully conscious, and his fastening on the scene tells us that he is a good literary critic. But he lets go much too quickly. This is an absolutely essential episode, as Mr Alick West, in the best analysis of *Moll Flanders* I know, has well pointed out:

> The life the child wants — working for herself in freedom — is the con-trasting background to the life the woman gets in a world where a gentle-woman does not live on the threepences or fourpences she earns by her own labour, but on riches of unexplained origin.[8]

This sentence not only shows what *Moll Flanders* is about but illumi-nates the specific artistic pattern of the book. It leads us straight to what makes Moll at the same time splendid and contemptible. What makes her splendid — a great heroine — is that she wants her in-dependence, to work for herself in freedom. She is a woman who is determined to be a human being, not a servant, and the feeling of what it means to be a servant is what generates the impulses which carry her through most of the book, until she too has become a gentlewoman with servants, living on riches whose origin she likes to forget about or to confuse but which Defoe has only too clearly explained.

Unless we see Moll in history we cannot grasp her moral stature as a heroine. Instead, we will bring to her the flat and static sort of moral judgment which she herself (and one side of Defoe himself) brings when she is forced to enter the sphere she calls morality or religion. And here Virginia Woolf's feminist preoccupations offer a more central[62] and artistically relevant approach to the book than any other. The examination of Defoe's social and economic attitude that Mr Novak[9] has offered us is not, of course, irrelevant; nor are Mr Watt's observations on the significance of the criminal class at this period; but neither emphasis goes to the heart of the matter. Moll becomes a criminal because she is a woman, and it is not at all by a chance in the book's structure that she comes to her second career (that of a thief) by way of her first (that of a wife). Too little is known about the posi-tion of women in the eighteenth century, but the general outlines are clear enough and Mr Watt himself in the chapters on Richardson in *The Rise of the Novel* has notably contributed to our appreciation of many of the problems involved. So have recent emphases on the im-portance of arranged marriages and contemporary feelings about them

---

[8]*Mountain in the Sunlight* (London, 1958), p. 90.
[9]Maximillian E. Novak, *Economics and the Fiction of Daniel Defoe* (California, 1962).

in Restoration and eighteenth-century literature.[10] Such extra-literary confirmation is not irrelevant to a critical approach to *Moll Flanders* because only on the basis of a just assessment of the facts can we form an opinion as to whether Moll's childish fears about the consequences of not being a gentlewoman are justified—whether in fact they represent an amiable delusion or a naive but genuine moral insight. All the evidence points to the conclusion that Moll is right, that to become a maidservant in that period meant the end of any possibility that could conceivably be subsumed under the words freedom or independence, any possibility therefore of individual human development or flowering. The choice Moll makes is therefore one which, with whatever reservations, deserves our positive sympathy, and the moral tensions about which Defoe's novel is constructed are not trivial or arbitrary.

Not to stress this point is to prejudice artistic judgments. It is only within the social context that we can begin, for instance, to assess Defoe's treatment (or lack of it) of Moll's role as mother. Mr Watt writes:

> Here the conclusion about her character must surely be that, although there are extenuating circumstances, she is often a heartless mother. It is difficult to see how this can be reconciled either with her kissing the ground that Humphry has trodden, or with the fact that she herself loudly condemns unnatural mothers, but never makes any such accusation against herself even in her deepest moments of penitent self-reprobation.[11] [63]

This puts the cart before the horse. Surely the very point that Defoe has been making us understand is that Moll is *at the same time* unusually honest and extraordinarily dishonest, and that the significance of her situation (whether it be horror or irony) is that she dare not be any more compassionate than she is. What Mr Watt sees as inconsistency I see as profundity. Moll is genuinely sorry that she has been a heartless mother; but that is part of the price she pays *and has to pay* for her independence. The really dreadful aspect of the book lies in Moll's ultimate absorption, via her 'repentance', into the very way of life against which she has so vigorously rebelled.

The Newgate section of the book is an extraordinary achievement and not primarily on the level of verisimilitude. If Newgate is hell to Moll it is above all because it is a place where her habitual habits of self-deception cannot do their job, a real eighteenth-century *huis clos*. Newgate is reality, the eighteenth-century world with the lid off, the world from which Moll set out and to which she comes back, defeated, to emerge as a conformist.

[10]Especially C. Hill, 'Clarissa Harlowe and her Times' (*Essays in Criticism*, V (1955), 315–40) and P. F. Vernon, 'Marriage of Convenience and the Moral Code of Restoration Comedy' (*Essays in Criticism* , XII (1962), 370 –87).

[11]Op. cit., p. 110. [See also this volume, pp. 296–97.]

IV

It is worth looking at *Moll Flanders* in its historical context in a rather different sense from the one I have so far emphasized. Moll is perhaps the first major plebeian heroine in English literature. The Doll Tearsheets and Doll Commons of the Elizabethan drama are her literary ancestors, but they are never right at the centre of the plays they appear in, any more than the sensible peasant-bred servants in Molière. Moll is unique. And throughout the eighteenth century she remains so. For Pamela, precisely because she makes the opposite choice to Moll's, is not a heroine. She bears on her shoulders none of the weight of human aspiration which heroism — including the fictional kind — involves. Polly Peachum is nearer to being a heroine; but the Polly of *The Beggar's Opera* needs Lucy Lockit to complete her and together they do — also within the walls of Newgate — throw a great deal of light on the problems and emotions of eighteenth-century plebeian women. Strictly speaking, however, it is impossible to speak of a plebeian heroine after Moll until Jeannie Deans, who is different because she is a peasant, not a townswoman. If one looks further afield the important figure among Moll's successors is another peasant girl, Susannah (Mozart's even more than Beaumarchais'), who is an anti-Pamela and a great advance on the Molière servants. [64]

V

We must see the place of *Moll Flanders* in total history if we are to see it in literary history. The book is not to be judged as though it were an imperfect forerunner of *Pride and Prejudice* or *What Maisie Knew*. Behind almost all the unsatisfactory criticism of Defoe today is a predisposition to judge his books in terms relevant to the novel as it developed in the nineteenth century and to praise in Defoe primarily those aspects of his art which point, so to speak, in that direction. 'Dramatization' (or what Percy Lubbock calls 'scenic' presentation), a conscious manipulation of 'point of view' and a moral preoccupation of the sort one associates with, say, George Eliot: these are assumed to be the elements of maturity in a novelist's development. 'Personal relationships' in the more analytical and isolable sense of the term are seen as the proper, even the ultimate, subject of the novel. And, of course, in an important sense, this is true. Novels will always be about men and women in their living, and therefore personal, relationships.

The trouble with Moll Flanders, however, is that by her very mode of existence she is precluded from having personal relationships of the sort modern critics most value. Mr Watt seems to recognize this when he writes:

... it is certain that, at the end of the long tradition of the European novel, and of the society whose individualism, leisure and unexampled security allowed it to make personal relations the major theme of its literature, Defoe is a welcome and portentous figure. Welcome because he seems long ago to have called the great bluff of the novel — its suggestion that personal relations really are the be-all and end-all of life; portentous because he, and only he, among the great writers of the past, has presented the struggle for survival in the bleak perspectives which recent history has brought back to a commanding position on the human stage.[12]

But he is arguing here that Defoe's positive quality is his concentration on isolated individuals. I think this is a mistaken argument. Moll's life is not an isolated life; she has as many personal relationships as anyone else. That she is unable to have full and satisfactory personal relationships is due not to her individualism but to the actual problems she is faced with. Moll is forced to be an individualist by her decision to try to be free in the man's world of eighteenth-century England; but her impulse to be free is due not to individualism but to a desire for better relationships with other people than life as a servant will permit. [65]

The whole nature of Defoe's book — its construction, its texture, its detail, its vitality, its power to move us — is determined by his awareness of the contradiction between Moll's human aspiration and the facts of the human world she lives in. Because so much of the contradiction was, in the year 1722, insoluble and yet had to be resolved, much of the resolution takes the form of ambiguous or ironical statement.

It is interesting to compare Defoe's methods with those of a contemporary artist facing a comparable problem, the Italian novelist Pier Paolo Pasolini in his impressive film *Accattone*. Accattone, Pasolini's 'hero', is in many respects very like a twentieth-century Moll Flanders. He is a feckless young man who lives as a ponce in Rome, and the film treats his life episodically. There is one scene in particular reminiscent of Defoe's novel. Accattone, needing money to buy a present for his girl, steals a chain from the neck of his young son, telling himself all the time what a swine he is. The moral impact of the film is in one sense much the same as that of *Moll Flanders*: we feel a deep sympathy for Accattone without approving of him, and we are shocked at the human inadequacies of the total situation that is revealed. Yet the similarities are scarcely less striking than the differences, of which perhaps the most important is that we know precisely where Pasolini stands: there is no moral ambiguity in *his* attitude. Accattone is presented to us clearly, objectively, as a product of contemporary society, and although he is not sentimentalized or excused, the social situation of which he is a part, and at least to some extent a victim, is implicitly condemned.

[12]Op. cit., p. 133. [See also this volume, p. 306.]

This is not a matter of chance. Pasolini knows very well that Accattone is unable to resolve his problems; but he also knows that, in the middle of the twentieth century, Accattone's problems are not insoluble. Whereas, to Defoe, at the beginning of the eighteenth century, Moll's problem is indeed insoluble and this inevitably affects the whole nature of his artistic handling of it.

The question 'How far is Defoe's irony intentional?' is not really a fruitful question. For one thing, it is impossible to know the answer for sure; for another, it oversimplifies the nature of artistic consciousness and indeed of all consciousness. Defoe's writing was presumably not *un*intentional, not *un*conscious. He knew what he was doing. But, of course, he will not have been aware of all the implications of what he was doing; no one ever is. It is true that Defoe's own comprehension of some of the most important implications of Moll Flanders' story must seem to us to be incomplete. He underwrites her own [66] ultimate complacency, obviously taking her salvation much too much at its face value. But this limitation is far less important than that 'negative capability' which allowed him to reveal the humanity of Moll. What is important is that he tackled the big, central human problems of his time and went deep, revealing the contradictions as well as the surface qualities, and revealing them in a form which in itself illuminates their nature because it springs from them. [67]

Conscious Irony in *Moll Flanders*: Facts and Problems*

MAXIMILLIAN E. NOVAK

Discussions of irony in *Moll Flanders* are reminiscent of Sir William Petty's famous choice of weapons and site for a duel: axes in a dark cellar. Dorothy Van Ghent has put the problem very neatly. "We are left," she wrote, "with two possibilities. Either *Moll Flanders* is a collection of scandal sheet anecdotes naively patched together with the platitudes that form the morality of an impoverished soul (Defoe's), a 'sincere' soul but a confused and degraded one; or *Moll Flanders* is a great novel, coherent in structure, unified and given its shape and significance by a complex system of ironies." Miss Van Ghent concludes that it must be a great novel because we reread it with delight. "That it may be the latter is justified by the analysis it yields itself to, as an ironic structure, and most of all justified by our pleasure in it. Shall we, then, waive the question of Defoe's 'intention and 'sincerity'? Speculations as to these apparently can add nothing to the book nor can they take anything from it; the book remains what it is" (*The*

*Source: *College English*, XXVI (December, 1964), 198–204. Reprinted by permission of the author.

lish Novel: Form and Function [New York 1961], p. 42). She adds
t we have no way of measuring Defoe's "intention and sincerity,
in the deepest meaning of intention and sincerity," and that the
question is irrelevant.

Those critics who have doubted that *Moll Flanders* is ironic have
suggested that they have some knowledge of this intention and
sincerity. In his introduction to the Modern Library edition of
Moll Flanders Mark Schorer suggested that what appears like irony is
merely the result of Defoe's moral confusion—the "classic revelation
of the mercantile mind." And in what appears like a devastatingly
documented attack, Ian Watt, in *The Rise of the Novel*, claimed that all
the evidence points to Defoe's failure to write ironically. More
recently, in *To the Palace of Wisdom*, Martin Price has argued that
although Defoe seems to have been aware of the moral complexity
of his subject matter, he was not being ironic in *Moll Flanders*. All
of these writers claim special knowledge of Defoe's background.
Schorer appeals to the mercantilist mind; Watt has hooked Defoe up
to the Protestant Ethic dynamo of Weber and Tawney; and Martin
Price has appealed to Perry Miller and the puritan mind.

In the most current article on this subject, Howard Koonce's
"Moll's Muddle: Defoe's Use of Irony in *Moll Flanders*" (*ELH*, 30
[1963], 377–394), an essay mercifully free from references to mercantile ethics and puritanism, the critic ably refutes Ian Watt's conclusions
and demonstrates that whether we think Defoe's irony is good or bad
is a matter for critical [198] judgment but that there is no question
that *Moll Flanders* is an ironic novel. But he weakens his point by
remarking: "We shall probably never be able to separate with any
degree of certainty how much of the irony of *Moll Flanders* is due to
conscious authorial effort from how much of it is due to perceptions
we bring to rather than get from Defoe." I am in entire agreement
with Mr. Koonce and Miss Van Ghent on the irony of *Moll Flanders*,
but I cannot see why the areas of irony cannot be established. As
Wayne Booth argues in *The Rhetoric of Fiction*, "the question is an
important one: if we find ourselves laughing at the author along with
his characters, our opinion of the book as art must suffer." I have
examined the ironic implications of the first section of *Moll Flanders*
in my article on "Moll Flanders' First Love," and in my book *Economics
and the Fiction of Daniel Defoe* and will not repeat my conclusions
here. What I want to do in this article is to outline some of the general
areas of irony which the reader may pick out of *Moll Flanders*, to indicate those themes and elements of human behavior which Defoe
regarded as inherently paradoxical and hence subject to ironic treatment, and to assure those readers who have found irony in *Moll
Flanders* that Defoe was being consciously ironic.

Of course in order to do this, the critic must have read a good part of the five hundred and forty-seven items which appear in Professor John Robert Moore's *Checklist of the Writings of Daniel Defoe* (Professor Moore has subsequently added several more), but this is precisely what none of the critics appear to have done. Many of these works are long, some are dull, but all of them give us some insight into Defoe's mind. If an appeal to intention may seem a heresy in modern criticism, I can justify myself on the ground that the confusion concerning his irony is a result of appeals to sociological and biographical generalizations about Defoe's puritanism. One would think that the first job of such criticism would be to define Defoe's puritanism, to remember that he was more a contemporary of Swift, Addison, and Steele than of Milton, Baxter, and Bunyan, and to consider that during the last thirty years of his life he was a professional writer, not a tradesman.

We should begin by dispelling the idea implied by Professor Watt that *The Shortest Way with the Dissenters* is Defoe's only other work of irony. To the contrary, irony was one of his most common modes. Defoe was not being quite honest in claiming that *The Shortest Way* was an "irony not unusual." It was very unusual, and his usual method is much more blatant. More typical of his irony are the blame by praise techniques employed in his *A Letter to Mr. Bisset* (1709); the fallacious arguments of *Reasons against the Succession of the House of Hanover* (1713); and the suspension of moral judgments in *The Life of Jonathan Wild* (1725). He used the same techniques that appear in *The Shortest Way* in a work he must have written at the same time, *King William's Affection to the Church of England Examin'd* (1703), but he broke the illusion of his ironic mask, a fictional opponent of King William, before the end. *The Shortest Way* was, as Defoe confessed, deliberately intended to fool some people. It was the irony described by Kierkegaard in his paraphrase of Aristotle: an irony which "tends essentially towards one person" as the extent of its audience.

But let us start with Professor Watt's definition of irony to see how well Defoe's irony meets his demands. "Irony," writes Professor Watt, "in its extended sense expresses a deep awareness of the contradictions and incongruities that beset man in this vale of tears, an awareness which is manifested in the text's purposeful[199] susceptibility to contradictory interpretations. As soon as we have become aware of the author's ulterior purpose, we can see all the apparent contradictions as indications of the coherent attitude underlying the whole work." Defoe's irony will fit this definition if we make some qualifications. Defoe saw man's condition in terms of contradictions and incongruities, but he did not always resolve his position on these matters. As Martin Price has very accurately observed, "Like Mandeville, who struts much more in the role, he is one of the artists who makes our moral judgments more difficult." Secondly, we have ealize that Defoe regarded irony as a rhetorical trope. The only torician whom he quotes is Gerardus Vossius, and it is here that we must search for clues to Defoe's use of irony. Vossius separates irony as a way of life, the Socratic manner of dissembling and false humility, from the rhetorical concept in which "we speak in one way but our meaning bears no relation to what we literally say." He defines it as a form of "mockery" by means of "deception and trickery." Quoting Fabius he notes that irony is understood "either by the tone of voice, or by the character of the person speaking, or by the situation. For if any of those is discordant with the words, it is apparent that the meaning of the utterance is the opposite." And finally he warns of the difficulty of irony: "The circumstances and the rest should be given careful attention if we are to avoid suspecting irony where there is none, or where there is irony, taking the words literally."

If we grant Defoe's familiarity with such a theory we can stop worrying about his naiveté. Moll's words are those of a woman in a state of prosperity and repentance. As a character she tends to be blind to her situation and to reveal only the dimmest understanding of her true moral state. We cannot know her tone of voice, but Defoe will vary his style to suggest sincerity or sophistic rationalization. I want to turn now to consider the various points of incongruity where Defoe's irony may be measured:

1. MORALITY: In his fiction Defoe operated on two levels of morality. The first was a standard Christian morality with charity as the highest of virtues. It is difficult to determine the degree to which the Christianity of the fictions is eccentrically puritan. The second was that connected with natural law. This view sees man as a creature motivated mainly by self: self-love, self-interest, and self-defense. Natural law was codified by Grotius and Pufendorf in the seventeenth century, and Defoe drew upon them for his moral judgments concerning natural behavior. "Natural" is a key word in *Moll Flanders*, and Defoe draws some irony from the disparity between the judgments of the repentant Moll concerning her life passed under the laws of nature. Thus when she says that she was driven by the devil to steal and then excuses herself on the grounds of her poverty, we can see her upbraiding herself for an act which not for a moment could she have avoided. The great virtue of the heroic follower of natural morality is activity, and Moll is one of the most active of his protagonists. Vices include the unnatural: ingratitude, incest, and doing evil to others where there is no excuse to be found in self-preservation or self-interest. It is a moral code which is peculiarly modern in its implications, for it abstracts the individual from specific social institutions and religion and establishes a "natural" standard based on the sophisticated view of human customs which voyagers to foreign lands had made available to the European.

2. REPENTANCE: Defoe was not being ironic about Moll's repentance and conversion in Newgate. That we are told in the preface that she is no longer as penitent as she was may make us question some of the attacks upon her natural[200] morality in the name of a more conventional Christian morality, but the conversion and repentance in Newgate follows the pattern of a true repentance which appears in Defoe's other writings. Defoe would have allowed for the possibility that a woman like Moll could repent, and the sincerity of tone in these passages should leave little question about the suspension of irony. Here the repentant narrator is dealing with her greatest moment. The remark in the preface merely suggests that Moll remains true to her essential character — a character which fits ill with a perpetually fervent convert.

3. SEX, LOVE, AND MARRIAGE: Defoe once noted that God did not put the sexual instinct under the control of the reason, and in this it differed from the passions which might be controlled. Sex, then, subjects men and women to a universal comedy in which the main joke lies in the human condition. Thus his most sympathetic hero, Colonel Jacque, is continually cuckolded by his wives, and poor Robin, Moll's first husband, whose defense of marriage for love rather than money Defoe would have found admirable, marries his brother's mistress, who goes to the wedding like "a bear to the stake."

A large part of *Moll Flanders* is devoted to the comedy of sex, love and marriage, and Defoe's sympathies remain divided. He thought that the women were worse off than the men, for they cannot buy a husband if they do not have money, and once they marry, they are at the mercy of their husbands. Defoe's only solution was to advise women to become as capable as men — to educate themselves for survival in a masculine world. Moll's rather masculine nature does not appear until her disillusionment, and, unlike the feminist, Roxana, she always prefers to assume a feminine role. But her ideals should not be confused with Defoe's. Her desire for a "gentleman" husband, who proves useless in the American plantation, is part of the marriage comedy.

Defoe's ideal is one which we can still understand — a marriage for love, a wife who is understanding and helpful, a husband who is a companion and a conscientious provider. Ideally both should be religious and of the same religion. But Defoe seldom presented this ideal and regarded any workable compromise as acceptable. He did not regard polygamy as the worst of sins, for natural law had shown that it was a common institution, and by the same standard of natural law, he regarded desertion as equivalent to divorce. Incest was considered to be contrary to the law of nature, and Moll cannot endure her incestuous marriage to her brother. Even her desire for security must yield to her natural detestation of this relationship.

4. CHILDREN: The injunctions of natural law state that parents must care for and educate their children, but that in cases of necessity, they may give them away. Moll gives love and care where she has the money to afford it. The important point here is that self-preservation was allowed to take precedence over parental love. Defoe seems to have accepted Moll's attitude toward her children as natural enough.

5. SERVANTS: After her training with her foster mother, Moll becomes a servant in the home of the Colchester family. She speaks of herself as if she were an adopted daughter, but she is called Miss Betty (the generic name for chamber maids) and is at best a servant-companion to the daughters. Defoe wrote a variety of works attacking the insolence of servants, but he also admired the clever servant who has the ability to rise in the world. Like Mandeville, he knew that the social structure was in flux, but he was much more an exponent of *la carrière ouverte aux talents* than his contemporary. In Moll, then, Defoe illustrates the servant who is not clever enough to trick the [201] heir of the family into marriage but pretty enough to win a younger son. Defoe's attitude toward the young Moll, who dislikes servitude and admires the independence of the town whore, is detached, amused, critical, and ironic. The irony of the first part of the book which ends with the death of Robin is perfectly clear and free from the complications of more serious themes—the possibility of starvation and destitution.

6. POVERTY (NECESSITY): When a person falls into a state of destitution which makes starvation a possibility, he may do anything to preserve his life. Some writers on natural law believed that such a state dissolved the bonds of society and made all goods common. Defoe placed the following limitations on man's freedom when confronted by this "first and great principle of nature": a. He must not harm someone in the same condition as himself (a condition of equal poverty or danger). b. He must try to make restitution of whatever he steals or repair whatever harm he has done when it is possible. c. His degree of guilt depends to some extent on the degree to which he is to blame for falling into a state of necessity. When Moll blames herself for her crimes she judges herself from a standpoint of divine law and excuses herself on grounds of natural law. The paradox lies in the limitations of the human condition. She condemns herself for her failure to resist temptation, but then argues that human nature is too frail to resist the laws of nature.

7. POSITIVE LAW: Even Coke argued that no national law could overrule the laws of nature or the laws of God. Such laws could not be regarded as valid. But Moll lives in a society which will punish her for violating its laws. English law tells her that she cannot steal no matter how hungry she is, and she cannot remarry while her husband is alive. Moll always follows the laws of nature, but the contrasts

between the three levels of law are responsible for much of the paradoxical morality in *Moll Flanders* and in Defoe's other works.

8. THIEVES AND TRADESMEN: Defoe frequently contrasted the honesty of the thief who will steal through necessity and the dishonesty of the grasping tradesman. He suggested that the worst pirates were more honest than the capitalists of his time and superior in every way to the directors of the South Sea Company. He even suggests that Jonathan Wild destroyed honor among thieves when he organized them as an industrialist. Defoe blamed theft and piracy upon the laws of England and English society with its unfair treatment of debtors, its failure to care for the poor, and its ill treatment of seamen. But he also recognized that a society must punish crime or fall into anarchy.

9. PROSTITUTES: Defoe attacked Mandeville's suggestion concerning legalizing prostitution, but he objected to the manner rather than the matter. Defoe sympathized with the prostitute and argued that she does not support society by consuming its goods (as Mandeville suggested) and that her life is miserable, for he did not believe that she experienced any sexual pleasure in her job. In sketching the decline of women into prostitution he argued that the primary guilt lay with the man who first seduced her. Moll is hardly reluctant but the rake who seduces her is still more at fault.

10. GENTLEMEN: Moll has affairs with three "gentlemen." The first robs her of her virtue and refuses to marry her. The second is a "gentleman-tradesman," who spends all her money and leaves her destitute. The third is a "gentleman-highwayman" who tries to cheat her but proves to be a loving spouse. All of these men have in common an aspiration to a life of leisure. Moll's aspiration toward gentility and her disapproval of her Lancashire Husband's idleness in America suggests an appropriate "muddle" in [202] Moll's mind which is hardly in Defoe's. Defoe frequently attacked those rakish gentlemen who added nothing to the wealth of the society and were a plague to the women. The Lancashire Husband is the best of the group both because he reveals a good heart and because he led an active life of crime to support himself.

11. ECONOMIC INDIVIDUALISM: Defoe was fully aware of the movement in feeling and ideas which Tawney and Weber described and stood staunchly against it in the name of older mercantilist ideals. He was continually proposing state intervention in trade, the establishment of cooperative communities and societies from orphanages to homes for the aged. In 1704 he complained that "it is now almost become a Maxim with them [Dissenting ministers], that poverty proceeds from want of Grace, Inverting the Scriptures. That only with [rich?] Men, can enter the Kingdom of Heaven, at least into their Congregation." Though he dramatized the struggle for wealth in his fiction, Defoe's ideal was always that of retirement when a moderate

wealth was achieved. There may appear to be a paradox in his admiration for both activity and retirement, but Defoe did not insist that the activity had to be economic. Colonel Jacque seeks gentility and an education after he has gained wealth.

12.   PROJECTS: Defoe has Moll remind the reader that some nations have hospitals to take care of orphans and much time is spent on the home for expectant mothers operated by the woman who later becomes her "Governess." These are both ideas which Defoe is advancing with some seriousness, but in both cases he uses them dramatically. Moll is given what ought to be a perfectly good training for servitude by the parish. Her inability to accept servitude has something to do with heredity (she sucked her mother's milk in Newgate) and something to do with environment (she was raised by gypsies until the age of three). She should have been spared both experiences and trained more thoroughly. The Governess has some excellent ideas, but Defoe would have disapproved of her sly suggestion about abortion; and we are not surprised to find that the establishment slips into evil ways.

13.   COLONIAL PROPAGANDA: Defoe presents the possibility of a new life in America for the transported criminal in both his fiction and didactic works. He believed that the criminal might become a wealthy property owner through hard work and ingenuity. Though Jacque feels that he needs the official status of an army officer, education, and travel before he can regard himself as a gentleman, Defoe recognized the relativity of status in such a society.

It should be clear from this summary of themes in *Moll Flanders* that the underlying irony of the work is to be found in Moll's blindness or, as Mr. Koonce calls it, her "muddle." The fog that I wish to dispel is that which hangs over Defoe's puritanism and moral insensitivity. Defoe's sophisticated attitude toward human nature as governed by natural law allowed him to see mankind free from the claims of religion and social customs. His training in economics enabled him to dramatize some of the most fascinating sociological currents of his day. On the surface level of her narrative Moll sees her life as a Christian penitent. She is only dimly aware that she operates on a level of natural law, pursuing security through marriage and then self-preservation through theft. One is reminded of Marvin Mudrick's comment on Jane Austen's Emma when that peculiarly obtuse heroine repents her deeds: "the act of self-abasement that claims sin, in order to avoid the responsibility of self-knowledge." Moll never understands why she does not stop stealing after she has enough money to live on, but Defoe allows us to see the pleasure which she [203] takes in her craft. We see her self-satisfaction; we never see her self-recognition. Mr. Koonce suggests that to a certain extent Moll's blindness is our blindness. Whereas Roxana has Amy to talk with and to reveal herself to, Moll presents us with a closed world. Her husbands reveal little

about her and her Governess seems to be merely a reflection of
wishes. Like many people, she sees the world through her rationa,
tions and pretensions, and though we can see where these are gros._y
false, we can only guess at the rest. I would repeat the suggestion
which I made elsewhere that we take the suggestion in the preface of a
trilogy centered on Moll, her Lancashire Husband, and the Governess
more seriously. Defoe usually wrote in clusters. *Robinson Crusoe* became a trilogy and both *Captain Singleton* and *Colonel Jacque* grew out
of earlier works; there are two lives of Sheppard, two of Wild, and his
works on magic and the devil grew to three volumes. The preface
suggests that the two other accounts of Moll give a different view of
her personality, and it is possible that Defoe was saving some of his
material for other volumes.

Nevertheless what we have satisfies Miss Van Ghent's analysis of a
"complex system of ironies." As for Professor Watt's doubts about
Defoe's capacity for handling the rhetoric of irony, I would suggest
that Defoe's training in rhetoric at the Newington Green Academy
was very thorough. In his *Compleat English Gentleman* Defoe described
how Charles Morton taught his students to imitate the style of various
characters: "Some times they were Ministers of State, Secretaries and
Commissioners at home, and wrote orders and instructions to the
ministers abroad, as by order of the King in Council and the like. Thus
he taught his pupils to write a masculine and manly stile, to write the
most polite English, and at the same time to kno' how to suit their
manner as well to the subject they were to write upon as to the
person or degrees of persons they were to write to." It is clear that
Defoe learned his lessons well in this "class for eloquence."

That his readers frequently did not understand his irony is possible,
but if this is true, we may wonder why he continued to employ irony
in his writings throughout his life. And was Defoe's audience very
different from Swift's? The very realism of his fiction was considered
"low" and put it outside the pale of polite literature during his day.
But there is no reason to believe that it was not read and understood.
Professor Watt has raised some valuable questions; our answers to
these problems should begin with the unquestionable fact that *Moll
Flanders* is a work of irony.[204]

*Moll Flanders**

G. A. STARR

Spiritual autobiography pursued thematic coherence amid or
despite narrative incoherence: incoherence, that is, measured by the

*Source: G. A. Starr, *Defoe and Spiritual Autobiography* (Princeton, N.J.: Princeton
University Press, 1965), pp. 126–62. Reprinted by permission of Princeton University
Press. Copyright © 1965 by Princeton University Press.

more rigorous standards of plotting which the novel was to evolve. So long as the protagonist's inward vicissitudes obeyed the traditional pattern, either of growth or decay, and so long as individual episodes contributed to this pattern with some consistency, an autobiography might be regarded as structurally sound. Within such a convention, whose rationale lay in religious psychology rather than aesthetics, a logic of spiritual change within the character took precedence over a logic of outward action; within such a convention, discrete, apparently random episodes might be held to possess a unity both sufficient and meaningful. This convention, it seems to me, illuminates some basic features of the action and characterization of *Moll Flanders*.[1] The chronological sequence of events is halting and abrupt, and their [126] causal connection is arbitrary at best. Between one incident and the next there tends to be some such perfunctory transition as "At length a new scene opened" or "now a new scene of misfortunes attended me" (104, 86). And yet the fact that Moll's story unravels in a series of rather tenuously connected episodes does not rule out an underlying continuity of the kind just described, nor does the abruptness of the outward narrative preclude a gradual, fairly systematic development of the heroine's spiritual condition.

Crusoe's career begins with his running away from home: Defoe supplies no very complex motivation for his act, but anticipates it by establishing his unruliness and obstinacy. Perhaps no single deed so decisively launches the action in *Moll Flanders*, yet the seduction by the elder brother is in some respects comparable. Although Moll's first real act of will, there is little complexity in its motivation: Defoe marshals no more personality traits here than in the opening pages of *Robinson Crusoe*. What he does instead is to emphasize the predominance of a single characteristic — namely, Moll's vanity. Between the ages of eight and fourteen, she develops as strong an obsession about being a gentlewoman as Crusoe's about going to sea. In themselves, both desires may be innocent enough, but each represents a "station in life" which is altogether unnatural and inappropriate under the circumstances. When Moll first speaks of becoming a gentlewoman, she little understands the meaning of the word, but even her naïveté is made slightly ominous.[2] Moreover, from the time she is ten she [127] begins hearing herself spoken of as pretty, and she confesses that this

---

[1]Other important features of the book are of course traceable to different conventions, such as those of criminal biography: see Ernest Bernbaum, *The Mary Carleton Narratives 1663-1673* (Cambridge, Mass., 1914), *passim*, and Spiro Peterson, foreword to *The Counterfeit Lady Unveiled* (Garden City, 1961), pp. 4-7. Cf. also Paul Dottin, *Daniel De Foe et ses Romans*, 3 vols. (Paris, 1924), III, 645f.; and John Robert Moore, *Daniel Defoe Citizen of the Modern World* (Chicago, 1958), pp. 242f.

[2]Compare the following dialogue between Moll and her old nurse (14–15): "Naming a woman that mended lace and washed the ladies' laced heads; 'she,' says I, ' is a gentlewoman, and they call her madam.'

made her "not a little proud" (15). When at fourteen she enters the family of the Colchester merchant, these combined strains of vanity contribute at least as much as the wiles of the elder brother to her undoing.

That Moll's ambition to become a gentlewoman is not merely an amusing, innocuous irony can be shown in various ways. For one thing, although Defoe was a pioneering advocate of female education, he never speaks of it as a means of social betterment; on the contrary, he always stresses the importance of educating youths not only according to their natural capacities, but according to their expectations.[3] In *Moll Flanders*, the contrast between Moll and the sisters in the family makes clear that her natural capacities are great, but it makes equally clear the discrepancy between her genteel attainments and her prospects in the world.[4] A recurrent theme of contemporary sermons[128] and educational tracts was that any such discrepancy is dangerous; Bishop Fleetwood is typical in arguing that "A Parent is to take good heed that he never educate his Children above the Provision he designs to make for them; ... it being much more easy to bear with a mean Condition constantly, than to fall into it from a plentiful and good one; which is the Case of People better educated than provided for: The soft and tender Usage of People, whilst young, and capable of undergoing Labour and more Hardship, is truly a Diskindness to them, without an answerable Provision for them afterwards; for whenever they are left to shift for themselves, they are no better than expos'd naked, as it were, and defenceless, unable to procure themselves a Livelihood, and in much worse Condition than their Inferiours." The fate of women brought up in such a way, Fleetwood continues, is that they "fall to[o] often into the Hands of wicked Tempters, through want of Ability to employ themselves in honest Courses, and an utter Incapacity of maintaining their Condition; their Poverty makes them unfit for their *Equals*, and their soft Education ... [makes] their *Inferiours* afraid to match with them."[5] To be sure, Moll does not

" 'Poor child,' says my good old nurse, 'you may soon be such a gentlewoman as that, for she is a person of ill fame, and has had two bastards.'
"I did not understand anything of that; but I answered, 'I am sure they call her madam, and she does not go to service nor do house-work'; and therefore I insisted that she was a gentlewoman, and I would be such a gentlewoman as that."
[3]Cf. *Serious Reflections*, pp. 63–66. In the section of *An Essay upon Projects* called "An Academy for Women," his proposals are egalitarian only in a special, limited sense: namely, in maintaining that the capacity and the need for education are as great in women as in men. Raising poor orphans to the plane of gentlewomen is not his object.
[4]Compare the sister's speech on p. 20: "Betty wants but one thing, but she had as good want everything, for the market is against our sex just now; and if a young woman has beauty, birth, breeding, wit, sense, manners, modesty, and all to an extreme, yet if she has not money, she's nobody, and had as good want them all." Cf. also *Little Review*, July 4, 1705, p. 33.
[5]*The Relative Duties of Parents and Children, Husbands and Wives, Masters and Servants;*

experience the precise ill effects[129] that Fleetwood predicts, yet the point is made that her education not only exceeds her provision but renders her vulnerable to temptation. Thus the very word "gentle-woman" at first means no more than self-support, and later signifies genteel appearance and attainments; yet it becomes increasingly associated with money, so that the longer Moll's education in gentility continues, the more susceptible she is to gold as well as "fine words" (24).

At all events, Defoe takes care to indicate that it is vanity rather than love or lust which animates her at the beginning. Although in the course of time she does become passionately attached to the elder brother, this does not seem to be a factor in her initial seduction. When the elder brother's declarations of love "fire her blood," it is her vanity which is enflamed;[6] and when the courtship is well under way, she makes the significant distinction that "This gentleman had now fired *his* inclination as much as he had *my* vanity."[7] Throughout the book Defoe is careful to distinguish between what is done from "gust" or "inclination" and what is done from other motives. Here, instead of positively denying that Moll shares the brother's "inclination," he remains silent about this possibility, and makes Moll dwell exclusively on the element of vanity. The reason, I think, is not that he intends to lessen her[130] guilt by clearing her of any anticipatory relish for the deed itself, but on the contrary that he wants to stress her own vanity as the force that really prevails over her virtue.[8] By furnishing the elder brother with subtlety and cash, and by placing Moll in what amounts to the situation of a chambermaid[9] — an extremely vulnerable one at the time, as Pamela Andrews was to discover — Defoe does take into account the external forces that contribute to her seduction; but such forces by no means lessen her own responsibility for the deed. They scarcely even complicate her choice, but instead give impetus to that vanity which alone determines her behavior.

It has seemed worth dwelling on this initial action for several

---

Consider'd in Sixteen Practical Discourses ..., 3rd edition (1722), pp. 100–01, 102; cf. Robert Moss, *The Providential Division of Men into Rich and Poor, and the respective Duties thence arising* ... (1708), p. 22. Moss's is a charity-school anniversary sermon; such occasions frequently called for remarks resembling Fleetwood's.

[6] Thus Moll reports that "my head ran upon strange things, and I may truly say I was not myself, to have such a gentleman talk to me of being in love with me, and of my being such a charming creature, as he told me I was. These things I knew not how to bear; my vanity was elevated to the last degree" (21–22).

[7] 23; italics mine. Even at the climactic moment (26), it is the sight of the purse and the fire of the proposal that cause Moll's color to come and go, not any passion on her part.

[8] Moll states emphatically that "that which I was too vain of was my ruin, or rather my vanity was the cause of it" (19); and she calls herself "a fair memento to all young women whose vanity prevails over their virtue" (24).

[9] On this point, see Novak, *Economics and the Fiction of Daniel Defoe*, pp. 84–85.

reasons. In the first place, it must be acknowledged that Defoe takes pains with the narrative itself, but his attitude towards it resembles that of a recent fictional narrator who declares, "I have always been deeply interested in the administrative side of love.... What Lady Chatterley and her gamekeeper did in the woods is, to me, of only passing interest, compared with how they got there."[10] Insofar as Defoe is concerned with the outward story of the seduction, it is "the administrative side" that absorbs his attention, as the elder brother's final elaborate ruse well illustrates. The economic implications of the deed [131] fall into this category, it seems to me. While it is true that they figure more prominently than any erotic aspects of the affair, they remain one item in "the administrative side," rather than themselves constituting the controlling factor, or the ultimate significance of what takes place.[11]

Indeed, a second reason for looking closely at these early scenes is that they show, in a way that seems characteristic of Defoe, economic considerations being subsumed under moral ones; gold takes its place, along with flattery but no more crucially, as one of the stimuli to Moll's vanity. And although various forces act on Moll from without, they do not make for a corresponding complexity of "personal characteristics": the complexity remains external, while she herself is dominated by the single characteristic of vanity. Her vanity may itself take various outward forms, but nevertheless provides a radically simple basis for Moll's thoughts and actions at this point in the book.

This, then, is a final reason for attending to the preliminaries of Moll's seduction, for despite the complication of the external narrative, there is nothing very intricate about Moll's own character. Without wishing to generalize from this single episode, one might anticipate her subsequent treatment by saying it consists of complex outward manifestations of inward states that are in fact rather simple. To return to the initial argument, the book's real coherence seems to lie in the gradual unfolding of these inward states, not [132] in the overt action by which they are revealed. If we take Moll's vanity as a point of departure, analogous to Crusoe's rebelliousness, we find a certain consistency in the vicissitudes that follow, however disconnected they may be outwardly.

There are several points of comparison, in fact, between Moll's and Crusoe's spiritual careers. In the first place, each has the repeated option of altering his course after the original misdeed. In Crusoe's case, unmediated acts of Providence function as calls to conversion

---

[10]Malcolm Muggeridge, *Affairs of the Heart*, quoted in *New York Times* review by Nigel Dennis, March 5, 1961, VIII, 5.

[11]For a reading of *Moll Flanders* which places greater emphasis on its economic aspects, see Denis Donoghue, "The Values of *Moll Flanders*," *Sewanee Review*, LXXI (1963), pp. 287–303.

which go unheeded. Moll remains within society, and is less subject to direct, elemental threats and deliverances, but in the course of her dealings with other people she experiences recurrent promptings to repentance. Instead of resisting or neglecting them, as does Crusoe, she entertains them momentarily, or partially, or insincerely, so that her career is marked by a series of false starts. Secondly, lacking religious conviction to direct or sanction her behavior, Moll acts (to use a phrase from *Robinson Crusoe*) "like a mere brute from the principles of Nature, and by the dictates of common sense only, and indeed hardly that" (p. 97). As in *Robinson Crusoe*, Defoe indicates that practical reason is a weak and faltering guide; not only is Moll's judgment overcome on crucial occasions by external pressures or inducements, but it is rendered ineffectual by the gradual enslavement of her will. Finally, there is an essential likeness in the kind of spiritual development Crusoe and Moll undergo: indeed, the two features just noted can be seen as corollaries of this more basic pattern. Gradual hardening characterizes Crusoe's career prior to conversion, although this is made fully explicit only when he comes to repent. Moll's actions lack the traditional symbolic overtones[133] that Crusoe's have; to compensate for this, and to make clear that she is undergoing the classic process of hardening, the significance of many episodes is spelled out as they occur.

As for the first of these three features, Moll's abortive repentances begin fairly soon after the seduction. When the younger brother proposes marriage, she exclaims that "I was now in a dreadful condition indeed, and now I repented heartily my easiness with the eldest brother; not from any reflection of conscience, for I was a stranger to those things, but I could not think of being a whore to one brother and a wife to the other" (28). Here "repentance" is largely a matter of worldly prudence, and is very remote from its true nature, as defined in Defoe's other works and later in this one. But that Moll is not speaking altogether casually is indicated by the parenthesis, "not from any reflection of conscience, for I was a stranger to those things." Here and in similar passages, Defoe clearly means to stress the ironic contrast between Moll's passing qualms and real repentance.[12]

Sometimes Moll does not speak of repenting, but describes herself as seriously considering or reflecting. Again there is often a more or less explicit contrast with the opening stage of genuine repentance, discussed earlier. On these occasions, however, the irony[134] of the

---

[12]The conclusion of the passage introduces a note of squeamishness which also deserves comment. As the story proceeds, Moll repeatedly draws lines at certain kinds of wrongdoing out of a bizarre compunction, less moral than aesthetic or sentimental, and balks at actions scarcely more wicked than those which have become habitual to her. Besides being a piece of femininity that contributes to the book's "formal realism," this trait should probably be regarded as a specimen of Moll's tendency to swallow camels and strain at gnats, about which more will be said.

contrast tends to be less pronounced than when Moll actually talks of repentance. Thus when the younger brother persists in his open courtship, and Moll's dilemma requires the elder brother's advice, she says "Upon serious consideration, for indeed now I began to consider things very seriously, and never till now, I resolved to tell him of it" (29). When she is living in the Mint, and finds she is "not wicked enough for such fellows" as the debauched debtors who take refuge there, she asserts that "I began to consider here very seriously what I had to do; how things stood with me, and what course I ought to take" (56). When her liaison with the man at Bath is over, she reports that "I cast about innumerable ways for my future state of life, and began to consider very seriously what I should do" (103). When she has parted with her Lancashire lover and returns to lodgings in London, she says that "here being perfectly alone, I had leisure to sit down and reflect seriously upon the last seven months' ramble I had made" (127). Soon after the delivery of her son by this "marriage," she receives a letter from her London clerk, in which he announces his divorce, the suicide of his ex-wife, and his hope of seeing Moll again: her reaction is that "I was exceedingly surprised at the news, and began now seriously to reflect on my circumstances" (136).

These are a few of the reflections and considerations that punctuate Moll's career before she commits her first theft. Each bout comes at a crucial point in her affairs, but dissipates itself in worldly scheming. I do not wish to imply that Defoe invariably associates the terms "serious consideration" and "serious reflection" with incipient repentance, so that any other use of them on Moll's part involves irony. But it does appear[135] significant that each time she is afforded an opportunity to review and alter her course of action, her attention quickly shifts from self-scrutiny to outward reconnoitering. In any case, subsequent passages lend weight to the supposition that her terminology in the above instances is not entirely casual or unconscious. When she later describes the character of the gentleman she meets at Bartholomew Fair, she recognizes that his capacity for making "just reflections" on his behavior falls considerably short of genuine, durable repentance (186). And when she comes to describe her own "lethargy of soul" in Newgate, she begins by putting it negatively: she has no sense of her condition despite the fact that, as she admits, "I had a weight of guilt upon me, enough to sink any creature with the least power of reflection left" (218). In other words, her lowest spiritual ebb is marked by the loss (or total abeyance) of that "power of reflection" which she had long stifled, or at best diverted to external, worldly matters from its proper object: the state of her soul.

Taken by themselves, Moll's spells of serious reflection may seem inconclusive. Running parallel to them, however, is the series of insincere or incomplete repentances mentioned earlier. One instance has already been cited. A more striking one, which could be called a case of sentimental repentance, occurs at the time of her marriage to the London clerk. When she accepts the clerk's proposal, he is "so overcome with the satisfaction of it" that "tears stand in his eyes," upon which Moll declares that "I turned from him, for it filled my eyes with tears too, and asked him leave to retire a little to my chamber. If I had a grain of true repentance for an abominable life of twenty-four years past, it was then" (144). And after she is [136] married, she reports that "I sat many an hour by myself, and wept over the remembrance of past follies, and the dreadful extravagances of a wicked life, and sometimes I flattered myself that I had sincerely repented" (149). Weeping may, as we have seen, be a symptom of genuine "conviction," but here it merely provides emotional release. Moll's tearful sentimentality might, like her squeamishness, be no more than a feminine trait included for the sake of realism, and accounts of her outward personality should certainly mention her frequent weeping along with her unscrupulous hardness. But such sentimentality actually provides a further contrast with the nature of true repentance. This is made particularly clear when Moll steals the bundle of plate from the burning house. She confesses that "the inhumanity of this action moved me very much, and made me relent exceedingly, and tears stood in my eyes upon that subject; but with all my sense of its being cruel and inhuman, I could never find in my heart to make any restitution. The reflection wore off, and I quickly forgot the circumstances that attended it" (163). Here most of the ingredients of repentance already singled out are strikingly combined: what with tears and revulsion, relenting and reflecting, Moll would seem to be in a fair way to repent, yet her remaining moral awareness spends itself in sentimental indulgence, and the upshot is only further hardening.[13]

The full significance of this series of abortive repentances [137] will become clear when the final, effectual one is examined. One further passage may be noted, however, since it illustrates Defoe's care in distinguishing real repentance from false or partial versions. When Moll is first committed to Newgate, she makes the following statement: "Then I repented heartily of all my life past, but that repentance yielded me no satisfaction, no peace, no, not in the least, because, as I said to myself, it was repenting after the power of further sinning was taken away. I seemed not to mourn that I had committed such crimes, and for the fact, as it was an offense against God and my neighbour, but that I was to be punished for it. I was a penitent, as I thought, not

[13]It is also at this point that the pretense of necessity gives way to frank avarice; indeed her refusal to make restitution marks not only the remoteness of this outburst from true repentance, but also the obsessive wish to gain "a little more, and a little more" (163).

that I had sinned, but that I was to suffer, and this took away all the comfort of my repentance in my own thoughts" (215). The implied distinction is a sophisticated but important one, as contemporary discussions of fear as a basis for repentance strongly indicate. Within a very few pages Moll is to undergo a repentance that is clearly meant to be valid, but here, to offset any suspicion that she is a mere gallows-penitent, Defoe gives us a brief specimen of this kind of pseudo-repentance, and makes the point that it *is* hollow and ineffectual. Prompted by the imminence of punishment, rather than by actual abhorrence of sin, and seeking neither forgiveness nor comfort from God, such "repentance" can issue only in despair: thus Moll is oppressed by thoughts of "nothing night or day, but of gibbets and halters, evil spirits and devils" (217). These partial or false repentances contribute to the book in several ways. Through their very recurrence, they provide one thematic link between outwardly diverse episodes; through their implicit contrast with real repentance, [138] they help to characterize Moll's spiritual state as they occur; finally, they are among the factors that heighten the significance of the genuine repentance which finally takes place.

I have described a second feature of Moll's vicissitudes, between her initial misstep and her conversion, as an adherence to that weak and faltering guide, her own reason. Much has been written about Defoe's faith in human reason, but the evidence in *Moll Flanders*, as in *Robinson Crusoe*, points to an attitude by no means sanguine. Moll's reasoning is mentioned almost as frequently as her reflecting and considering, but it is no more reliable a guide. Indeed, on two crucial occasions she speaks of being "reasoned out of her reason." This is the phrase she uses first to describe the effect of the elder brother's arguments in favor of her marrying the younger brother (48), and she uses it again to characterize the governess's sophistic invalidation of her Lancashire marriage (137). Perhaps the most notable instance in Defoe's fiction of the speciousness of "reason" when pitted against morality occurs in *Roxana*, in the long debate with the Dutch merchant over female independence (Aitken edition, I, 1967f.), but these two scenes in *Moll Flanders* make the same point. With "reason" (such as it is) as her guide, rather than religious conviction, Moll is vulnerable to the plausible arguments of wicked counselors.

If this were all, however, we might be justified in regarding "reason" as merely one of the external forces which Moll alleges in extenuation of her misdeeds. But Defoe goes further, to lay responsibility squarely with Moll herself. He displays the fundamental inadequacy of reason to cope not only with the devil's advocates, but also with Moll's own conflicting inclinations. In [139] other words, even when reason is not threatened by sophistry from without, it is liable to be undermined from within by emotions too strong for it. Thus we find Moll admitting, when she determines to marry the "gentleman tradesman," that "I was hurried on (by my fancy to a gentleman) to ruin myself in the grossest manner that ever woman did" (51). We may recall Crusoe confessing in the same vein that in undertaking the slaving voyage "I was hurried on, and obeyed blindly the dictates of my fancy rather than my reason" (p. 43). Defoe appears to have believed that no principle, however rationally discovered or adhered to, is proof against the power of "fancy" or irrational impulse unless it is buttressed by religious conviction.[14] Earlier discussion of Robinson Crusoe's and Robert Drury's motives for going to sea has shown how much force Defoe attaches to "inclination" as a spring of action, and how deeply skeptical he is of it. He not only fails to share the optimistic faith, becoming [140] current in his day, that human "gust" or impulse is naturally towards the good, but he doubts that inclination, even when it is clearly malignant, can be checked by mere reason. This belief might be shown by tracing the workings of reason and inclination in greater detail, but it also emerges from the portrait of Moll's gradual hardening.

I have suggested that between her seduction and her conversion, a process of hardening makes up the basic pattern of her spiritual development. That she undergoes some kind of hardening is clear from her own repeated admissions, so that even critics who deny the presence of any meaningful structure in the book recognize this as a prominent feature of Moll's psychological make-up. But the traditional significance of this hardening process and its specific function in the book remain to be investigated. Earlier chapters have alluded to it briefly, pointing out that in both spiritual autobiography and its fictional derivants, some degree of hardening inevitably attends any prolonged delay in conversion, and that the stages of such hardening often supply the principle for selecting and organizing the events narrated prior to conversion.

The first thing to emphasize about hardness of heart is that it is in fact a spiritual state, not merely a psychological one. To be sure, its manifestations are of a kind nowadays approached psychologically. But so long as men continued to believe in the reality and importance

---

[14]The behavior of Moll's Bath lover affords a good illustration of this. He spends a night in bed with her, but she reports that he "rose up and dressed him in the morning, and left me as innocent for him as the day I was born"; nor, as she is careful to observe, "did he act thus on a principle of religion at all, but of mere affection" (94). "I own it was a noble principle," she further remarks, and he manages to maintain it for some time. But one night, "owing to our having yielded too far to our mutual inclinations," as Moll explains (97), she "exchanged the place of friend for that unmusical, harsh-sounding title of whore" (95). Thus a "principle" of behavior, unfortified by religious conviction, ultimately gives way before powerful inclination. Cf. also Defoe's remark in *Applebee's Journal* for March 18, 1721, that "It is Religion alone, which is the Bond of Virtue in the World; the Awe of a Divine Power, and a Sense of the Majesty and Vengeance of Heaven, being alone able to restrain the Vices and Lusts of Men" (Lee, *Life and Recently Discovered Writings*, II, 353).

of the soul, psychology remained largely a method of analyzing and describing the state of a soul through its outward workings. It is not that the psychological and the spiritual were opposed: the description and analysis might have the precision we associate with science, but their ultimate object was spiritual. [141] The evidence for these contentions has already been given. They are reintroduced here as a reminder that hardness of heart is essentially a spiritual phenomenon, and that even the most painstaking narrations of it may have spiritual assessment rather than psychological realism as their purpose.

A second and more obvious point about spiritual hardening is precisely that it is a process. Like regeneration, the term "hardness of heart" can represent a fully realized state, but it more commonly stands for an ongoing, cumulative development.[15] It is not reached instantaneously, through a single misdeed, any more than is regeneration achieved through the bare experience of conversion: each requires time and persistence.[16] In any case, a traditional conception of hardness of heart as something essentially spiritual, not merely psychological, and as an unfolding process, not an absolute state, stands in the background of Defoe's treatment of the theme in *Moll Flanders*. [142]

It is true that Moll's hardening is portrayed in greatest detail during her actual criminal career, and some critics have seen it as beginning only with her first theft. Nevertheless it can be maintained that she undergoes gradual hardening from the point of her seduction, so that the process gives a continuity to her behavior throughout the larger part of the book.[17] She explicitly alludes to it on more than one occasion, but her very qualms and revulsions afford evidence that

[15]The notion of hardness of heart as a gradual process gave rise to fairly elaborate attempts at schematization. But owing perhaps to the wide variation between observed cases, or perhaps simply to the lack of authoritative Biblical or patristic models, the steps in hardening were never entirely standardized. What may be the most ambitious "brief of the degrees of hardness" during the period is the section of Joseph Caryl's commentary on Job 9:4, in which nine separate steps are distinguished: see his *Exposition...of Job*, I, 763–64. Cf. also Samuel Wright, *A Treatise on the Deceitfulness of Sin; And its leading Men to Hardness of Heart: With the Means Appointed to prevent both its Hardning and Deceiving*, 5th edition (1735; 1st edition, 1726), pp. 62–71.

[16]On the role of custom or habit in hardening the heart, see Robert Bolton, *Some Generall Directions for a Comfortable Walking with God*, 5th edition (1638), p. 233; William Bates, "How to Bear Afflictions," *Cripplegate Exercises*, II, 590; Taylor, *Unum Necessarium*, in *Works*, VII, 151; Tillotson, "Of the Difficulty of reforming Vicious Habits," in *Works*, II, 195.

[17]Even while she remains in Colchester, her initial vanity grows into something more baneful, as her remarks on the death of the younger brother indicate (50). Bearing in mind the care taken to establish vanity rather than lust as the basis of her initial compliance, one sees that her guilt is compounded, not reduced, when the younger brother makes her an honest woman. The trouble is not that she fails to love him, but that her attachment to the elder brother, which she retains rather than repents, assumes new proportions.

this is actually her situation. It may seem paradoxical to argue that her recurrent squeamishness is a symptom of hardening, but I think this is the case. If so, it helps to solve a problem in her characterization that has disturbed various critics. This problem, and one possible solution to it, are stated as follows in James Sutherland's stimulating introduction to a recent edition of the book: "As Moll grows old in crime, Defoe is concerned to show us how her moral arteries harden, and it may now be objected, more plausibly than ever, that such a woman would no longer be capable of the tenderness and the moral scruples that Moll continues from time to time to show. But to say that is to have too rigid a conception of human character.... Moll has the inconsistency that comes from being alive; she lives for the moment, and she changes with circumstances." [18]

The inconsistency may be only apparent, however. [143] If we take into account the kind of behavior traditionally associated with hardening, Moll's periodic scruples are not really self-contradictory. They tend to follow the pattern described in a typical sermon "Of the Danger, Nature, and Malignity of a Hard-Heart": "... it is with Conscience, as with a Dog that keeps a Country-House, tho' he opens and runs fiercely at a Stranger, yet he lies still and is silent when any of the Family comes in; and the frequent Conversation at the House, will in some time so perfectly reconcile him to the Stranger, that he will not bite, nor so much as move his Tongue against him. We may easily observe in Men great Reluctance to some new Sins, who indulge themselves at the same time in others never a whit less criminal; and a little Time and familiar Practice will take off their Prejudice against those Vices, at which for the present they are very clamorous." [19] Naturally what William Hopkins has in mind is most pronounced at the very outset of a sinful career, and this part of his argument is duplicated by various writers on habitual sin. [20] But what is particularly relevant to the issue raised by Mr. Sutherland is the observation that men have "great Reluctance to some new Sins, who indulge themselves at the same time in others [144] never a whit less criminal"; for it is this tendency that largely accounts for Moll's scruples, and resolves their apparent inconsistency. I have spoken of the way her sentimental and partial repentances reveal, by ironic contrast with real repentance, her actual impenitence, and the way her fleeting "reflections"

[18](Boston, 1959), p. xv.
[19]*Seventeen Sermons of the Reverend and Learned Dr. William Hopkins* (1708), p. 294; cf. pp. 299–300.
[20]Indeed, the idea traces back to Augustine, who had asserted that "At first we are ashamed of sin; but custom makes us bold and confident, apt to proclaim, not to conceal our shame. For though at first it seemed great, yet every day of use makes it less, and at last all is well, it is a very nothing" (paraphrased by Jeremy Taylor, *Unum Necessarium*, in *Works*, VII, 170). Cf. Tillotson's simile comparing sinners with travellers, in his sermon "Of the Deceitfulness and Danger of Sin," *Works*, I, 207.

and "considerations" indicate, through a similar contrast with genuine self-scrutiny, her actual spiritual torpor. Her scruples should probably be regarded in the same light: they do not belie her hardening, but illustrate its very progress; they do not contradict but confirm it.

Turning to specific instances, we find that Moll is subject to various scruples after parting from her Lancashire husband, and before marrying the London clerk. She proves pregnant, which is "a perplexing thing" on several accounts. She declares at one point that "indeed I would have been glad to miscarry, but I could never entertain so much as a thought of taking anything to make me miscarry; I abhorred, I say, so much as the thought of it" (128; cf. 134). The child is born, but must be gotten out of the way if Moll is to marry the London clerk. As mentioned earlier, she has scruples even about the legality of contracting a new marriage, but her governess manages to reason her out of her reason. The old lady, whom Moll has learned to call mother, is equally resourceful and accommodating in the matter of disposing of the child. She proposes that Moll "must do even as other conscientious mothers have done" before her, and give it to one of the people who are paid "to take the child off the parent's hands, and to take care of it as long as it lives" (139), although as Moll recognizes, the practice amounts to "a contrived method for murder; that [145] is to say, killing [one's] children with safety" (137).[21] But Moll strenuously dissociates herself from the whores, the "conscientious mothers" who avail themselves of all the governess's facilities: "let me be what I would," she affirms, "I was not come up to that pitch of hardness, common to the profession" (139). She lays particular stress on the bonds of nature and affection which link her to the child, contrasting herself with the governess, who, "as she was hardened in these things beyond all possibility of being touched with the religious part, and the scruples about the murder, so she was equally impenetrable in that part of which related to affection" (138).

What are we to make of Moll's protestations throughout this scene? On the assumption that they are genuine, is it Defoe's intention that we admire and sympathize with her? If so, does the whole bizarre setting make her nevertheless an object of unintended irony? Or does Defoe mean us to condemn Moll? Has he made her sympathetic in spite of himself? A case could be made for each possibility, but I believe the third is the correct one. We are to take Moll at her word. She puts things comparatively: she is not as hardened as the other inmates at the Sign of the Cradle, or its proprietor. She has become reconciled to a great deal, but she still has strong qualms about abortion and infanticide, and faint residual scruples about bigamy. In Hopkins's terms, she shows "great Reluctance to some new Sins,"

---

[21]On this practice, see Defoe's proposal for erecting a foundling hospital in *Augusta Triumphans* (1728).

even though her old ones do not weigh heavily upon her. She is not altogether hardened, but hardening, and because this is a gradual [146] process, not a simple state of being, she can accept some things and balk at others without real self-contradiction. What is required for consistency's sake is merely that she accept more and more, and balk at less and less.

Nor do I think the essentially critical view of Moll at this stage of her career is weakened, much less negated, by anything unintentionally sympathetic in the portrait. I have spoken of Moll's recurrent tearfulness as a characteristic of her shallow and abortive pseudo-repentances, and there is little reason to suppose that her sentimentality on this occasion is any more redeeming. Moreover, it is significant that she appeals to nature and affection in her abhorrence of doing away with the child. Here, as in her discussion of the Bath lover's "noble principle," she sharply distinguishes between religion and affection as sanctions of action. By this time there should be little doubt that Defoe attaches a very equivocal value to "affection," and regards it at best as a fitful and precarious guide.[22] When he speaks of "affection," he invests it with little intrinsic or independent merit as a moral sentiment, and displays little faith in benevolence and fellow-feeling: it may place scruples in the way of [147] vice, but, if unsupported by religious conviction, it cannot withstand strong temptation or contrary inclination.

The scruples to which Mr. Sutherland actually refers, however, are those that continue to beset Moll after she has begun her career of theft. These may admit of the same explanation: rather than belying her hardening, they are symptomatic of it. All her palpitations over the first theft might seem to indicate that her hardening really begins only at this point. Her initial essay in shoplifting undeniably marks another fresh start in the narrative, but there does not seem to be any comparable break in her spiritual development. We may recall that she says of her years with the banker's clerk, "sometimes I flattered myself that I had sincerely repented." Partial repentance may cause a change in outward behavior, and, given favorable circumstances, such changes may be lasting. But such "repentance" does not alter, or even interrupt, one's inward decline. As we observed in connection with Crusoe's career, the failure to repent efficaciously of old sins is spiritually equivalent to the commission of new ones. In

---

[22]For Defoe's evaluation of "affection," compare n. 14 above, and the following passage from *Street-Robberies, Consider'd* [1728], p. 10: "I was no sooner brought into this World to breath freer Air, but my Mother thought me as great a Burthen to her as she did the Day before I was Born, therefore thought of many Stratagems to get rid of me, at least to procure something for my Support; for she own'd she had some small Affection for me. She got a Hand-Basket, into which, pretty late, she put my Worship, and ty'd me Decently to a Knocker of a Door in *Cornhill*, (for I was a Citizen born) and then stood aloof to see the Event."

these terms, then, Moll's five virtuous years do not preclude the continuity of her spiritual decay. In other words, her career in crime is not so much a case of innocence giving way to guilt, as of existing guilt taking on new degrees and dimensions. It is true that she is moved to steal out of necessity. Her initial theft is extenuated, if not fully condoned, by the fact that there are "temptations which it is not in the power of human nature to resist."[23] But she notes in the same [148] sentence that "as covetousness is the root of all evil, so poverty is the worst of all snares"; what is so sinister about the first theft is that poverty opens a breach for covetousness. As she had observed of an earlier lapse, with the Bath lover, "the way being thus cleared, and the bars of virtue and conscience thus removed, we had the less to struggle with" (95). Thus necessity may justify the initial misdeed, but if repentance does not follow, the lapse becomes a settled course of action, which in turn is culpable whatever the original provocation.[24] In taking this attitude towards Moll's [149] crimes, Defoe is neither rigid nor lax, but stands in a humane tradition. Admitting a legitimate plea in defense of an isolated lapse, he nevertheless deplores the tendency of one sin to make way for others, and treats the habitual sin with due severity. His demonstration of the way single misdeeds become habitual sins, however, is more interesting than his judgment of the one or the other.

This process begins with the scene following the theft. At first Moll is under "dreadful impressions of fear, and in such terrors of mind,

[23]149; cf. Maximillian Novak's interesting article on "The Problem of Necessity in Defoe's Fiction," *PQ*, XL (1961), pp. 513–24. Mr. Novak is most informative on secular theories of natural law in the seventeenth century; on one point, however, his remarks seem to me misleading. Speaking of Defoe's "failure to distinguish between poverty and necessity," Mr. Novak says that "If he has little authority from the philosophers for this radical departure, he has even less from the religious treatises of his fellow Dissenters," and he goes on to quote Matthew Henry and Richard Baxter to the effect that necessity is not a sufficient justification for theft. But for the equation between poverty and necessity, see Timothy Cruso, *Discourses Upon the Rich Man and Lazarus* (1697), p. 24; for the same equation, and the view that necessity may justify theft, see Francis Osborne's essay on Proverbs 30:8 in his *Works*, 8th edition (1682), pp. 514, 518–19 and *passim*. For further evidence that Defoe's equation of poverty and necessity marks no "radical departure," compare the following statement by Samuel Butler: "Poverty and want are greater Temptations than Riches; when our Savior had fasted 40 days, and as many Nights, the Devil thought it the fittest time to attack him: and St. Peter denyd and forswore Christ when he saw him in Affliction. For wealth and Luxury can but Tempt: Necessity compel's." ("Religion," in *Characters and Passages from Note-Books*, edited by A. R. Waller [Cambridge, 1908], p. 298.) A very ample and intelligent discussion of these questions, which Defoe is likely to have read, occurs in Part IV of Jeremy Collier's *Essays upon several Moral Subjects* (1709); "Of Theft" occupies pp. 264–361, and these topics are considered especially at pp. 326–31.

[24]It should be noted that it is the *anticipation* of poverty, rather than the *fact* of it, that afflicts Moll: thus she says "I saw nothing before me but the utmost distress; and this represented itself so lively to my thoughts, that it seemed as if it had come, before it was really very near" (150).

though I was perfectly safe, that I cannot express the manner of it" (152). She speculates that she may have robbed some poor widow like herself, and this thought torments her for several days.[25] Yet her own distresses silence these reflections, and she reports that "the prospect of my own starving... hardened my heart by degrees" (153). She is still able to pray for deliverance, although she confesses that "my prayers had no hope in them... it was all fear without and dark within; and I reflected on my past life as not repented of, that Heaven was now beginning to punish me, and would make me as miserable as I had been wicked" (*ibid.*). Her final comment is that "Had I gone on here I had perhaps been a true penitent," but as on previous occasions her "reflections" and convictions subside. At this point, then, her criminal career is at a stage frequently described by divines by the simile of a spring, easily dammed at first but quickly becoming [150] a flood if allowed to proceed. A notable statement from Jeremy Taylor enforcing the argument that sins eventually "destroy the soul by their abode, who at their first entry might have been killed with the pressure of a little finger," has already been quoted.[26] This principle finds expression in autobiographical narrative in *An Alarme for Sinners* (1679). Robert Foulkes, who could speak with some authority, observes that "the heights of wickedness appear so monstrous at a distance to one that is but newly entering upon it, that he flatters himself he shall never come thither; but after long continuance in it, and suppressing many Convictions, violating our Vows and Resolutions, after many Evasions to shift off the imputation, apologies to excuse of lessen it,... a man becomes strangely altered" (pp. 9–10). By failing to repent of this sin at its "first entry," Moll eases the way for its further onsets. Moreover, once she has quelled her first "dreadful impressions," she readily finds the kind of evasions and apologies that Foulkes speaks of. Thus her second "adventure," when she takes the child's necklace, causes her "no great concern": she rationalizes that "as I did the child no harm, I only thought I had given the parents a just reproof for their negligence, in leaving the poor lamb to come home by itself, and it would teach them to take more care another time" (154). The phrase "I only thought" should perhaps be emphasized; Defoe makes clear that this is the way Moll excused or lessened the crime at the time, not when she came to write of it.[27] [151]

[25]For partial analogues to this scene, see *Colonel Jacque*, I, 72–73, 96–100; *Street-Robberies, Consider'd*, p. 20f.

[26]The same image is used by Whichcote, *Select Sermons* (Edinburgh, 1742), p. 93; cf. also Austen, *The Spirituall use of an Orchard*, p. 98.

[27]On this passage, see Watt, *The Rise of the Novel*, p. 124. Postulating a Puritan "tendency for the individual to be mercifully blind to his own faults"—a tendency scarcely characteristic of the diarists and autobiographers we have examined—Mr. Watt maintains that Moll Flanders frequently exemplifies it, and cites this passage as evidence. But what Defoe gives us here is the immediate response of Moll the protagonist, not the

In the episodes that follow, Defoe skillfully undermines Moll's "Evasions to shift off the imputation." We have seen that he makes Crusoe repeat the substance of his original sin, so that what might have seemed an isolated lapse is shown to become an ingrained pattern of action. He achieves the same effect here by placing Moll in the household of her old governess. Here she is able to live cheaply, and to farm out her son by the banker's clerk (which she now does with no compunction); most important, she gets "some quilting work for ladies' beds, petticoats, and the like" (157). The result is that her pretexts for thieving are removed: "but as poverty brought me in," she confesses, "so avarice kept me in, till there was no going back" (160).[28] Thus covetousness, rather than [152] narrow circumstances, becomes her sole motivation. From the first she had been legally guilty; now the moral blame too is entirely hers.

It is clear from Defoe's other works that he believed in the existence of the devil, and it is worth inquiring briefly whether Moll's allusions to him involve any lessening or transfer of her own responsibility. It seems to me that they do not. At first it was the devil who "laid the snare" and prompted her, "as if he had spoke," to snatch the bundle from the apothecary's shop: yet there is no attempt to represent the actual theft as anything other than a fully voluntary act. But when she reaches the point that avarice "keeps her in," Moll speaks of the devil as follows: "Thus I, that was once in the devil's clutches, was held fast there as with a charm, and had no power to go without the circle, till I was engulfed in labyrinths of trouble too great to get out at all" (160). This might seem to imply that some external power, rather than Moll herself, is responsible. But this is probably

retrospective judgment of Moll the narrator. In an autobiography, real or fictional, such phrases as "I only thought" make a great difference; by means of them, Defoe can differentiate between Moll's initial evasiveness and her point of view as regenerate narrator. For another view of this scene, however, see Howard L. Koonce, "Moll's Muddle: Defoe's Use of Irony in *Moll Flanders*," *ELH*, XXX (1963), pp. 378–79. Cf. also A. A. Mendilow, "The Time Locus of the Pseudo–Author," in *Time and the Novel* (1952), pp. 89–93; and Wayne Booth, *The Rhetoric of Fiction* (Chicago, 1961), pp. 321–22.

[28].The following remarks in the second volume of *The Compleat English Tradesman* (1727) illuminate the connection between necessity and avarice: "every Station of Life has its Snares attending it, and every Degree of Business has its Invitation to do Evil:
1. Necessity tempts the poor Man.
2. Avarice tempts the rich.
It is true, they are both, to the last Degree, criminal in yielding to the Temptation; but the latter much more than the former; for he is tempted by that which is in itself a Crime: 'Tis not criminal to be poor; Necessity is no Offence till it makes itself a Snare, and places itself in the *Devil's* Stead: But *Avarice* is a Crime in its Nature;...The first is an Accident to the Man, a Circumstance of Life, and comes from without; but Avarice is within the Man; 'tis mingled, as we say, with his Animal Life; it runs in his Blood; it has insinuated itself into his very Species, and he is truly, as the Text says, *drawn aside by his own Lust, and enticed*" (Introduction, pp. 21–22).

not Defoe's intention. Instead, he may be representing her spiritual condition in quite conventional terms, for hardening in sin had long been described as a kind of impotence, and as a kind of slavery to Satan. The origin of these metaphors is Biblical: thus Tillotson points out that "to express to [153] us the miserable condition of such persons, [Scripture] representeth them as perfect slaves to their vices, that have sold themselves to do wickedness, and *are led captive by Satan at his pleasure.*"[29] These remarks are typical of seventeenth- and early-eighteenth-century discussions of habitual sin, of which the most powerful and influential may be the fifth chapter of Jeremy Taylor's *Unum Necessarium*. In any case, they provide a helpful gloss to Moll's talk about being held fast in the devil's clutches, and having no power to get out of them. Far from diminishing her own guilt, such statements seem intended to show just how grave her situation has become.[30]

Moreover, the passage just quoted helps to account for the "moral scruples" she continues to feel. Hardened by success, her will is becoming enslaved, but her understanding is not yet darkened. Her case still resembles that expressed by St. Paul's "What I would, that do I not, but what I hate, that do I" (Romans 7:15), [154] and by the frequently quoted lines, "*Video meliora, proboque, /Deteriora sequor*"; so that rather than being implausible or self-contradictory, Moll's recurrent qualms actually emphasize the hold avarice now has upon her.[31]

One could trace the continuation of this process through her subsequent crimes, but it is worth turning directly to her imprisonment in Newgate. Defoe's picture of this "emblem of hell" has been regarded quite rightly as a forcible indictment of contemporary penal conditions, which served to harden criminals more often than reclaim them. His characterization of the Newgate Ordinary, for instance, preaching confession and repentance in the morning, and drunk

[29]"Of the Deceitfulness and Danger of Sin," in *Works*, I, 209; he is paraphrasing John 8:44. Elsewhere he observes that "Habit and Custom is a kind of second nature; and so far as any thing is natural, so far it is necessary, and we cannot do otherwise. By passing from one degree of sin to another, Men become fix'd and harden'd in their Wickedness, and do insensibly bring themselves into that state, out of which they are utterly unable to recover themselves" ("The Necessity of Supernatural Grace, in order to a Christian Life," in *Works*, VIII, 504). Cf. also Edward Waple, *Thirty Sermons*, p. 94.

[30]Moll's references to fate are probably to be regarded in the same light; compare, for instance, the statement that "It seemed to me that I was hurried on by an inevitable fate to this day of misery" (215). Defoe holds that the Devil really does exist and that "Fate" does not, but the point is that neither power actually dictates Moll's behavior from without; both serve primarily to objectify compulsions within her, for which she herself is responsible.

[31]The lines from Ovid (*Met.* VII, 20) are quoted by Tillotson in his sermon "Of the Difficulty of reforming Vicious Habits," in *Works*, II, 196.

with brandy by noon, is a powerful expression of reforming indignation. Yet his undeniable concern, here as elsewhere, with the force of external environment does not preclude a more fundamental interest in the spiritual processes taking place within Moll. Throughout the book society is responsible, to a large extent, for her outward vicissitudes, but her own reactions to them give rise to her spiritual predicament. For the latter, she alone is responsible, and to this Defoe devotes the bulk of his attention, even while he is chronicling the horrors of Newgate. In other words, he reports "the hellish noise, the roaring, swearing and clamour, the stench and nastiness, and all the dreadful afflicting things" that Moll sees there, not merely because of the exotic appeal of such a narrative to his respectable readers, which it would surely have, or merely because he regards the place as a foul blemish on [155] English justice and humanity, which he clearly does, but because of its hideous effect on the souls of its inmates, who generally enter it in a hardened state only to be further hardened while they remain there. In such a place they seal their damnation, rather than avert it.

Moll's last pseudo-repentance has already been mentioned: soon after she is committed she repents of the crimes that had brought her there, not because they were sinful in themselves, but simply because she was now to suffer for them. We have seen in Crusoe's case that even genuine convictions lead to a sense of helpless despondency, out of which the penitent is rescued only by the intervention of God's grace, and here Moll undergoes a grim parody of the process. Fearing for her neck, not her soul, her convictions are lame. They lead to despair over her bodily, not her spiritual fate, and from this she is rescued, not by God's grace, but by "the indefatigable application of [her] diligent governess," who arranges a delay in her trial. Moll describes the result very vividly, declaring that "I ought to have esteemed it as a space given me for repentance, and have employed it as such, but it was not in me. I was sorry, as before, for being in Newgate, but had few signs of repentance about me.

"On the contrary, like the water in the hollows of mountains, which petrifies and turns into stone whatever they are suffered to drop upon; so the continual conversing with such a crew of hell-hounds had the same common operation upon me as upon other people. I degenerated into stone; I turned first stupid and senseless, and then brutish and thoughtless, and at last raving mad as any of them" (218).

The process I have been tracing is thus extended to [156] its furthest point. Each of Moll's abortive repentances has left increased hardness in its wake, but despite the gradual enslavement of her will, she has retained some capacity to reflect on her actions. Her judicial power has survived her executive power; now, however, that too is lost. She supplements the above confession by recording that "a certain strange lethargy of soul possessed me. I had no trouble, no apprehensions, no sorrow about me ... my sense, my reason, nay, my conscience, were all asleep.... I neither had a heart to ask God's mercy, or indeed to think of it. And in this, I think, I have given a brief description of the completest misery on earth" (218–19). As her very anguish ceases, her spiritual condition becomes completely wretched. With this step, the process of hardening reaches its climax.

The traditional stages of repentance have been examined in previous chapters, and it is unnecessary to recapitulate them here. It is enough to say that when Moll finally does repent, the genuineness of the process is emphasized not only by its contrast with all the insincere and incomplete versions that have preceded it, but also by its conformity to the classic pattern of spiritual rebirth. Consideration was commonly regarded as the first step towards repentance, and long discussions of it were extrapolated from Luke 15:17, "And when he came to himself...". In Moll's case, the reunion with her Lancashire husband, and the news that she is to be tried at the next Session, cause her "wretched boldness of spirit" to abate. "I began to think," she says, "and to think indeed is one real advance from hell to heaven. All that hardened state and temper of soul ... is but [157] a deprivation of thought; he that is restored to his thinking, is restored to himself" (221).[32] Her consideration does not merge directly into conviction, however; when one of the keepers advises her to prepare for death, she is still not brought, as she puts it, "to any sense of being a miserable sinner, as indeed I was, and of confessing my sins to God, and begging pardon for the sake of Jesus Christ" (222). Nevertheless her reawakening out of utter "lethargy of soul" does make her amenable to the exhortations of the minister who visits her after her trial, and his earnest discourses do evoke genuine convictions in her. She now reviews and laments her past, not merely out of dread of human punishment, but with a sense of having offended God and man, and with a concern for her eternal welfare.[33] The confession that the minister draws from her represents a further phase of her convictions, but the actual culmination of her repentance comes the following morning, with "the excellent discourses of this extraordinary man" again acting as a catalyst. Moll reports that "he revived my heart, and brought me into such a condition that I never knew anything of in my life before. I was covered with shame and tears for things past, yet

[32]In view of her condition, this may seem a very sanguine notion of what is required for self-restoration, but Moll is describing merely the coming-to-oneself which is the necessary preliminary to repentance; compare Crusoe's description of the same process: "Conscience, that had slept so long, began to awake" (Aitken edition, p. 99).

[33]"It was now that, for the first time, I felt any real signs of repentance. I now began to look back upon my past life with abhorrence, and having a kind of view into the other side of time, the things of life ... began to look with a different aspect, and quite another shape, than they did before" (225).

had at the [158] same time a secret surprising joy at the prospect of being a true penitent, and obtaining the comfort of a penitent — I mean the hope of being forgiven" (226). We may recall Crusoe lifting his heart as well as his hands up to heaven, "in a kind of ecstasy of joy," upon discovering the text of Acts 5:31, and affirming that "from this time I began to have hope that God would hear me." Moll's joy and hope are of the same kind. We have seen that Defoe tends to describe conversion in a rather subdued manner, and that by his time, few besides Baptists and Quakers retained the old enthusiastic way of revelling in the transports of rebirth. It should be stressed again, however, that this wariness of presumption and cant on the part of Anglicans and conservative Nonconformists implies no lessening of the importance attached to conversion, and no real change in the conception of it. The difference is essentially one of style or tone, with a decorous restraint moderating the jubilant excesses of the past.

Moll's regeneration is portrayed in far less detail than Crusoe's. In the first chapter we stated as a kind of structural law of spiritual autobiography that the greater the attention paid to events before conversion, the less the emphasis given to what happens afterwards, and vice versa. A work that traces in detail the progress of sin, with conversion finally snatching the sinner from the very jaws of hell, will rarely have much to say about subsequent trials or relapses, and this is the case in *Moll Flanders*.[34] While conversion [159] supplies the point of view of the narrator, and the resolution towards which the narrative itself moves, the main substance of the narrative is the spiritual decay that makes repentance ever more necessary, but ever more difficult. By now it should be clear that conversion can provide the organizing principle of a narrative, most of which actually runs directly counter to it. There is a similar paradox in many novels and plays that have marriage as their organizing principle, yet whose actual content consists mainly

[34]The indications of Moll's altered spiritual state may be noted briefly. For one thing, the references to being hurried on by Fate which marked her earlier career now give way to acknowledgments of the existence and goodness of Providence. More subtle is the equation Defoe creates between two kinds of new life, the one physical or geographical, the other spiritual. Thus even when Jemmy is arguing against going to Virginia, and finds "the passage into another state much more tolerable at the gallows" (236), the pun helps to suggest the fundamental change which transportation can involve; sailing from England to America is comparable to passing through death from this life to another. Again, Moll's arguments in favor of transportation more directly contribute to the equation, especially when she speaks of living "as new people in a new world," and of launching out "into a new world, as I may call it." As she uses it, the term is not merely a geographical cliché: the change of surroundings can and should be matched by a change of heart on the part of the transported convicts. It is true that in the "Author's Preface" (p. 7) we are told that Moll "lived, it seems, to be very old, but was not so extraordinary a penitent as she was at first." This follows a return to the *Old* World, however, and is qualified by the remark that "indeed she always spoke with abhorrence of her former life, and of every part of it." Although the completeness of her regeneration is called into question, the genuineness of her conversion is not.

of the delays and obstructions besetting the ultimately happy pair. In much the same way, conversion can give thematic orientation to a chronicle of sin and hardening, these being the delays and obstructions peculiar to it.

The spiritual evolution I have traced not only helps to account for the apparent inconsistency of Moll's "moral scruples" but also affords grounds for questioning [160] certain graver criticisms of the book. The episodic nature of the plot, with all its abruptnesses and discontinuities, has led many critics to doubt the presence of any coherent initial plan on Defoe's part, or of any internal consistency in the action itself. My response to this has been that a work may possess thematic coherence despite any amount of incoherence in the outward narrative, and that a conventional pattern of spiritual decay supplies this coherence in *Moll Flanders*. In the second place, various critics have found Moll's own character as uneven as the story of her adventures: what she is has seemed as inconsistent as what she does. This view has been countered with evidence that many apparent ambiguities or self-contradictions in her character are owing not to any "double vision" on Defoe's part, but rather to a traditional conception of the sinner's progress, which Moll's portrayal largely embodies.

If my arguments do lessen the force of some recent criticisms of *Moll Flanders*, other difficulties remain. I have suggested, for instance, that the achievement of a balance between narrative and spiritualization may be the most basic criterion of literary merit that one can apply to spiritual autobiographies. Since *Moll Flanders* owes much to the autobiographical tradition, it is appropriate to inquire how well the book satisfies this norm. My opinion is that the two elements are not so fully in equilibrium as in *Robinson Crusoe*, but that narrative has not yet outstripped spiritualization as drastically as in some of Defoe's other fiction. As we have seen, a good deal of the narrative in *Robinson Crusoe* requires no explicit "improvement": many of the episodes possess conventional spiritual overtones, so that Defoe need not define their significance. In *Moll Flanders*, on the other hand, most of the actions [161] have no traditional metaphoric meaning, so that their implications have to be spelled out by the narrator. This is managed less arbitrarily than in certain genuine autobiographies, but there is a baldness about some of Moll's commentary that *Crusoe* generally avoids through its use of symbolic action and deft allusion. It is better, after all, for spiritual meaning to be embedded in the narrative itself than to be attached to the narrative through interpretative labels. Thus the lack of actions that carry in themselves familiar, well-defined spiritual significance may place *Moll Flanders* at a certain disadvantage relative to *Robinson Crusoe*.

A more basic departure from the convention of spiritual autobiography is that some portions of the narrative are not spiritualized at all, either implicitly or explicitly; or, at any rate, they are not fully assimilated into the spiritual framework which has been described. We have seen that the impulse to narrate an event for its own sake is latent even in the true spiritual autobiography, although there it tends to be repressed by the demand for spiritual significance. What we find in *Moll Flanders* is that this impulse sometimes has its way: other strains in the heredity of the book assert themselves along with—and contrary to—the autobiographical one. Despite the presence of a thematic pattern which is firm and coherent, there are various passages to which it does not extend. As comments on woman's role in society, as reflections on commerce, crime, and colonization, or simply as gobbets of "narrative realism," many of these passages have an undeniable vitality of their own. At the same time, their very effectiveness tends to obscure the structural integrity which, as I have tried to show, the book as a whole does possess. [162]

APPENDIXES

Appendix A: THE MISPLACED PASSAGE

The passage below was included in both the first and third editions of *Moll Flanders*, but it was clearly out of place in both editions. (In the first edition, the passage was placed between the paragraph ending "... splitting the Chest to peices." and the one beginning "The Ship began now to fill..." [p. 244 of the present edition]; in the third edition, the passage was between the paragraph ending "... or with what he had, but by Directions." and the one beginning "Our first business..." [p. 243 of the present edition].) I have here placed the passage in an appendix because I believe that it is not only out of place in either of those two locations, but does not really belong in the text at all. Much of the material included is substantially the same as that in the two paragraphs beginning "Then I read..." and "She soon agreed..." (p. 243 of this edition), and the length is almost exactly the same. My guess is that the passage below was originally in the manuscript in the place of those two paragraphs, and that Defoe decided to revise the passage to make the governess's role more prominent. The printer, according to my theory, printed the new passage (the two paragraphs on p. 243) but failed to eliminate the rejected passage. (The printer had clearly been having severe difficulty with the manuscript just before, and the text there is in the worst shape of any place in the entire volume.) If this theory is correct, it would also explain the first edition confusion on p. 249 (see the note there): that section was probably written before the new passage was inserted, and when the new passage changed the status of Moll's husband, the rest of the manuscript was not revised to conform with the new information.

In this Condition I lay for three Weeks in the Ship, not knowing whether I should have my Husband with me or no; and therefore not resolving how, or in what manner to receive the honest Boatswain's proposal, which indeed he thought a little strange at first.

At the End of this time, behold my Husband came on Board; he look'd with a dejected angry Countenance, his great Heart was swell'd with Rage and Disdain; to be drag'd along with three Keepers[1] of *Newgate*, and put on Board like a Convict, when he had not so much

---

[1]Men who had long resided in Newgate. "Keepers" is used elsewhere in the novel to mean prison officials, and it is possible that the text should read "drag'd along by three Keepers...."

351

as been brought to a Tryal; he made loud complaints of it by his Friends, for it seems he had some interest;[2] but his Friends got some Cheque in their Application, and were told he had had *Favour enough*, and that they had receiv'd such an Account of him since the last Grant of his Transportation, that he ought to think himself very well treated that he was not prosecuted a new. This answer quieted him at once, for he knew too much what might have happen'd, and what he had room to expect; and now he saw the goodness of the Advice to him, which prevail'd with him to accept of the offer of a voluntary Transportation, and after his chagrine at these Hell Hounds, *as he call'd them*, was a little over; he look'd a little compos'd, began to be chearful, and as I was telling him how glad I was to have him once more out of their Hands, took me in his Arms, and acknowledg'd with great Tenderness, that I had given him the best Advice possible: *My Dear*, says he, *Thou hast twice sav'd my Life, from hence forward it shall be all employ'd for you, and I'll always take your Advice.*

---

[2]Influence due to personal connection.

Appendix B: PARALLEL PASSAGES FROM FIRST AND THIRD EDITIONS

The following eight passages illustrate some of the differences between the first and third editions of *Moll Flanders*. Passages from the first edition appear on the lefthand page, parallel passages from the third on the facing righthand page. Each passage has been exactly transcribed line for line from the University of Illinois copy of the first edition and from the Newberry Library copy of the third edition.

*Passage 1. See p. 15 of the present edition; this passage is from pp. 10–11 of
the first edition.*

I was now about ten Years old, and began
to look a little Womanish, for I was mighty
Grave and Humble; very Mannerly, and as I had
often heard the Ladies say I was Pretty, and
would be a very handsome Woman, so you may
besure, that hearing them say so, made me not a
little Proud; however, that Pride had no ill effect
upon me yet, only as they often gave me Money, and I gave it my old Nurse, she *honest Woman*, was so just to me, as to lay it all out again for
me, and gave me Head-Dresses, and Linnen, and
Gloves and Ribbons, and I went very Neat, and al-
waysClean; for that I would do,and if I had Rags on,
I would always be Clean, or else I would dabble
them in Water myself; but *I say*, my good Nurse,
when I had Money given me, very honestly laid it
out for me, and would always tell the Ladies, this,
or that, was bought with their Money; and this
made them oftentimes give me more; Till at last, I
was indeed call'd upon by the Magistrates as I
understood it, to go out to Service, but then I
was come to be so good a Workwoman myself,
and the Ladies were so kind to me, that it was
plain I could maintain myself, that is to say, I
could Earn as much for my Nurse as she was able
by it to keep me; so she told them, that if they
would give her leave, she would keep the Gentlewoman as she call'd me, to be her Assistant, and
teach the Children, which I was very well able to
do; for I was very nimble at my Work, and had a
good Hand with my Needle, though I was yet very
young.

From pp. 9–10 of the third edition.

I was now about Ten Years old, and began to look a little Womanish, for I was mighty Grave, very Mannerly, and as I had often heard the Ladies say I was Pretty, and would be very Handsome, you may be sure it made me not a little Proud: However, that Pride had no ill Effect upon me yet, only as they often gave me Money, and I gave it my old Nurse, she, *honest Woman*, was so just as to lay it out again for me, and gave me Head-Dresses, and Linnen, and Gloves, and I went very Neat, for if I had Rags on, I would always be Clean, or else I would dabble them in Water my self; but *I say*, my good Nurse, when I had Money given me, very honestly laid it out for me, and would always tell the Ladies this, or that, was bought with their Money; and this made them give me more, till at last, I was indeed call'd upon by the Magistrates to go out to Service; but then I was become so good a Workwoman my self, and the Ladies were so kind to me, that I was past it; for I could Earn as much for my Nurse as was enough to keep me; so she told them, that if they would give her leave, she would keep the Gentlewoman as she call'd me, to be her Assistant, and teach the Children, which I was very well able to do; for I was very nimble at my Work, tho' I was yet very young.

Passage 2. See p. 40 of the present edition; this passage is from p. 50 of the first edition.

Well, *says the Mother*, then there's one Son lost; and she said it in a very mournful Tone, as one greatly concern'd at it.

I hope not Madam, *says* Robin, no Man is lost, when a good Wife has found him.

Why but Child, *says the* old Lady, she is a Beggar.

Why then Madam, she has the more need of Charity *says* Robin; I'll take her off of the hands of the Parish, and she and I'll Beg together.

Its bad Jesting with such things, *says the Mother.*

I don't Jest Madam, *says* Robin: We'll come and beg your Pardon Madam; and your Blessing Madam, and my Fathers.

This is all out of the way Son, *says the Mother*, if you are in Earnest you are Undone.

I am afraid not *says he*, for I am really afraid she won't have me, after all my Sisters huffing and blustring; I believe I shall never be able to persuade her to it.

From p. 43 of the third edition.

Well, *says the* Mother, Then there's one Son lost; and she said it in a very mournful Tone, as one greatly concern'd at it. I hope not Madam, *says* Robin, no Man is lost, when a good Wife has found him. Why but Child, *says the old Lady*, she is a Beggar. Why then Madam, she has the more need of Charity *says* Robin; I'll take her off the hands of the Parish, and she and I'll Beg together. Its bad Jesting with such things, *says the Mother*. I don't Jest Madam, *says* Robin: We'll come and beg your Pardon, Madam; and your Blessing Madam, and my Father's. This is all out of the way Son, *says the Mother*, if you are in Earnest you are Undone. I am afraid not, *says he*, for I am really afraid she won't have me, after all my Sisters huffing, I believe I shall never be able to persuade her to it.

Passage 3. See pp. 63–64 of the present edition; this passage is from p. 88 of the first edition.

But I come now to my own Case, in which there was at this time no little Nicety. The Circumstances I was in, made the offer of a good Husband, the most necessary Thing in the World to me; but I found soon that to be made Cheap, and Easy, was not the way: It soon began to be found that the Widow had no Fortune, and to say this, was to say all that was Ill of me; for I began to be dropt in all the Discourses of Matrimony: Being well Bred, Handsome, Witty, Modest and a-greeable; all which I had allowed to my Chara-cter, whether justly, or no, is not to the Purpose; I say, all these would not do without the Dross, which was now become more valuable than Virtue itself. In short, *the Widow*, they said, *had no Money*.

I resolv'd therefore, as to the State of my pre-sent Circumstances; that it was absolutely Ne-cessary to change my Station, and make a new Appearance in some other Place where I was not known, and even to pass by another Name if I found Occasion.

From pp. 74–75 of the third edition.

But I come now to my own Case, in which there was at this time no little Nicety. The Circumstances I was in, made the Offer of a good Husband, the most necessary thing in the World to me; but I found soon that to be made Cheap and Easy, was not the way: It soon began to be found that the Widow had no Fortune, and to say this, was to say all that was Ill of me: Being well Bred, Handsome, Witty, Modest and Agreeable; all which I had allow'd to my Character, whether justly, or no, is not to the Purpose: I say, all these would not do without the Dross. In short, *the Widow they said had no Money!*

I resolv'd therefore that it was necessary to change my Station, and make a new Appearance in some other Place, and even to pass by another Name if I found Occasion.

Passage 4. See p. 65 of the present edition; this passage is from p. 90 of the first edition.

It was enough to tell her Husband this, there needed nothing on my Side; I was but to sit still and wait the Event, for it presently went all o-ver the Neighbourhood that the young Widow at Captain ——s was a Fortune, that she had at least 1500 *l.* and perhaps a great deal more, and *that the Captain said so*; and if the Captain was ask'd at any time about me, he made no scru-ple to affirm it, tho' he knew not one Word of the Matter, other than that his Wife had told him so; and in this he thought no Harm, for he really believ'd it to be so, because he had it from his Wife; so slender a Foundation will those Fel-lows build upon, if they do but think there is a Fortune in the Game: With the Reputation of this Fortune, I presently found myself bless'd with ad-mirers enough, and that I had my Choice of Men, as scarce as they said they were, *which by the way con-firms what I was saying before*: This being my Case, I who had a subtile Game to play, had nothing now, to do but to single out from them all, the pro-perest Man that might be for my Purpose; *that is to say*, the Man who was most likely to depend upon the *hear say* of a Fortune, and not enquire too far into the particulars; and unless I did this, *I did nothing*, for my Case would not bare much Enquiry.

From pp. 76–77 of the third edition.

It was enough to tell her Husband this, there needed nothing on my Side; I was but to sit still and wait the Event, for it presently went all over the Neighborhood that the young Widow at Captain ——'s was a Fortune, that she had at least 1500 *l.* and perhaps a great deal more, and *that the Captain said so*, and if the Captain was ask'd at any time about me, he made no scruple to affirm, tho' he knew not one Word of the Matter, other than that his Wife had told him so; and in this he thought no Harm, for he really believ'd it to be so. With the Reputation of this Fortune, I presently found my self bless'd with Admirers enough, and that I had my Choice of Men, as they said they were, *which by the way confirms what I was saying before*: This being my Case, I who had a subtil Game to Play, had nothing now to do but to single out from them all, the properest Man that might be for my Purpose; *that is to say*, the Man who was most likely to depend upon the *hear say* of Fortune, and not enquire too far into the Particulars; and unless I did this, *I did nothing*, for my Case would not bear much Enquiry.

Passage 5. See pp. 101–2 of the present edition; this passage is from pp. 150–51 of the first edition.

Then I represented my own Circumstances to him in the most moving Terms that I was able: I told him that those unhappy Distresses which first mov'd him to a generous and an honest Friendship for me, would, I hope, move him to a little concern for me now; tho' the Criminal part of our Correspondence, which I believed neither of us intended to fall into at that time, was broken off; that I desir'd to Repent as sincerely as he had done, but entreated him to put me in some Condition, that I might not be expos'd to the Temptations which the Devil never fails to excite us to from the frightful prospect of Poverty and Distress; and if he had the least Apprehensions of my being troublesome to him, I beg'd he would put me in a Posture to go back to my Mother in *Virginia*, from whence he knew I came, and that would put an end to all his Fears on that account; I concluded, that if he would send me 50 *l.* more to facilitate my going away, I would send him back a general Release, and would promise never to disturb him more with any Importunities; unless it was to hear of the well-doing of the Child, who if I found my Mother living, and my Circumstances able, I would send for to come over to me, and take him also effectually off of his Hands.

Then I represented my own Circumstances to him
in the most moving Terms: I told him that those
unhappy Distresses which first mov'd him to a generous Friendship for me, would, I hope, move him
to a little Concern for me now; tho' the Criminal
part of our Correspondence, which I believed neither
of us intended to fall into at that time, was broken
off, that I desir'd to repent as sincerely as he had
done, but intreated him to put me in some Condition, that I might not be expos'd to Temptations from
the frightful prospect of Poverty and Distress; and if
he had the least Apprehensions of my being troublesome to him, I beg'd he would put me in a Posture
to go back to my Mother in *Virginia*, from whence
he knew I came, and that would put an end to all
his Fears on that account; I concluded, that if he
would send me 50 *l.* more to facilitate my going away,
I would send him back a general Release, and would
promise never to disturb him more with any Importunities; unless it were to hear of the well-doing of
the Child who, if I found my Mother living, and my
Circumstances able, I would send for and take him
also off of his Hands.

Passage 6. See p. 190 of the present edition; this passage is from p. 297 of the first edition.

> Some of the Servants likewise us'd me saucily, and had much ado to keep their Hands off of me, the Master indeed was civiler to me than they; but he would not yet let me go, tho' he owned he could not say I was in his Shop before.

Passage 7. See p. 221 of the present edition; this passage is from p. 347 of the first edition.

> While I was under these influences of sorrow for him, came Notice to me that the next Sessions approaching, there would be a Bill preferr'd to the Grand Jury against me,and that I should be certainly try'd for my Life at the *Old-Baily*: My Temper was touch'd before, the harden'd wretch'd boldness of Spirit, which I had acquir'd, abated, and Conscious in the Prison Guilt began to flow in upon my Mind: In short, I began to think, and to think is one real Advance from Hell to Heaven; all that Hellish harden'd state and temper of Soul, which I have said so much of before, is but a deprivation of Thought; he that is restor'd to his Power of thinking, is restor'd to himself.

From p. 254 of the third edition.

The Servants likewise us'd me saucily, and had much ado to keep their Hands off me, the Master indeed was civiler to me than they; but he would not let me go, tho' he own'd I was in his Shop before.

From p. 298 of the third edition.

While I was under these Influences of Sorrow for him, came Notice to me that the next Sessions there would be a Bill preferr'd to the Grand Jury against me, and that I should be try'd for my Life: My Temper was touch'd before, the wretched Boldness of Spirit, which I had acquir'd, abated, and conscious Guilt began to flow in my Mind: In short, I began to think, and to think indeed is one real Advance from Hell to Heaven; all that harden'd State and Temper of Soul, which I said so much of before, is but a Deprivation of Thought; he that is restor'd to his Thinking, is restor'd to himself.

Passage 8. See pp. 249–50 of the present edition (paragraph beginning
"When we drew near..."); *this passage is from p. 395 of the first
edition.*

> ...He told me I must get some Body in the
> Place to come and buy us as Servants, and who
> must answer for us to the Governor of the Coun-
> try, if he demanded us; I told him we should do as
> he should direct; so he brought a Planter to treat
> with him, as it were for the Purchase of these
> two Servants, my Husband and me, and there we
> were formally sold to him, and went a Shore with
> him: The Captain went with us, and carried us
> to a certain House whether it was to be call'd a
> Tavern or not, I know not, but we had
> a Bowl of Punch there made of Rum, &c. and
> were very Merry. After some time the Planter
> gave us a Certificate of Discharge, and an Ac-
> knowledgement of having serv'd him faithfully,
> and we were free from him the next Morning, to
> go whether we would.

... He
told me I must get some Body in the Place to
come and buy me as a Servant, and who must answer for me to the Governor of the Country, if
he demanded me; I told him we should do as he
should direct; so he brought a Planter to treat
with him, as it were for the Purchase of me for a
Servant, my Husband not being order'd to be Sold,
and there I was formally sold to him, and went
a Shore with him: The Captain went with us, and
carried us to a certain House whether it was to be
call'd a Tavern or not, I know not, but we had a
Bowl of Punch there made of Rum, &c. and were
very Merry. After some time the Planter gave us
a Certificate of Discharge, and an Acknowledgement of having serv'd him faithfully, and I was
free from him the next Morning, to go whether
I would.

APPENDIX C: MODERNIZED SPELLING IN THE TEXT

whether/whither
"whether" of first edition here changed to "whither"

PAGE	LINE	PAGE	LINE	PAGE	LINE
11	18	26	12	52	4
52	5	53	11	86	25
98	25	105	23	113	37
123	38	123	41	151	30
151	32	152	17	153	24
170	33	172	33	186	6
250	10				

off/of
"off" of first edition here changed to "of"

PAGE	LINE	PAGE	LINE	PAGE	LINE
23	26	48	34	82	4
203	15	229	19	238	4

of/off
"of" of first edition here changed to "off"

PAGE	LINE
72	31

ought/aught
"ought" of first edition here changed to "aught"

PAGE	LINE	PAGE	LINE	PAGE	LINE
14	13	14	17	33	35
36	22	137	28	139	9
155	19	171	34	179	16
180	3	212	2		

loose/lose
"loose" of first edition here changed to "lose"

PAGE	LINE	PAGE	LINE	PAGE	LINE
137	42	179	33	204	19

"looser" of first edition here changed to "loser"

PAGE	LINE
195	40

chose/chuse (choose)
"chose" of first edition here changed to "chuse"
(the usual spelling of the singular in Defoe's time)

PAGE	LINE	PAGE	LINE
246	6	249	2

then/than
"then" of first edition here changed to "than"

PAGE	LINE	PAGE	LINE	PAGE	LINE
23	32	213	40	219	15
220	13	223	40		

than/then
"than" of first edition here changed to "then"

PAGE	LINE	PAGE	LINE	PAGE	LINE
34	37	43	36	45	7
229	20				

Appendix D: TABLE OF DATES

1660	Daniel, son of James and Alice Foe, born in London.
c. 1674–79	Defoe attended a dissenters' academy in Newington Green.
1683–92	Engaged in various kinds of trade, as merchant, wholesaler, and importer, mainly in London. In 1692 he was bankrupt for £17,000.
1684	Married Mary Tuffley.
1685	Involved in Monmouth's Rebellion.
1688–1702	Served William III in various capacities. Especially close to William after 1697.
1701	*The True-Born Englishman*, a poem defending William and his Dutch ancestry.
1702	*Reformation of Manners, A Satyr.*
	The Shortest Way with the Dissenters, an ironic tract that pretended to favor brutal treatment of religious dissenters.
1703	Arrested for writing *Shortest Way*, charged with seditious libel, fined, imprisoned, and pilloried.
	A Hymn to the Pillory.
	Two published collections of his writings, one unauthorized.
1703–30	Served the English government in various places and capacities, mainly performing secret-service and journalistic functions for the successive ministries.
1704–13	Wrote and published *The Review*, a popular periodical.
1704	*The Storm: Or, A Collection of the most Remarkable Casualties and Disasters Which happen'd in the Late Dreadful Tempest.*
1705 or 1706	*A True Relation of the Apparition of one Mrs. Veal.*
	[Between *True Relation* and *Family Instructor*, Defoe published more than 200 titles, mostly on political and economic subjects.]
1715, 1718	*The Family Instructor*, 2 vols.
1719	*The Life and Strange Surprising Adventures of Robinson Crusoe.*
	The Farther Adventures of Robinson Crusoe.
	The Dumb Philosopher; or Great Britain's Wonder, a life of Dickory Cronke.
	The King of Pirates: Being An Account Of The Famous Enterprises of Captain Avery.

1720	*The History of the Life and Adventures of Mr. Duncan Campbell.*
	Memoirs of a Cavalier.
	The Life, Adventures, and Pyracies, of the Famous Captain Singleton.
	Serious Reflections During The Life And Surprising Adventures of Robinson Crusoe, With His Vision Of The Angelick World.
1722	*The Fortunes and Misfortunes of the Famous Moll Flanders.*
	Due Preparations for the Plague As well for Soul as Body.
	Religious Courtship.
	A Journal of the Plague Year.
	The History and Remarkable Life of the truly Honourable Col. Jacque, Commonly Call'd Col. Jack.
1724	*The Fortunate Mistress* [Roxana].
	A New Voyage Round the World.
	The Jack Sheppard "lives."
1724–26	*A Tour Thro' the Whole Island of Great Britain*, 3 vols.
1724, 1728	*A General History of the Robberies and Murders Of the most notorious Pyrates.*
1725	The Jonathan Wild "lives."
	The Complete English Tradesman, 2 vols.
1726	*An Essay upon Literature.*
	The Political History of the Devil.
1727	*Conjugal Lewdness: Or, Matrimonial Whoredom.* (Also published under the title, *A Treatise Concerning The Use and Abuse Of The Marriage Bed*).
	An Essay on the History and Reality of Apparitions.
	A New Family Instructor.
1728	*Augusta Triumphans.*
	The Memoirs of an English Officer.
1729	*Madagascar: or, Robert Drury's Journal.*
1731	Died April 24, in Ropemaker's Alley, London.

BIBLIOGRAPHY
A Selected List of Biographical and Critical Studies

Defoe

Hans H. Anderson, "The Paradox of Trade and Morality in Defoe," *Modern Philology*, XXXIX (1941), 23–46.

Rodney M. Baine, *Daniel Defoe and the Supernatural*, Athens, Ga., 1968.

Jonathan Bishop, "Knowledge, Action and Interpretation in Defoe's Novels," *Journal of the History of Ideas*, XIII (1952), 3–16.

Paul Dottin, *Daniel Defoe et ses romans*, Paris, 3 vols., 1924. Volume I has been translated into English by Louise Ragan as *The Life and Strange and Surprizing Adventures of Daniel Defoe*, London, 1928.

Virginia Harlan, "Defoe's Narrative Style," *Journal of English and Germanic Philology*, XXX (1931), 55–73.

J. Paul Hunter, *The Reluctant Pilgrim: Defoe's Emblematic Method and Quest for Form in Robinson Crusoe*, Baltimore, 1966.

William Lee, *Daniel Defoe: His Life and Recently Discovered Writings 1716–1729*, London, 3 vols., 1869.

Alan Dugald McKillop, *The Early Masters of English Fiction*, Lawrence, Kans., 1956, Chapter 1.

John Robert Moore, *Daniel Defoe: Citizen of the Modern World*, Chicago, 1958.

———, *Defoe in the Pillory and Other Studies* (Indiana University Humanities Series, No. 1), Bloomington, 1939.

Maximillian E. Novak, *Defoe and the Nature of Man*, London, 1963.

———, "Defoe's Use of Irony," in *The Uses of Irony*, ed. H. T. Swedenberg, Los Angeles, 1966.

———, *Economics and the Fiction of Daniel Defoe* (University of California English Studies, No. 24), Berkeley and Los Angeles, 1962.

V. S. Pritchett, "Defoe," in *The English Novel*, ed. Derek Verschoyle, London, 1936.

Gerridina Roorda, *Realism in Daniel Defoe's Narratives of Adventure*, Wageningen, 1929.

Arthur W. Secord, *Studies in the Narrative Method of Defoe* (University of Illinois Studies in Language and Literature, Vol. IX, No. 1), Urbana, 1924.

Sri C. Sen, *Daniel Defoe, His Mind and Art*, Calcutta, 1948.

Michael Shinagel, *Daniel Defoe and Middle-Class Gentility*, Cambridge, Mass., 1968.

R. G. Stamm, "Daniel Defoe: An Artist in the Puritan Tradition," *Philological Quarterly*, XV (1936), 225–46.

G. A. Starr, *Defoe and Spiritual Autobiography*, Princeton, 1965.

Sir Leslie Stephen, *Hours in a Library*, London, 1917, I, 1–43.

James Sutherland, *Defoe*, London, 1937.

Alan Swallow, "Defoe and the Art of Fiction," *Western Humanities Review*, IV (1950), 129–36.

W. P. Trent, *Daniel Defoe: How to Know Him*, Indianapolis, 1916.

Ian Watt, *The Rise of the Novel*, London, 1957, pp. 60–134.

Walter Wilson, *Memoirs of the Life and Times of Daniel Defoe*, London, 1830.

Moll Flanders

John Peale Bishop, "Moll Flanders' Way," in *Collected Essays*, ed. Edmund Wilson, New York, 1948, pp. 47–55. (Originally appeared in *Story*, 1937.)

Robert R. Columbus, "Conscious Artistry in *Moll Flanders*," *Studies in English Literature*, III (1963), 415–32.

Denis Donoghue, "The Values of *Moll Flanders*," *Sewanee Review*, LXXI (1963), 287–303.

Robert Alan Donovan, "The Two Heroines of *Moll Flanders*," Chapter 2 in *The Shaping Vision: Imagination in the English Novel from Defoe to Dickens*, Ithaca, 1966.

E. M. Forster, *Aspects of the Novel*, New York, 1927, pp. 87–99.

George E. Gifford, Jr., "Daniel Defoe and Maryland," *Maryland Historical Magazine*, LII (1957), 307–15.

Theodore M. Hatfield, "*Moll Flanders* in Germany," *Journal of English and Germanic Philology*, XXXII (1933), 51–65.

C. A. Johnson, "Two Mistakes of Geography in *Moll Flanders*," *Notes & Queries*, CCVII (1962), 455.

Arnold Kettle, "In Defense of 'Moll Flanders,'" in *Of Books and Humankind*, ed. John Butt, London, 1964, pp. 55–67.

Howard L. Koonce, "Moll's Muddle: Defoe's Use of Irony in *Moll Flanders*," *ELH: A Journal of English Literary History*, XXX (1963), 377–94.

Pierre Legouis, "Marion Flanders est-elle une victime de la société?" *Revue de l'Enseignement des Langues Vivantes*, XLVIII (1931), 289–99.

Terence Martin, "The Unity of *Moll Flanders*," *Modern Language Quarterly*, XXII (1961), 115–24.

Maximillian E. Novak, "Conscious Irony in *Moll Flanders*: Facts and Problems," *College English*, XXVI (1964), 198–204.

———, "Moll Flanders' First Love," *Papers of the Michigan Academy of Science, Arts, and Letters*, XLVI (1961), 635–43.

A. E. Rodway, "*Moll Flanders* and *Manon Lescaut*," *Essays in Criticism*, III (1953), 303–20.

Mark Schorer, "A Study in Defoe: Moral Vision and Structural Form," *Thought*, XXV (1950), 275–87.

G. A. Starr, *Defoe and Spiritual Autobiography*, Princeton, 1965, chapter 4.

Dorothy Van Ghent, *The English Novel: Form and Function*, New York, 1953, pp. 33–43, 296–307.

Tommy G. Watson, "Defoe's Attitudes toward Marriage and the Position of Women Revealed in *Moll Flanders*," *Southern Quarterly*, III (1964), 1–8.

Ian Watt, "The Recent Critical Fortunes of *Moll Flanders*," *Eighteenth-Century Studies*, I (1967), 109–26.

———, *The Rise of the Novel*, London, 1957, pp. 93–134.

Virginia Woolf, "Defoe," in *The Common Reader*, London, 1925, pp. 121–31.

3- 1303 - 0004 - 6147